W9-CUD-995

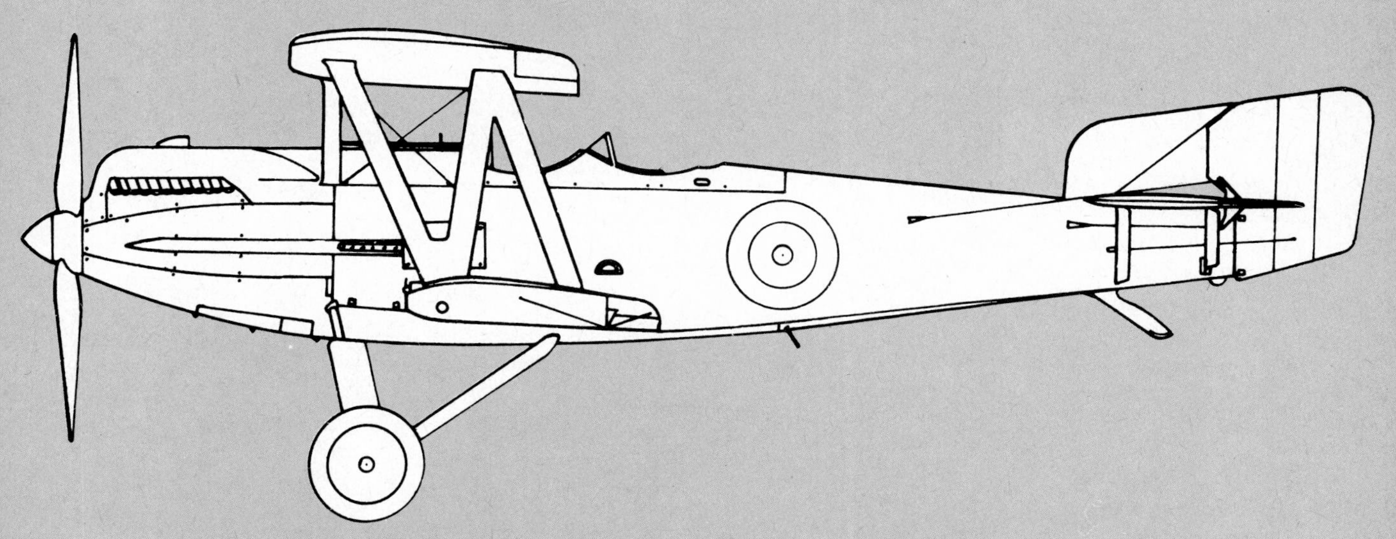

The Illustrated Encyclopedia of 20th Century

WEAPONS AND WARFARE

03EA61

13A

VOLUME 10
Form/General E

The Illustrated Encyclopedia of 20th Century

WEAPONS AND WARFARE

COLUMBIA HOUSE/New York

Distributed by Columbia House, a Division of CBS Inc.,
1211 Avenue of the Americas, New York, New York 10036
Printed in the U.S.A.

"Hit hard, hit fast, hit often."
—William Frederick Halsey, Jr.

CU
ROYAL NAVY
44
CU
ROYAL NAVY
45

INTRODUCTION

The full circles that often seem to be traced in the development of weapons have seldom been more graphically illustrated than by a selection of the entries in Volume 10 of the *Illustrated Encyclopedia of 20th Century Weapons and Warfare.*

The machine gun invented by Richard Jordan Gatling first appeared in the 1860s, and after initial resistance to the idea had been overcome, the **Gatling** gun went on to become the best-known of all the mechanical machine guns, though in many ways the contemporary **Gardner** was a better weapon. In its various forms it was sold and used throughout the world and it continued in service into the early years of the 20th century.

One of the most promising lines of development of the Gatling had been an electric-powered version developed by its inventor in 1893, but by this stage the Maxim, which needed no external power source, had diverted attention from mechanical weapons, and there was little interest in the idea.

In the 1940s however, the multibarrel concept, which was also investigated in Germany during the Second World War, was revived in the search for new aircraft guns with a much higher rate of fire than could be achieved by more conventional machine guns. In order to test the idea, an original Gatling was retrieved from a museum, fitted with an electric motor —and it worked. Moreover, it delivered an astonishing 5,000 rounds per minute, which as well as being a tribute to the soundness of Gatling's original design, was an unprecedented rate of fire.

The project was continued, and the code-name Vulcan was applied to the first and most famous of the modern Gatling guns. The subsequent development of multibarrelled aircraft guns is outlined in the general entry on **'Gatling'** weapons, as they have come to be known, and some of the specific examples are described and illustrated under the **General Electric** heading.

These weapons have come to be used not only as aircraft armaments, but in a variety of other roles. Their voracious appetite for ammunition makes them unsuitable for normal ground use, but they provide admirable point defense weapons against aircraft, and are widely carried by helicopter gunships. Perhaps the most dramatic illustration of their capabilities, though, is their success as the US Navy's Close-in Weapon System. In this system a 20-mm Vulcan with automatic ammunition feed is linked to a fire-control radar and computer which analyze potential targets, lock on the gun and open fire until the target is destroyed. The only drawback of the Vulcan Phalanx, as the weapon is known, is its rapid consumption of ammunition, which might not be sufficient to deal with a number of missiles.

For a time it appeared that anti-ship missiles such as the Israeli **Gabriel** posed an insuperable threat to surface vessels. But the ability of the Vulcan Phalanx, as fitted to the **Forrest Sherman** Class destroyer *USS Bigelow*, to deal with such missiles—and there are other forms of automatic weapon which have been similarly successful in this role—has caused a major revision of this theory.

One of the indirect ancestors of the modern ship-launched cruise missile was the German **FZG-76** flying bomb, more commonly known as the V-1 or "buzz-bomb". Examples of this weapon were shipped back to the United States during the Second World War and reassembled, and an American copy appeared as the JB-2 Loon. Over 1,200 were produced, and in the last month of the war a JB-2 unit embarked aboard an escort carrier ready to take part in the projected invasion of Japan.

Subsequently, Loons were fitted to specially-equipped *Balao* Class submarines. These were the first operational submarines equipped to launch guided missiles, and the Loon provided the United States with its first postwar guided surface-to-surface missile system. Among the Loon's descendants can be counted such missile systems as the Regulus, Matador, Mace and Navaho.

HMS *Formidable* with the battleship *Nelson* in the western Mediterranean covering operations in North Africa during the Second World War

Formidable

British aircraft carrier, completed 1940. She was the sixth ship to be called *Formidable* and was ordered in 1938 as the third member of the *Illustrious* Class of 23 000-ton armoured fleet carriers. She was, in fact, the second to be completed, being accepted from the builders, Harland and Wolff, on November 24, 1940, 41 months after she had been laid down.

After a very brief workup, *Formidable* left the Clyde in company with a convoy bound for Capetown on December 18. *Illustrious* was badly damaged in the Mediterranean on January 10, 1941, and *Formidable* was allocated to replace her, arriving at Alexandria on March 9. En route, her Fairey Albacore torpedo bombers had attacked Italian harbours at Mogadishu and Massawa.

Formidable took part in four major operations with the Mediterranean Fleet between March 26 and May 25, 1941. The first saw her aircraft scoring hits on the battleship *Vittorio Veneto* and the cruiser *Pola* off Cape Matapan—British battleships finished off the cruiser and two sister-ships. The fleet then covered convoys and bombarded Tripoli, between April 18 and 23, before fighting a convoy through from Malta to Alexandria, between May 6 and 12. The carrier was extremely short of Fairey Fulmar fighters and not until May 25 did she have sufficient to enable her to sail to attack Axis airfields supporting the Crete invasion. On May 26, she was found and attacked by Junkers Ju 88 dive-bombers which scored a direct hit with an 1100-lb (500-kg) bomb and inflicted extensive damage, obliging her withdrawal to the US for repairs.

Formidable returned to the United Kingdom in December 1941 and embarked her aircraft in February 1942. She was deployed in the Indian Ocean, where she remained from March 10 to August 24, encountering the enemy only once, in July, when her Grumman Martlet fighters destroyed a Japanese reconnaissance aircraft to the east of Ceylon.

Returning to the UK on September 18, she remained for only a month before sailing again with *Victorious* to support the Allied landings in Algeria—Operation Torch. The carriers operated off Oran and Bone between November 8 and 13, when shore-based aircraft took over the task. *Formidable* remained in the Western Mediterranean, based on Gibraltar and Oran, until early October 1943. During this time, she took part in only two major operations, the invasion of Sicily in July and the Salerno invasion in September. Her Martlets shot down an Italian seaplane during the latter operation—her first victim since the previous November.

Formidable undertook one convoy support mission in the Arctic in October 1943 before commencing a six-month refit. In early July 1944, she embarked 24 Barracudas and 16 Vought F4U Corsairs which, on July 17, took part in an unsuccessful attack on the battleship *Tirpitz*, lying in a northern Norwegian fjord. On August 22, 24 and 29, a further 103 sorties were flown against *Tirpitz*, the target's smoke screens again preventing the dive-bombers from scoring hits.

Sailing for the Far East on September 16, 1944, *Formidable* suffered from a machinery breakdown which kept her at Gibraltar until January 15, 1945, and it was not until April 16 that she saw action again, joining the British Pacific Fleet in place of the damaged and defective *Illustrious*. She flew strike missions against targets in the Sakishima Gunto (archipelago), south-west of Okinawa, on 13 days up to May 22. Hit by kamikazes on May 4 and 9, she was able to operate aircraft within hours of each attack, thanks to her 3-in (76-mm) armoured flight deck, and sustained only 55 casualties.

The carriers of the joint US Navy-Royal Navy fleet struck at the Japanese home islands between July 17 and August 10, most of the British ships withdrawing on the latter date. *Formidable*'s Corsairs of No 6 Naval Fighter Wing were particularly effective, claiming over 60 aircraft destroyed or damaged on the ground and several escort vessels sunk or damaged. It was during a shipping strike on August 9 that Lieutenant R H Gray DSC RCNVR, flying a Corsair of 1941 Squadron, lost his life in earning the Fleet Air Arm's second Victoria Cross of the war.

After her return to Sydney on August 23, *Formidable* was employed as a personnel transport, returning Allied prisoners of war from Japan to Australia and subsequently plying as a troopship between the United

Aircraft complements:	(Squadron Nos in parentheses)
December 1940:	12 Fulmars, 12 Albacores (803, 826, 829)
April 1941:	16 Fulmars, 9 Albacores, 9 Swordfish (803, 806, 826, 829)
April 1942:	16 Martlets, 21 Albacores (888 & 820)
November 1942:	24 Martlets, 6 Seafires, 12 Albacores (885, 888, 893, 820)
September 1943:	32 Martlets, 5 Seafires, 12 Albacores (as November 1942)
August 1944:	30 Corsairs, 24 Barracudas (1841, 1842, 826, 828)
May 1945:	36 Corsairs, 18 Avengers (1841, 1842, 848)
July 1945:	36 Corsairs, 6 Hellcats, 12 Avengers (1841, 1842, 1844, 848)

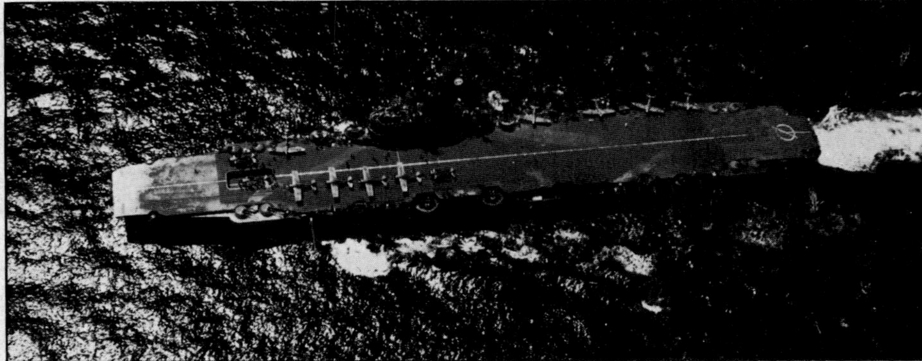

IWM

Formidable at sea with Seafires and Martlets on deck, one of which is on the forward elevator

Kingdom and the Far East. Her last trooping voyage ended in November 1946, and she was reduced to reserve at Rosyth in March 1947. Although plans were drawn up for her modernization, these were never implemented and she was scrapped in November 1953.

Displacement: 23 000 tons *Length:* 205.13 m (673 ft) pp *Beam:* 29.18 m (95 ft 9 in) *Draught:* 7.31 m (24 ft) *Machinery:* 3-shaft geared turbines, 110 000 shp=31 knots *Protection:* 114 mm (4.5 in) main belt; 114 mm (4.5 in) hangar side; 76-63.5 mm (3-2.5 in) deck *Armament:* 16 4.5-in (114-mm) dual purpose (8×2); 48 2-pdr AA (6×8); 8 20-mm (0.79-in) (8×1) *Aircraft:* 72 *Crew:* 1392

Formidable

British battleship class. The three ships of this class were constructed under the 1897 Programme at an average cost of £1 million each. All were laid down in Royal dockyards during 1898—*Formidable* at Portsmouth, *Irresistible* at Chatham, and *Implacable* at Devonport. The first pair were launched in 1898 and completed in 1901 and 1902, respectively, while *Implacable* was launched in 1899 and completed in 1901.

In the previous *Canopus* Class, advantage had been taken of the weight savings provided by the adoption of Krupp armour and water tube boilers to reduce size and cost. In the *Formidable* design it was decided to return to the size of the earlier *Majestic* Class and to utilize these weight savings to improve the protection and main armament. The arrangement of protection was generally similar to that in *Canopus* but with the side armour increased in thickness from 152 mm to 229 mm (6 in to 9 in) and a few other improvements including increases in the thickness of turrets and decks. A new gun, the 12-in (305-mm) Mk IX, was adopted for the main armament in place of the 12-in (305-mm) Mk VIII of the *Canopus* and *Majestic* Classes. It fired the same 385-kg (850-lb) shell as its predecessor but was of 40-cal length, instead of 35, giving a muzzle velocity of 792 m/sec (2600 ft/sec) and a theoretical penetration of 330-mm (13-in) Krupp armour at 4400 m (4800 yd) compared with 731 m/sec (2400 ft/sec) and 2834 m (3100 yd) in the Mk VIII.

A new twin mounting was designed for these weapons which allowed for the guns being loaded at any angle of training or elevation. It was, however, heavier than earlier mountings. The designed load displacement was 15 000 tons, but careful atten-

HMS *Formidable*, one of a class of three battleships constructed in 1897 which included the *Irresistible* and *Implacable*. Only the *Implacable* survived the First World War: *Formidable* was hit by two torpedoes from *U24* and sank off Portland Bill in January 1915, while *Irresistible* hit a mine in the Dardanelles and was sunk by gunfire from the Turkish Forts on March 18, 1915

IWM

tion to detail while the ships were under construction resulted in an average saving of 500 tons.

All three ships served in the Mediterranean until 1908, when they returned to home waters. On the outbreak of war, they formed part of the 5th Battle Squadron and operated mainly in the English Channel during 1914-15, during which time they covered the passage of the British Expeditionary Force (BEF) to France. Early on January 1, 1915, while patrolling in the Channel off Portland Bill, *Formidable* was struck by a torpedo on the starboard side amidships. Shortly afterwards she was hit by a second torpedo on the port side and about two hours later rolled over and sank. At the time the weather was very bad and 547 of the crew of 780 were lost. The torpedoes were fired by the German submarine *U24*. In February 1915, *Irresistible* was transferred to the Mediterranean where she joined the Dardanelles bombardment force. On March 18, while bombarding the Narrows forts, she struck a mine on the starboard side amidships. Immobilized with both engine rooms flooded, she drifted towards the enemy forts and was sunk by gunfire about three hours later.

In March 1915, *Implacable* was also transferred to the Dardanelles and covered the Gallipoli operations before being transferred to the Adriatic in May 1915. During 1915-16, she operated between Egypt and the East Indies and then returned to the Mediterranean. During 1916-17 her eight main deck 6-in (152-mm) guns were removed and the gun ports plated over. Four of these guns were repositioned on the upper deck where they displaced the 12-pdr battery and reduced the 12-pdr armament to eight. She also carried by this time three 3-pdr AA guns and two 2-pdr pom-poms. In 1918 *Implacable* returned to home waters and served in the Northern patrol until 1919. She was sold for scrap in 1921.

Displacement: 14 500 tons (normal), 15 800 tons (full load) *Length:* 131.60 m (431 ft 9 in) *Beam:* 22.85 m (75 ft) *Draught:* 7.62 m (25 ft) *Machinery:* 2-shaft triple-expansion steam engines, 15 000 ihp= 18 knots *Protection:* 229 mm (9 in) sides; 305 mm (12 in) barbettes; 254 mm (10 in) turrets; 152 mm (6 in) casemates; 76 mm to 25 mm (3 in-1 in) decks *Armament:* 4 12-in (305-mm) (2×2); 12 6-in (152-mm) (12×1); 16 12-pdr (16×1); 4 18-in (46-cm) submerged torpedo tubes *Crew:* 780

National Maritime Museum

The *Formidable* Class battleship HMS *Implacable* just before the outbreak of war in 1914

Forrestal

US aircraft carrier class. The first entirely new carrier design to be ordered and built after the Second World War, the *Forrestal* Class represented a major advance in all those aspects affecting aircraft operation at sea. Intended from the outset to operate jets and strategic bombing aircraft, they were large ships, displacing about 60 000 tons when light and little less than 80 000 tons at full load, and boasting a flight-deck area of nearly 2 hectares (4½ acres) in order to be able to stow and operate the 100 aircraft which 1943-45 Pacific operations had shown to be the ideal air group.

The name-ship of the class was authorized as CVB-59 (battle carrier) on March 10, 1951, during the Korean war. The general re-designation of large carriers in October 1952 placed her in the attack carrier (CVA) category, where the class was to remain for the next 20 years. The building time was remarkably short for such a huge ship—laid down in July 1952, *Forrestal* was launched on December 11, 1954, and was commissioned on October 1, 1955. The other three ships of the class, *Saratoga* (CVA-60), *Ranger* (CVA-61) and *Independence* (CVA-62) were completed in 1956, 1957 and 1959, respectively.

The recent British developments of the angled deck, steam catapult and mirror landing-aid were all incorporated, the length of the unobstructed landing area being 187 m (613 ft)—greater than the full length of the 1943 *Independence* Class light carrier's flight deck. Four catapults, capable of launching 36 290-kg (80 000-lb) aircraft at over 100 knots, were fitted: two in the conventional bow position and two amidships on the port side of the flight deck, in what became known as the 'waist' position. All four of the aircraft lifts were installed at the deck edge, three to starboard and one to port, all but the last being clear of the landing area and catapult tracks. Initially, the ships were able to carry their full intended complement of over 100 fighter and attack aircraft, but as the size of aircraft increased this figure was progressively reduced, until by the mid-1970s the normal air group embarked consisted of about 85 aircraft. Jets being thirsty aircraft, no less than 2 840 000 litres (625 000 Imp gal; 750 000 US gal) of aviation fuel were provided in *Forrestal*— more than four times as much as in the *Essex* Class.

In keeping with previous US Navy practice, the ships were powerful and very fast: the name-ship was fitted with machinery of a type dating from the Second World War, but her sisters had higher-pressure boilers which produced an additional 20 000 shp and made them the most powerful ships afloat. The high-speed seakeeping was improved by the extension of the bow plating up to flight-deck level, all US carriers after the first *Saratoga* having been built with bow gun-sponsons.

Conventional gun armament was reduced to just eight single 5-in (127-mm)/45-cal dual-purpose mountings, disposed in pairs—fore and aft, to port and starboard—below the level of the flight deck. Even though they were set well back from the bows, the forward sponsons were subject to slamming and they and their guns were removed in all the ships but *Ranger*. *Forrestal* lost her four after guns during repairs following the serious fire in 1967 and she appeared next with a close-range self-defence Sea Sparrow missile system, later to be known as the Basic Point Defence Missile System (BPDMS). A second BPDMS was fitted in *Forrestal* in 1972 and during the next two years *Saratoga* and *Independence* were each fitted with a pair of BPDMS and their guns removed. *Ranger*, however, retained her guns, reduced to two 5-in (127-mm), until 1976 before replacing

No and name	commissioned	builder
(CVA-59) *Forrestal*	1/10/55	Newport News
(CVA-60) *Saratoga*	14/4/56	New York navy yard
(CVA-61) *Ranger*	10/8/57	Newport News
(CVA-62) *Independence*	10/1/59	New York navy yard

US Navy

USS *Bigelow*, showing her Vulcan Phalanx 20-mm (0.79-in) CIWS forward of her aft turret

them with the Sea Sparrow missile system.

Forrestal, like *Saratoga* and *Independence*, served in the Atlantic and Mediterranean until the mid-1960s. From the autumn of 1965, however, *Independence* joined Task Force 77 in the Gulf of Tonkin, attacking targets in North and South Vietnam. *Ranger*, deployed with the Pacific Fleet since commissioning, had been involved since February 1965, when regular attacks on the North had begun. *Forrestal* joined TF 77 in 1967, but on July 29 a mishap on deck started fires which raged on the flight and hangar decks for 13 hours and caused 194 casualties and the loss of 21 aircraft; repairs took seven months to complete.

Saratoga, which had never left the Atlantic Fleet, was redesignated as a CVS in 1972, following a refit to install antisubmarine command and control facilities. The addition of the ASW role to the continuing attack task marked a new departure in US Navy carrier policy but was made necessary by the withdrawal of the *Essex* Class CVS-designated ASW carriers. By June 1975, all four ships of the class had been fitted for ASW and were operating one fixed-wing and one helicopter squadron each, in addition to their three attack and two fighter squadrons.

The heaviest aircraft operated by the class was the 36 290-kg (80 000-lb) North American RA-5C Vigilante, embarked in 4-6 aircraft detachments up to the mid-1970s. Subsequently the Grumman F-14 Tomcat interceptor has been the heaviest aircraft aboard, grossing 32 885 kg (72 500 lb), and is not likely to be overtaken during the remaining life of the ships.

By 1978 the *Forrestal*s were between 20 and 23 years old and were expected to require replacement some time towards the end of the 1980s.

Displacement: 60 000 tons (standard) (*Forrestal* 59 650 tons), approx 78 000 tons (full load) *Length:* 316.7 m (1039 ft) oa (*Independence* 319 m [1046 ft 6 in]); 301.8 m (990 ft) wl *Beam:* 76.8 m (252 ft) flight deck (*Ranger* 79.2 m [260 ft]), 39.5 m (129 ft 6 in) wl *Draught:* 11.3 m (37 ft) *Machinery:* 4-shaft Westinghouse General Electric geared turbines 280 000 shp= 34 knots. (*Forrestal* 260 000 shp= 33 knots) *Armament:* (As designed) 8 5-in (127-mm)/54-cal DP (4×2); 18 3-in (76-mm)/50-cal AA (*Forrestal* only); (As modernized) 2 or 3 Sea Sparrow BPMS; 4 5-in (127-mm)/54-cal DP (2×2) (*Ranger* only) *Aircraft:* 85-100 *Crew:* 4950 approx

Forrest Sherman

US destroyer class built 1953-59. These were the first new destroyers designed for the US Navy after the Second World War, and were authorized under the FY 1952-56 programmes. Although basically similar to the *Gearing* design they differed from conventional destroyers in several ways. Apart from being nearly 50% larger, they had aluminium superstructures to reduce topweight; the only torpedo armament carried was four fixed antisubmarine tubes amidships, and more guns were mounted after than forward.

Twin 5-in (127-mm)/38-cal guns were dropped in favour of a new 5-in (127-mm)/54-cal Mk 42 in a single mounting, one forward and two aft. The close-range AA armament comprised two pairs of 3-in (76-mm)/70-cal—later replaced by 3-in (76-mm)/50-cal—one in B position and one between the after fire-control director and the superimposed 5-in (127-mm) gun. The antisubmarine armament comprised two Hedgehogs on B gundeck and four fixed Mk 25 21-in (53-cm) torpedo tubes amidships.

Forrest Sherman (DD.931), *John Paul Jones* (DD.932), *Barry* (DD.933), *Manley* (DD.940), *Du Pont* (DD.941), *Bigelow* (DD.942), *Hull* (DD.945), *Edson* (DD.946) and *Somers* (DD.947) were built by Bath Iron Works, Maine.

Decatur (DD.936), *Davis* (DD.937), *Jonas Ingram* (DD.938), *Blandy* (DD.943) and *Mullinnix* (DD.944) were built by Bethlehem Steel, Quincy; *Morton* (DD.948) and *Parsons* (DD.949) by Ingalls shipbuilding, Pascagoula; *Richard S Edwards* (DD.950) and *Turner Joy* (DD.951) by Puget Sound Bridge and Dry Dock, Bremerton.

Note that the 'missing numbers' in the sequence belonged to earlier destroyers, DD.934 was ex-Japanese *Hanazuki*, DD.935 was ex-German *T.35* and DD.939 was ex-German *Z.39*.

The ships have all lost their forward 3-in (76-mm) AA mountings (and in many cases both) and the Hedgehogs, while the Mk 25 torpedo tubes have been replaced by triple Mk 32 tubes. In 1965-68 the *Decatur*, *John Paul Jones*, *Parsons* and *Somers* underwent major modernization to guided missile-armed destroyers, and are now rated as DDG.31-34. Two massive lattice masts have replaced the tripods and a single-arm Tartar missile-launcher and a hangar for a DASH helicopter were built on the extended after gundeck. However, when the DASH system failed, an Asroc launcher was added between the after funnel and hangar. The two after 5-in (127-mm) guns were suppressed, leaving only one

USS *Bigelow* (DD.942), before her alterations in 1976, on a courtesy visit to South Africa

gun, in A position, while the triple torpedo tubes were moved forward to the former B gundeck.

Eight of the unconverted ships were given a major overhaul of their antisubmarine capability in 1967-71; *Barry, Davis, Du Pont, Jonas Ingram, Manley, Blandy, Morton* and *Richard S Edwards*. They were given an Asroc missile-launcher in place of the after superimposed 5-in (127-mm) gun, and variable depth sonar, and the after deckhouse was extended to full width of the upper deck. A big square lattice mast replaced the tall tripod foremast. In 1974-75 *Hull* was given the prototype 8-in (203-mm) Mk 71 Major Calibre Lightweight Gun (MCLWG) in place of her forward 5-in (127-mm) gun, to test the feasibility of a destroyer firing such a heavy projectile. The tests proved successful, even with standard cruiser-ammunition instead of the laser-guided shells planned for the production version. In 1976 *Bigelow* appeared with the second example of the Vulcan Phalanx 20-mm (0.79-in) Close-In Weapon System (CIWS) mounted on the after superstructure.

There are a number of minor differences between individual ships. For example, the later ships have slightly higher bows, and *Barry* has a stem anchor to clear her bow sonar, the first SQS-23 set fitted in a US navy ship. *Edson* was reduced to reserve status in 1977 for training duties, and it is expected that her unmodernized sisters will all be downgraded in a similar manner. The DDGs will probably be equipped with a LAMPS multi-purpose helicopter in the near future.

See also Asroc, DASH.

Displacement: 2800 tons (standard), 4050 tons (full load) DDG conversions about 100 tons more *Length:* 127.41 m (418 ft) oa *Beam:* 13.71 m-13.77 m (45 ft-45 ft 2 in) *Draught:* 6.09 m (20 ft) *Machinery:* 2-shaft geared steam turbines, 70 000 shp= 32.5 knots *Armament:* (as built) 3 5-in (127-mm)/54-cal Mk 42 DP (3×1); 4 3-in (76-mm)/50-cal Mk 33 (2×2); 4 21-in (53-cm) torpedo tubes (4×1) (DDG conversions) 1 5-in (127-mm)/54-cal Mk 42 (Mod) DP; 1 single Tartar Mk 13 SAM system; 1 8-barrelled Asroc A/S missile system; 6 12.75-in (32.4-cm) Mk 32 torpedo tubes (2×3) *Crew:* 292-364

Forward

British cruiser class, built 1903-05. Four pairs of scout cruisers were ordered from various builders in 1903, the contracts for two, *Forward* and *Foresight* being placed with Fairfields. Although constructed to the same basic specification, the detailed design was left to the builders. This resulted in sufficient differences to place them in four groups (*Adventure, Forward, Patrol* and *Sentinel* Classes). The two Fairfield ships differed most noticeably from the other vessels of the group in having a poop deck, and these two were the last cruisers constructed for the Royal Navy with this Victorian feature. Both vessels were laid down in 1903, launched in 1904 and completed in 1905.

As designed, they mounted ten 12-pdr guns, but this was considered too weak (even though speed was regarded as more important than armament for their scouting role) and before completion, the number of guns was increased to 14. These weapons were disposed three on the poop, three on the forecastle and three on each side of the waist. With the introduction of the 4-in (102-mm) gun for destroyers, the armament was again reviewed and during 1911-12 both vessels were re-equipped with nine 4-in (102-mm) guns (9× 1), two on the forecastle, one on the poop and six in the waist. During the war, both were fitted with a 6-pdr AA gun abaft the third funnel while *Forward* also mounted a 3-pdr AA gun on her poop. The side armour was of KNC (Krupp Non-Cemented) and covered the machinery compartments while a protective deck was provided fore and aft of this.

Foresight was leader of the 6th Destroyer Flotilla based at Dover and *Forward* leader of the 7th Destroyer Flotilla in the Humber during 1914-15, after which both vessels transferred to the Mediterranean where they remained until the end of the war. *Foresight* was sold for scrap in 1920 and *Forward* followed in 1921.

Displacement: 2860 tons (normal), 3210 tons (full load) *Length:* 115.52 m (379 ft) *Beam:* 11.66 m (38 ft 3 in) *Draught:* 4.27 m (14 ft) *Machinery:* 2-shaft triple-expansion engines, 16 500 ihp= 25 knots *Protection:* 51 mm (2 in) sides, 28.5-15.8 mm (1.12-0.62 in) deck *Armament:* 14 12-pdr (14× 1); 2 46-cm (18-in) torpedo tubes (surface)

USS *Parsons* (DDG.33), *Forrest Sherman* Class destroyer, off Hong Kong in 1975. The hangar for the DASH helicopter can be seen on the extended after gundeck with the Tartar launcher

US Navy

***Foudre*, a French torpedo boat depot ship, later floatplane carrier and depot ship, which served in the Mediterranean between 1915-18**

Foudre

French torpedo boat depot ship, later floatplane carrier and depot ship, launched 1895. The career of *Foudre* (which means thunderbolt) can appropriately be described as chequered. Inspired by the doctrines of the *Jeune Ecole*, the influential school of French naval strategy, the vessel was laid down in the yards of Ch de la Gironde, Bordeaux, in 1892. She was completed in 1896 and commissioned a year later.

As built, she was depot ship for eight torpedo boats. These craft were carried in cradles and launched and recovered by booms. Six years after she had been completed, the advent of the ocean-going torpedo boat destroyer, which simultaneously replaced and countered the torpedo boat, made *Foudre* redundant. Thus, following a mission to ferry four coastal submarines to Indo-China after the end of the Russo-Japanese war in 1905 she was laid up. In 1907 *Foudre* was converted into a repair ship, and three years later into a minelayer with a capacity for 80 mines.

On March 1, 1912, she was commissioned as a floatplane depot ship. As well as the workships which she had inherited from her days as a torpedo boat carrier, *Foudre* was equipped with a 14 m×9 m×4 m (46 ft×29 ft 6 in×13 ft) hangar abaft the aftermost of her three funnels. The hangar opened on to a 14 m×11 m (46 ft×36 ft) handling deck from which two floatplanes could be transferred between ship and water.

Trials and evaluation occupied *Foudre* during most of 1912 and in the spring of 1913 she took part in the annual Mediterranean fleet exercise, scouting in the approaches to Toulon. Results were not entirely satisfactory, due to the small number and limited performance of her aircraft. In the late autumn of the same year, during a refit, a second large hangar was added between the forward funnel and the bridge, and a flying-off platform was erected over the forecastle. *Foudre* could now carry five small Nieuport 80-hp seaplanes or four of the larger Breguets or Voisins. The flying-off platform was used for the first time on May 8, 1914, when René Caudron flew one of his own G.III amphibians from it—nine months after a similar aircraft had flown from the British pioneer aircraft carrier *Hermes*. Caudron's feat was not repeated and the flying-off platform was later dismantled.

During the First World War, *Foudre* served in the Adriatic and the Levant before joining the Allied expedition to the Dardanelles in 1915. Later in the year, she left her aircraft at Mudros and operated as a light cruiser during the blockade of the Syrian coast. However, she was too valuable for such service, her workshops proving necessary for the maintenance of small ships as well as her own aircraft, and she returned to duties as a seaplane depot and general fleet maintenance ship, serving in the Aegean and the Levant until the end of the war.

After the war, the French navy laid up *Foudre* since she was no longer capable of operating the more modern aircraft and her workshops were no longer needed on distant stations. She was finally sold for scrap in 1921.

Displacement: 6100 tons *Length:* 116 m (380 ft 6¾ in) *Beam:* 16 m (52 ft 6 in) *Draught:* 7.1 m (23 ft 3½ in) *Machinery:* 2-shaft triple-expansion, 12000 shp=19.6 knots (1897 trials) *Protection:* 100-90 mm (3.9-3.54 in) main deck *Armament:* 8 100-mm (3.9-in); 4 65-mm (9-pdr); 2 47-mm (3-pdr) (as TB depot ship) 8 18.5 m (60 ft 8½ in) torpedo-boats (14.4 tons, 250 shp=17.5 knots, 1 14-in (35.5-cm) torpedo tube *Aircraft:* 2 (1912) 5 (1914) 8 (1915)

The Fox combat reconnaissance car can swim at a speed of 4 knots with flotation screen erected

Fox during trials with the British Army in Germany at Münchengladbach in February 1977

Fouga 90

French trainer and light attack aircraft. Since 1960 the giant nationalized Aérospatiale group has been seeking a successor to the mass-produced Magister (originally a Fouga design, then taken over by Potez and finally absorbed into Aérospatiale). In the early 1970s the decision was taken to concentrate on a derivative rather than a completely new design, and the full-scale mock-up of the resulting project, the Fouga 90, was displayed in public at the Paris air show in May 1977.

Though similar in configuration to the existing Magister, with tandem cockpits and a V-type butterfly tail, the Model 90 would have virtually no parts in common and would need completely new tooling for manufacture. Instead of the 400-kg (880-lb) thrust Turboméca Marboré turbojet the engines would be a pair of the same company's Astafan geared turbofans, which are extremely efficient (specific fuel consumption only 0.38 at maximum power) geared fan engines with variable-pitch blades (in theory they could have reverse pitch for braking after landing). Takeoff thrust of each engine is 848 kg (1870 lb) for Astafan III and 1230 kg (2710 lb) for Astafan IV. The rear (instructor) cockpit would be raised well above the front, giving a hump-backed appearance, and the wing would be more advanced than that of the Magister.

Existence of some 300 Magisters with the Armée de l'Air and Aéronavale has delayed go-ahead. Data available in 1978 were not firm enough to publish.

Fox

British all-aluminium combat reconnaissance car. It was developed by the Daimler company in conjunction with the Fighting Vehicles Research & Development Establishment, and is currently in service with the British Army. It is a development of the Ferret but designed to improve on that vehicle's performance and carry a more effective armament.

The hull is of welded aluminium alloy armour plate, and carries a turret mounting a 1.18-in (30-mm) Rarden cannon and a coaxial 0.30-in (7.62-mm) machine-gun. The Rarden cannon can deal with light AFVs out to ranges in excess of 1000 m (3280 ft) by using armour-piercing discarding-sabot (APDS) projectiles, while the HE projectile can be used against low-flying aircraft. The Fox carries a flotation screen which, when erected, allows the vehicle to swim, propelled by the paddle-wheel action of the road wheels and reaching a speed of about four knots. It is also light enough to be easily airlifted and it can be dropped by parachute. The three-man crew are liberally provided with optical and image-intensifying sights, while infrared equipment, short radar and navigational equipment can also be fitted.

Weight: 5670 kg (12 500 lb) *Length:* 5.10 m (16 ft 9 in) *Width:* 2.08 m (6 ft 10 in) *Height:* 2.13 m (7 ft) *Armament:* 1 1.18-in (30-mm); 1 0.30-in (7.62-mm) MG *Crew:* 3 *Powerplant:* Jaguar XK 6-cylinder 4.2 litres, 195 bhp at 5000 rpm *Speed:* Not known *Range:* Not known

Fox churns up the dust at Bovington tank training area, Dorset, in July 1976. Its aluminium armour gives a total weight of 5670 kg (12 500 lb) which makes Fox air-portable and light enough to be air dropped. The armoured car can also swim using a flotation screen

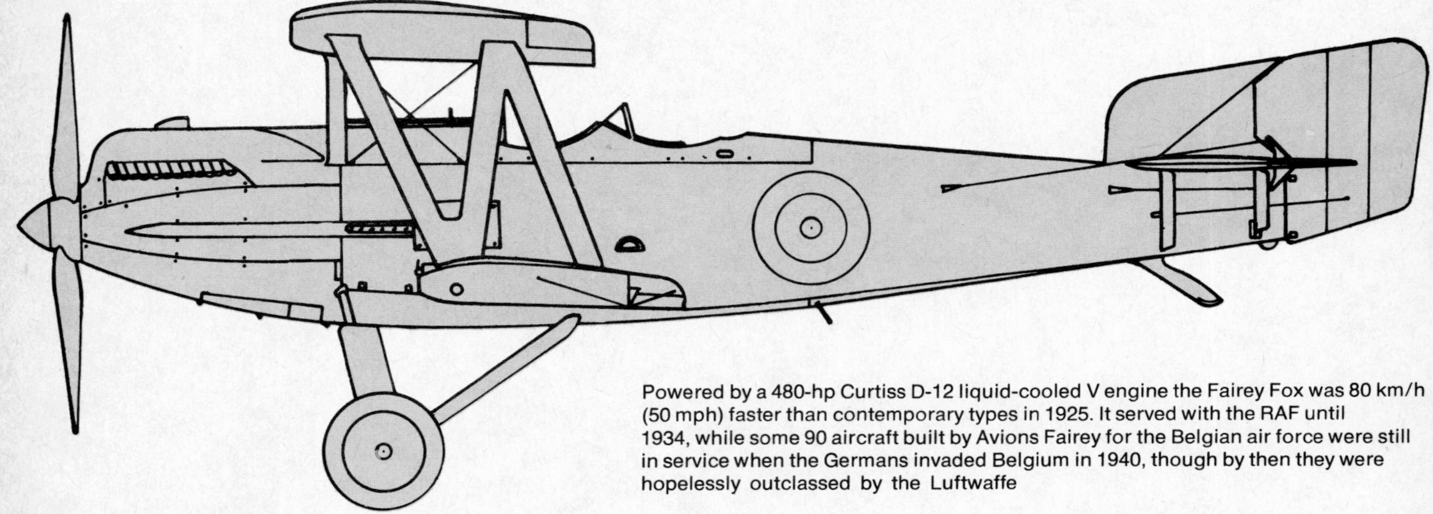

Powered by a 480-hp Curtiss D-12 liquid-cooled V engine the Fairey Fox was 80 km/h (50 mph) faster than contemporary types in 1925. It served with the RAF until 1934, while some 90 aircraft built by Avions Fairey for the Belgian air force were still in service when the Germans invaded Belgium in 1940, though by then they were hopelessly outclassed by the Luftwaffe

Fox, Fairey

British bomber aircraft. During 1923, on a visit to the US, Richard Fairey saw the 480-hp Curtiss D-12 liquid-cooled V engine as a potential powerplant for a new British aircraft. Around this was designed the Fairey Fox, a single-bay biplane of wood and metal construction with the engine enclosed in a compact cowling faired into the fuselage. The aerodynamically clean lines of the aircraft, together with the low drag of the powerplant installation, made the Fox 80 km/h (50 mph) faster than any of its contemporaries when it was flown for the first time on January 3, 1925. Air Chief Marshal Sir Hugh Trenchard was impressed to the extent that he ordered a complete squadron of Foxes to be built for the RAF. These were built to Air Ministry Specification 21/25 and designated Fox Mk I. They were delivered to No 12 Squadron at Andover in 1926, where they served for five years.

The Fox I was armed with a specially mounted 0.303-in (7.7-mm) Lewis machine-gun, installed in the observer's cockpit, and a single fixed Vickers gun of the same calibre, operated by the pilot, synchronized to fire forward between the propeller blades. Bomb load was 209 kg (460 lb). The aircraft gave exceptionally good performance in service, but due to strict economies being made by the British government at the time only 28 of these aircraft were built. Some were later fitted with 480-hp Rolls-Royce Kestrel IB engines and redesignated Mk IA. No 12 Squadron, which had taken a fox's head as its official emblem, had its Foxes replaced by Hawker Harts in 1931, but some remained in RAF service until 1934.

In September 1931, Fairey had set up a subsidiary company in Belgium, Avions Fairey, to build the Firefly for that country's air force, the Aéronautique Militaire. This was followed in 1933 by orders from the Belgian air force for 31 Fox IIs and 65 Fox IIIs (licence-built versions of the British-designed all-metal Fox IIM, with an enlarged vertical tail and a ventral radiator). The Fox design was now nine years old, but continual development had kept the type in demand and Avions Fairey decided to improve it still further. The Fox VI was a version re-engined with an 860-hp Hispano-Suiza 12 Ydrs 12-cylinder V engine; a cockpit canopy and wheel fairings were added; and the armament comprised two 0.30-in (7.62-mm) FN-Browning machine-guns, one on each side of the forward fuselage. About 85 of this model were built, some being used, under the designation Fox VIR, as fighter-reconnaissance aircraft with an additional machine-gun in the rear cockpit. The standard Belgian fighter version was known as the Fox VIC (for Chasse).

The Fairey Fox I in service with No 12 Squadron RAF at Andover in 1926. They operated Foxes for five years before converting to Harts

IWM

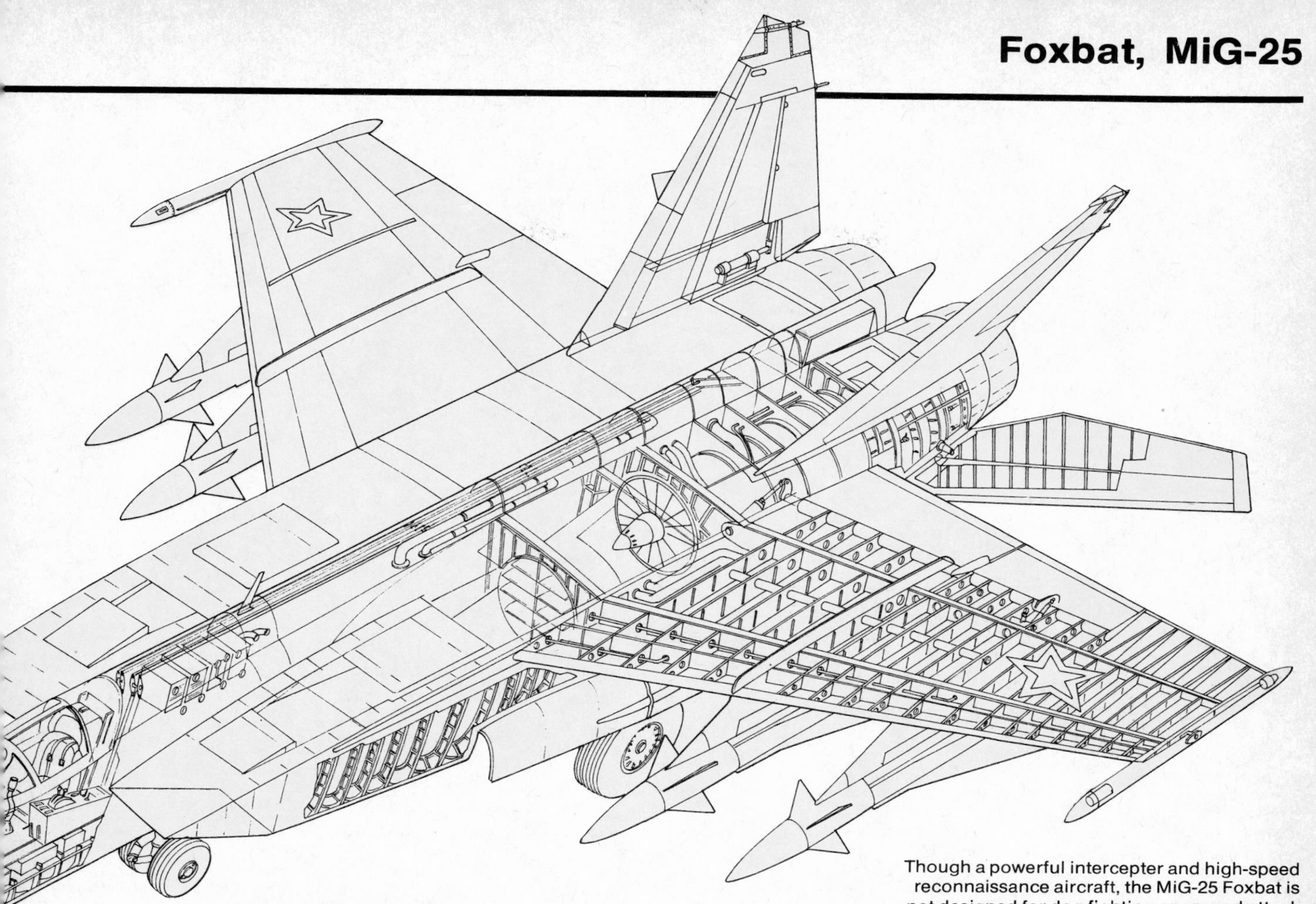

Though a powerful intercepter and high-speed reconnaissance aircraft, the MiG-25 Foxbat is not designed for dog fighting or ground attack

When Belgian production ended in 1939 a total of just over 170 Foxes had been built by Avions Fairey, including six Fox IV floatplanes exported to Peru; two Fox VIs for Switzerland; two Mk VIs converted to single-seat fighter configuration (Mono Fox or Fox VII), with two machine-guns in the fuselage and four in the upper wings; and 12 Fox VIIIs, an improved version of the Mk VI. About 90 Foxes were still in Belgian air force service when the Germans invaded in May 1940.

(Fox 1) *Span:* 11.58 m (38 ft) *Length:* 9.50 m (31 ft 2 in) *Gross weight:* 1867 kg (4116 lb) *Maximum speed:* 252 km/h (156.5 mph)

(Fox VIR) *Span:* 11.58 m (38 ft) *Length:* 9.37 m (30 ft 9 in) *Gross weight:* 2345 kg (5170 lb) *Maximum speed:* 360 km/h (224 mph)

Foxbat, MiG-25

Soviet intercepter and reconnaissance aircraft. For ten years this remarkable aircraft has been the fastest combat aircraft in the world, and, except for the specialized SR-71 reconnaissance aircraft of Strategic Air Command (SAC), the fastest aircraft of any type. It was designed in the late 1950s as an intercepter to shoot down the B-70 Valkyrie bomber. When in 1961 this was cut back to a research programme, the MiG-25 was not cancelled but continued. Subsequently it was diversified into three main families of aircraft, a strategic intercepter, a reconnaissance aircraft and a conversion trainer.

The Soviet design bureau number was E-266, and in April 1965 the prototype, flown by Alexander Fedotov, set a world 1000-km (620-miles) circuit record with 2000-kg (4409-lb) payload at 2320 km/h (1441 mph). In July 1967 four examples flew over Domodedovo airfield at high speed during a flying display, these clearly being development prototypes with various electronic and equipment installations. At first erroneously believed to be the MiG-23 in the West, it was assigned the Air Standards Coordinating Committee (ASCC) reporting name of 'Foxbat', and this immediately became a major scareword in the Pentagon and other NATO defence establishments. No Western aircraft could even approach the Foxbat in speed or altitude performance, and it was the remarkable potential of this aircraft that led to the USAF FX competition as a result of which McDonnell Douglas built the F-15. At the same time, it must be emphasized that the two aircraft are in no way comparable. The F-15 is very much slower, but is an all-round combat aircraft. The E-266/MiG-25 is a straightline aircraft intended to stand off and release missiles from a distance, or fly high-level reconnaissance missions. It has never been intended for rapid manoeuvre, air combat or ground attack.

Records fell to early MiG-25s like nine-pins. The 1000-km (620-mile) circuit with load was pushed up to 2921 km/h (1815 mph) and the 500-km (311-mile) circuit to no less than 2982 km/h (1853 mph). Fedotov set a new world altitude record at 36 240 m (118 900 ft) and also set a mark with 2000-kg (4409-lb) payload by climbing to 35 230 m (115 584 ft). Today an E-266M with up-rated engines currently holds the two top time-to-height records by reaching 25 000 m (82 020 ft) in 2 min 34.2 sec and 30 000 m (98 425 ft) in 3 min 9.7 sec; Fedotov even set a new mark, above all previous time-to-height records, by blasting to 35 000 m (114 830 ft) in 4 min 11.3 sec. The current absolute height record, also set by an E-266M, is 37 650 m (123 520 ft), again by Fedotov.

Except for the pioneer A-5 Vigilante, the MiG-25 was the first aircraft to have a narrow body blended into an extremely broad box-like fuselage with the sides occupied by the engine installations, the top and bottom being almost flat. The wing is naturally very thin but almost unswept, and provided with shallow fences above and below, aligned with pylons in some versions. There are small plain flaps and inboard ailerons, the outer panels and leading edges being fixed. A novel feature, later used in several fighters, was twin vertical tails inclined outwards; these are so close to the wing that much of each fin is above the wing, and there is little body between the high wing and the lower-mounted slab tailplanes which are acutely swept back. It is believed that differential tailplane deflection is the primary control in roll at high speeds.

The two Tumansky TRD-31 single-shaft afterburning turbojets are each rated at 11 000 kg (24 250 lb) takeoff thrust. They are fed via long ducts of tall rectangular cross-section, with wedge inlets fitted with hinged lower lips scheduled by the engine control system to open downwards at takeoff or at low speeds and close upwards at increasing Mach numbers. Water/methanol injection is fitted as standard, and used for all maximum-power or high-Mach modes of flight. The very large nozzles are of convergent/divergent form with variable profile and area, and at Mach numbers near 3.0 almost all the thrust is produced by the inlets, three-ring afterburners and nozzles. Special Y-6 fuel, with flash point of 54.5° C and good anticoking and heat-sink properties, is housed in novel structural tanks forming a second fuselage inside the first, backed up by saddle tanks above and around the inlet ducts and integral tanks forming the entire wing box out to the outboard fence. Fuel capacity is about 14 000 kg (30 865 lb).

Nearly all the MiG-25 airframe is steel, titanium being used only for relatively minor parts including the leading edges. It had been expected that the MiG-25 would be a titanium aircraft, a metal not in short supply in the Soviet Union, and it was a great surprise when observers were able to dissect a Foxbat in September 1976. The weight penalty is large and the advantages of steel obscure (cost would not be important).

The basic intercepter, called Foxbat A, has a single seat, a nose filled with a very large radar (called Fox Fire by NATO) and four of the world's biggest air-to-air missiles (AAMs) under the wings. The interception radar is of 1959 vintage, with a large number of thermionic valves (vacuum tubes). Its high average power of 600 watts is used not so much for long range as to burn through any hostile electronic countermeasures (ECM) and unfailingly lock-on and track targets out to the effective limit of range of the missiles. The latter, called 'AA-6 Acrid' by NATO, are carried in two pairs, the inboard pairs usually having IR, heat-homing, guidance and the outers semiactive radar homing. As noted in Part 2 of *Weapons and Warfare*, the range of these missiles is, perhaps quite wrongly, estimated by NATO observers at very short limits, around 19 km (12 miles) for the IR version and about twice this distance for the radar pattern. Yet the missile is very much larger than the US Navy Phoenix, which has a range exceeding 210 km (130 miles), and long missile range was a basic Foxbat parameter, as was the ability to engage targets very much lower or higher than the launch aircraft.

In early 1971 four MiG-25R reconnaissance aircraft were airlifted in Antei transports to Egypt, where after reassembly and checkout they operated from Cairo West in bold overflights of Israel and several other countries. On several occasions Israeli F-4E Phantoms attempted to effect a missile interception using the Sparrow AAM but failed. Today it is known that there are at least two MiG-25R versions, one having five cameras in the forward fuselage and many other sensors, including a side-looking airborne radar (SLAR), and the other, Foxbat D, having a larger and relocated SLAR but no cameras. An odd feature is that all reconnaissance versions have straight wing leading edges, unlike other variants.

The only other model known to the West is the MiG-25U (Uchelono, or instructional) trainer with an additional (pupil) cockpit ahead of and below the original, necessitating deletion of the radar. Full air-data, navigation and ECM systems are carried but no sensors or weapon subsystems.

Lieutenant Viktor Belenko, who in September 1976 defected and flew his intercepter version from the TA-PVO base at Sukhanovka to Hakodate, Japan, told his interrogators that at that time more than 400 MiG-25s were in service. He mentioned an improved version with uprated engines, a strengthened airframe for full-throttle flight at low levels and increased manoeuvre capability, and with an improved radar and two body pylons to increase the number of AAMs carried to six. In 1975 an E-266M set various records with 'RD-F' engines rated at 14 000 kg (30 864 lb) thrust, and it is believed that an R-266F engine at the same thrust is fitted to the improved intercepter, which one report designates MiG-25MP (Modifikatsirovanny Perekhvatchik, or modified intercepter).

Span: 13.95 m (45 ft 9 in), reconnaissance versions 13.40 m (44 ft) *Length:* 22.3 m (73 ft 2 in) *Gross weight:* Foxbat A 36 200 kg (79 800 lb) *Max speed:* intercepter Mach 2.8; reconnaissance, emergency, Mach 3.2, 3380 km/h (2100 mph)

Foxtrot

Soviet submarine class, built 1956-68. The Soviet navy started production of a conventional (diesel-electric) class in the mid-1950s to follow the *Zulu* type, and even when the first nuclear submarines were built their enormous cost led the Russians to continue the conventional programme to boost numbers.

The *Foxtrot* is believed to have the same propulsion as the interim missile-firing *Golf* type, and it is thought of as a very successful design. Western sources claim that 60 are in service, and they are certainly the most frequently sighted. The Indian navy has eight: *Kalvari* (S.121), *Kanderi* (S.122), *Karanj* (S.123), *Kursura* (S.124), *Vela* (S.40), *Vaqir* (S.41), *Vagli* (S.42) and *Vagsheer* (S.43). They were delivered between 1968 and 1975, and Libya took delivery of the *Babr*, first of seven, in 1977. It is not clear if these are new construction or serving boats from the total of 60 mentioned above, but it seems unlikely that the Russians would restart production of what is now a somewhat

A Soviet *Foxtrot* Class submarine during operations in an Arctic theatre in the 1970s. It has a bow guard fitted for protection against ice

dated design. It is likely that *Foxtrots* will replace the ageing *Whiskeys* in Eastern bloc navies in the next few years.

All *Foxtrots* were built at the Sudomech yard in Leningrad, and the first was sighted in 1958. Three names have been reported: *Pskovskii Komsomolets, Jaroslavskii Komsomolets* and *Vladimirskii Komsomolets.*

Displacement: 2000/2300 tons (surfaced/submerged) *Length:* 90.5 m (296 ft 11 in) oa *Beam:* 8.3 m (27 ft 2¾ in) *Draught:* 5.8 m (19 ft) *Machinery:* 2-shaft diesel-electric, 6000 shp=20/15 knots (surfaced/submerged) *Armament:* 10 53.3-cm (21-in) torpedo tubes (6 forward, 4 aft, 20 torpedoes carried) *Crew:* 70

MOD

A *Foxtrot* Class submarine photographed by an RAF Nimrod off the Faroes on August 23, 1974

FRAM

Acronym for Fleet Rehabilitation and Modernization, a massive effort to overhaul ageing ships of the US Navy in the fiscal years 1960-64. The modernization of the destroyers of the *Fletcher, Gearing* and *Allen M Sumner* Classes was so drastic that the ships formed new classes thereafter.

The reason for initiating the FRAM programme was primarily to offset the block obsolescence overtaking ships built in 1941-45 and to provide more effective antisubmarine ships by making use of the 15-17-year-old destroyers which no longer had any useful role to play, being designed for surface torpedo attack. Three new weapon systems were available, and it was hoped to incorporate all of them: the Mk 44 acoustic antisubmarine torpedo, the Asroc long-range antisubmarine (A/S) missile system and the DASH drone A/S helicopter.

The conversion of the destroyers was divided into two parts, the first being FRAM I, to extend the life of the hull by at least eight to ten years. FRAM II was to be less extensive, and would add at least five years to the ship's life. The long-hulled *Gearing* Class destroyers were the most suitable choice for FRAM I conversions and 79 hulls were earmarked. The work was to be done over a five-year period, eight ships under FY'60, 14 ships under FY'61, 14 ships under FY'62, 24 ships under FY'63 and 19 ships under FY'64. A further 16 *Gearings* were to be given the FRAM II conversion, with 33 *Allen M Sumners* and three *Fletchers*. It was hoped to extend the programme to include a further 17 *Fletchers* and *Sumners* in the FRAM II programme under FY'65 but this was subsequently cancelled.

Eleven shipyards took part in the programme, and all but eight of the destroyers were finished by December 1964. The cost worked out at about $11 million for a FRAM I conversion, and some $7 million for a FRAM II, making a total of $1100 million on the destroyers alone.

Other categories of ships were to be given FRAM II modernizations: 35 conventional submarines, six *Essex* Class antisubmarine carriers, 11 destroyer- and submarine-tenders

A *Foxtrot* in the Mediterranean, shadowing the USS *Jonas Ingram* in 1973. *Foxtrots* are the main Soviet submarine in the Mediterranean

US Navy

FRAM

A *Gearing* Class destroyer after her update in the FRAM I model A programme was fitted with Asroc, retaining one twin 5-in gun forward

J W Wood Associates

No and name	recom-missioned	disposal
DD.710 *Gearing*	10/1962	Stricken 7/1973
DD.711 *Eugene A Green*	10/1963	To Spain 8/1972 as *Churruca*
DD.714 *William R Rush*	4/1965	Serving 1978
DD.715 *William M Wood*	3/1965	Stricken 12/1976
DD.716 *Wiltsie*	9/1962	To Pakistan 1977
DD.717 *Theodore E Chandler*	1/1962	Sold 12/1975
DD.718 *Hamner*	11/1962	Serving 1978
DD.719 *Epperson*	12/1964	To Pakistan 1977
DD.743 *Southerland*	10/1964	Serving 1978
DD.763 *William C Lawe*	11/1961	Serving 1978
DD.782 *Rowan*	5/1964	To Taiwan 1977
DD.783 *Gurke*	5/1964	To Greece 1976
DD.784 *McKean*	11/1964	Serving 1978
DD.785 *Henderson*	4/1962	Serving 1978
DD.786 *Richard B Anderson*	7/1961	To Taiwan 1977
DD.787 *James E Kyes*	1/1963	To Taiwan 4/1973 as *Chien Yang*
DD.788 *Hollister*	12/1961	Serving 1978
DD.789 *Eversole*	2/1963	To Turkey 7/1973 as *Gayret*
DD.790 *Shelton*	6/1961	To Taiwan 4/1973 as *Lao Yang*
DD.806 *Higbee*	2/1964	Serving 1978
DD.808 *Dennis J Buckley*	10/1964	Serving 1978
DD.817 *Corry*	9/1964	Serving 1978
DD.818 *New*	12/1963	To South Korea 1977
DD.819 *Holder*	10/1963	Stricken 10/1976
DD.820 *Rich*	11/1963	Serving 1978
DD.821 *Johnston*	11/1962	Serving 1978
DD.822 *Robert H McCard*	12/1962	Serving 1978
DD.823 *Samuel B Roberts*	12/1962	Stricken 11/1970
DD.824 *Basilone*	4/1964	Serving 1978
DD.825 *Carpenter*	3/1965	Stricken 1977
DD.826 *Agerholm*	3/1961	Serving 1978
DD.827 *Robert A Owens*	11/1964	Stricken 1977
DD.829 *Myles C Fox*	10/1964	Serving 1978
DD.832 *Hanson*	12/1964	To Taiwan 4/1973 as *Liao Yang*
DD.833 *Herbert J Thomas*	8/1965	To Taiwan 5/1974 as *Han Yang*
DD.835 *Charles P Cecil*	5/1964	Serving 1978
DD.836 *George K Mackenzie*	12/1964	Stricken 10/1976

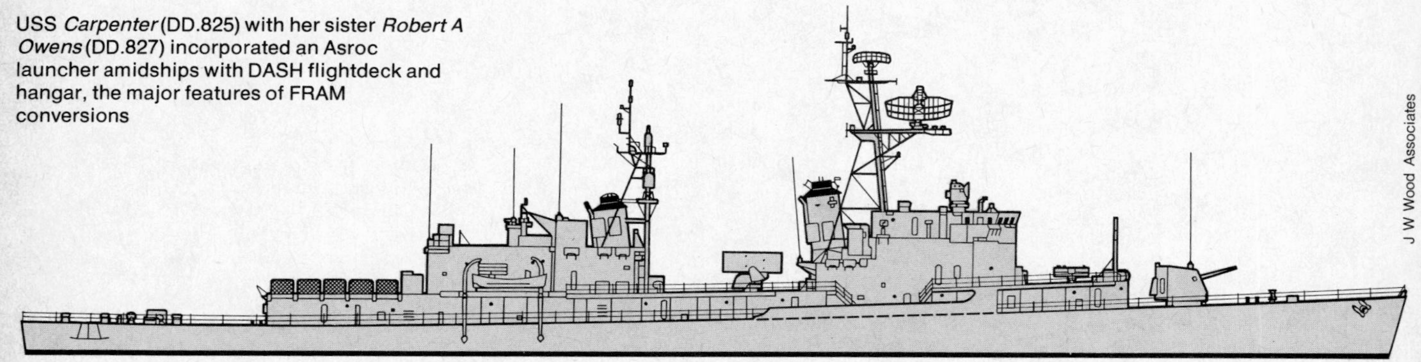

USS *Carpenter* (DD.825) with her sister *Robert A Owens* (DD.827) incorporated an Asroc launcher amidships with DASH flightdeck and hangar, the major features of FRAM conversions

J W Wood Associates

DD.837	***Sarsfield***	5/1963	To Taiwan 1977
DD.839	***Power***	1/1962	To Taiwan 1977-78
DD.840	***Glennon***	7/1963	Stricken 10/1976
DD.841	***Noa***	5/1961	To Spain 10/1973 as *Blas de Lezo*
DD.842	***Fiske***	1/1965	Serving 1978
DD.843	***Warrington***	5/1962	Stricken 10/1972
DD.844	***Perry***	5/1960	Stricken 7/1973
DD.845	***Baussell***	6/1961	Serving 1978
DD.846	***Ozbourn***	12/1961	Stricken 5/1975
DD.847	***Robert L Wilson***	11/1963	Stricken 9/1974
DD.849	***Richard E Kraus***	5/1964	To South Korea 1977
DD.850	***Joseph P Kennedy Jr***	5/1962	Stricken 7/1973 (museum ship)
DD.851	***Rupertus***	11/1963	To Greece 7/1973 as *Kountouriotis*
DD.852	***Leonard F Mason***	1/1964	Stricken 11/1976
DD.853	***Charles H Roan***	6/1962	To Turkey 9/1973 as *Cakmak*
DD.862	***Vogelgesang***	1/1963	Serving 1978
DD.863	***Steinaker***	3/1965	Serving 1978
DD.864	***Harold J Ellison***	1/1963	Serving 1978
DD.865	***Charles R Ware***	1/1962	Stricken 12/1974
DD.866	***Cone***	1/1963	Serving 1978
DD.867	***Stribling***	5/1961	Stricken 7/1976
DD.868	***Brownson***	5/1964	Stricken 9/1976

DD.869	***Arnold J Isbell***	5/1962	To Greece 12/1973 as *Sachtouris*
DD.870	***Fechteler***	12/1963	Stricken 9/1970
DD.871	***Damato***	2/1964	Serving 1978
DD.872	***Forrest Royal***	4/1962	To Turkey 3/1971 as *Adatepe*
DD.873	***Hawkins***	1/1965	Serving 1978
DD.875	***Henry W Tucker***	12/1963	To Brazil 12/1973 as *Marcilio Dias*
DD.876	***Rogers***	6/1964	Serving 1978
DD.878	***Vesole***	10/1964	Stricken 12/1976
DD.879	***Leary***	1/1965	To Spain 10/1973 as *Langara*
DD.880	***Dyess***	2/1965	Serving 1978
DD.881	***Bordelon***	12/1963	Stricken 2/1977
DD.882	***Furse***	10/1963	To Spain 8/1972 as *Gravina*
DD.883	***Newman K Perry***	2/1965	Serving 1978
DD.884	***Floyd B Parkes***	5/1963	Stricken 7/1973
DD.885	***John R Craig***	2/1963	Serving 1978
DD.886	***Orleck***	11/1963	Serving 1978
DD.887	***Brinkley Bass***	5/1962	To Brazil 12/1973 as *Mariz é Barros*
DD.888	***Stickel***	3/1964	To Greece 7/1972 as *Kanaris*
DD.889	***O'Hare***	12/1963	To Spain 10/1973 as *Mendez Nunez*
DD.890	***Meredith***	6/1961	Serving 1978

***Gurke*, one of the US Navy destroyers given an extended operational career by a FRAM I update**

and 40 amphibious ships. This was a less drastic overhaul than the one given to the FRAM II destroyers, and involved such items as renewing boiler-tubes, rewiring etc, as well as the updating of radar and sonar, all important items in larger ships but not resulting in major change to the ships' appearance.

The appearance of the ships was changed completely, with new funnel caps and the big Asroc 'Pepperbox' launcher amidships. The Model A group retained the twin 5-in (127-mm) in B position, but had the after mounting removed; Model B ships had the 5-in (127-mm) aft but not in B position, the Model C group had only one 5-in (127-mm) mount, in A position. All had a hangar and flight deck aft for the two QH-50A DASH drone helicopters. The triple Mk 32 torpedo tubes were mounted in various positions, on B gun deck, abreast of the after funnel, or, in one case, on the quarterdeck.

Most of the modernized *Gearing* Class destroyers were given the FRAM I conversions, and these are listed above and opposite, though the 16 listed overleaf, along with 33 *Alan M Sumner*s and three *Fletcher*s, received the FRAM II modifications.

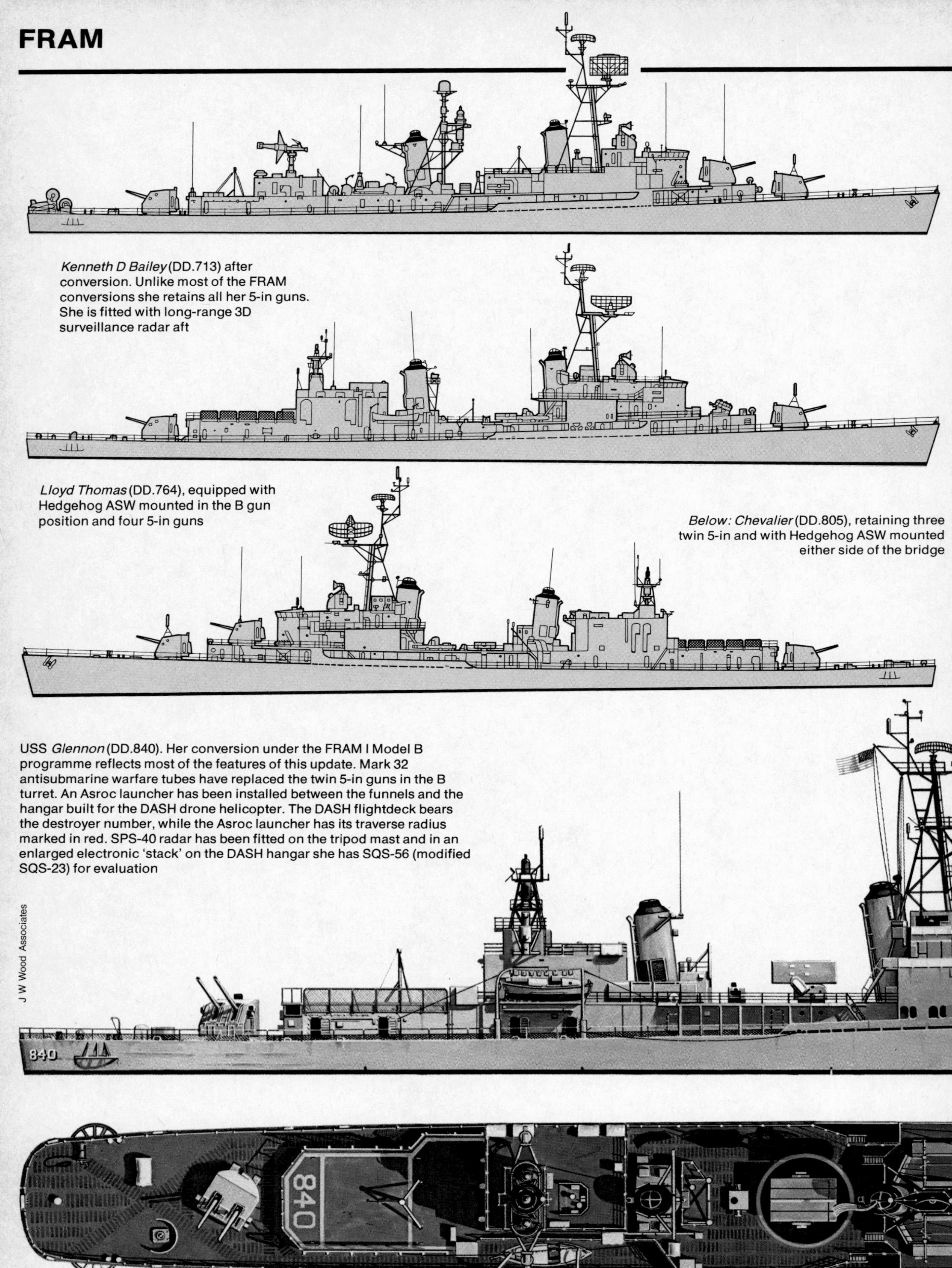

Kenneth D Bailey (DD.713) after conversion. Unlike most of the FRAM conversions she retains all her 5-in guns. She is fitted with long-range 3D surveillance radar aft

Lloyd Thomas (DD.764), equipped with Hedgehog ASW mounted in the B gun position and four 5-in guns

Below: Chevalier (DD.805), retaining three twin 5-in and with Hedgehog ASW mounted either side of the bridge

USS *Glennon* (DD.840). Her conversion under the FRAM I Model B programme reflects most of the features of this update. Mark 32 antisubmarine warfare tubes have replaced the twin 5-in guns in the B turret. An Asroc launcher has been installed between the funnels and the hangar built for the DASH drone helicopter. The DASH flightdeck bears the destroyer number, while the Asroc launcher has its traverse radius marked in red. SPS-40 radar has been fitted on the tripod mast and in an enlarged electronic 'stack' on the DASH hangar she has SQS-56 (modified SQS-23) for evaluation

J W Wood Associates

No and name	recom-missioned	disposal
DD.713 ***Kenneth D Bailey***	10/1960	Stricken 2/1974
DD.742 ***Frank Knox***	5/1961	To Greece 1/1971 as *Themistokles*
DD.764 ***Lloyd Thomas***	11/1961	To Taiwan 10/1972 as *Dang Yang*
DD.765 ***Keppler***	9/1961	To Turkey 6/1972 as *Tinaztepe*
DD.805 ***Chevalier***	8/1962	To South Korea 7/1972
DD.807 ***Benner***	2/1963	Stricken 2/1974
DD.830 ***Everett F Larson***	1/1963	To South Korea 10/1972 as *Jeong Buk*
DD.831 ***Goodrich***	9/1960	Stricken 2/1974
DD.834 ***Turner***	8/1960	Stricken 9/1969
DD.838 ***Ernest G Small***	8/1961	To Taiwan 2/1971 as *Fu Yang*
DD.858 ***Fred T Berry***	10/1961	Stricken 9/1970
DD.859 ***Norris***	10/1961	To Turkey 1975 as *Kocatepe I*
DD.860 ***McCaffery***	11/1961	Stricken 9/1973
DD.861 ***Harwood***	12/1961	To Turkey 12/1971 as *Kocatepe II*
DD.847 ***Duncan***	6/1961	Stricken 9/1973
DD.877 ***Perkins***	11/1962	To Argentina 1/1973 as *Py*

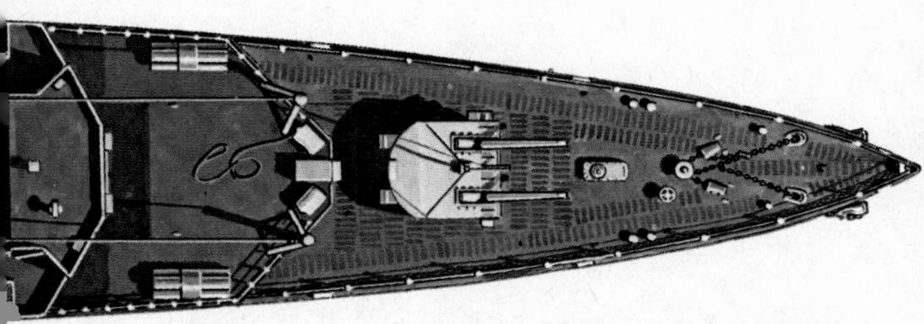

ex-*Allen M Sumner* Class

No and name	recom-missioned	disposal
DD.692 ***Allen M Sumner***	12/1961	Stricken 8/1973
DD.693 ***Moale***	12/1961	Stricken 7/1973
DD.694 ***Ingraham***	12/1961	To Greece 7/1971 as *Miaoulis*
DD.697 ***Charles S Sperry***	6/1960	To Chile 1/1974 as *Ministro Zenteno*
DD.698 ***Ault***	12/1962	Stricken 7/1973
DD.699 ***Waldron***	12/1962	To Colombia 10/1973 as *Santander*
DD.703 ***Wallace L Lind***	7/1962	To South Korea 12/1973 as *Dae Gu*
DD.704 ***Borie***	7/1962	To Argentina 7/1972 as *Bouchard*
DD.709 ***Hugh Purvis***	10/1960	To Turkey 7/1972 as *Zafer*
DD.723 ***Walke***	10/1961	Stricken 2/1974
DD.724 ***Laffey***	9/1962	Stricken 3/1975
DD.725 ***O'Brien***	10/1961	Stricken 2/1972
DD.727 ***De Haven***	8/1960	To South Korea 12/1973 as *Inchon*
DD.728 ***Mansfield***	9/1960	Stricken 2/1974
DD.729 ***Lyman K Swenson***	1/1961	Stricken 2/1974
DD.730 ***Collett***	8/1960	Stricken 2/1974
DD.744 ***Blue***	1/1961	Stricken 2/1974
DD.746 ***Taussig***	9/1962	To Taiwan 5/1974 as *Lo Yang*
DD.752 ***Alfred A Cunningham***	9/1961	Stricken 2/1974
DD.754 ***Frank E Evans***	10/1961	Stricken 1969 (See below)
DD.755 ***John A Bole***	8/1962	Stricken 4/1974
DD.757 ***Putnam***	3/1963	Stricken 8/1973
DD.758 ***Strong***	11/1962	To Brazil 10/1973 as *Rio Grande do Norte*
DD.759 ***Lofberg***	7/1962	Stricken 4/1974
DD.760 ***John W Thomason***	1/1960	To Taiwan 5/1974 as *Nan Yang*
DD.761 ***Buck***	7/1962	To Brazil 7/1973 as *Alagoas*
DD.770 ***Lowry***	12/1960	To Brazil 10/1973 as *Espiritu*
DD.776 ***James C Owen***	10/1962	To Brazil 7/1973 as *Sergipe*
DD.777 ***Zellars***	5/1960	To Iran 3/1971 as *Babr*

No and name		recom-missioned	disposal
DD.778	*Massey*	7/1960	Stricken 9/1973
DD.779	*Douglas H Fox*	10/1962	To Chile 1/1974 as *Ministro Portales*
DD.780	*Stormes*	1/1961	To Iran 2/1972 as *Palang*
DD.781	*Robert K Huntington*	9/1960	To Venezuela as *Falcon*

ex-*Fletcher* Class

No and name		recom-missioned	disposal
DD.446	*Radford*	11/1960	Stricken 11/1969
DD.447	*Jenkins*	1/1961	Stricken 7/1969
DD.449	*Nicholas*	7/1960	Stricken 1/1970

PPL

The ex-*Allen M Sumner* Class destroyer *Charles S Sperry* after FRAM II conversion and transferred to Chile as the *Ministro Zenteno*

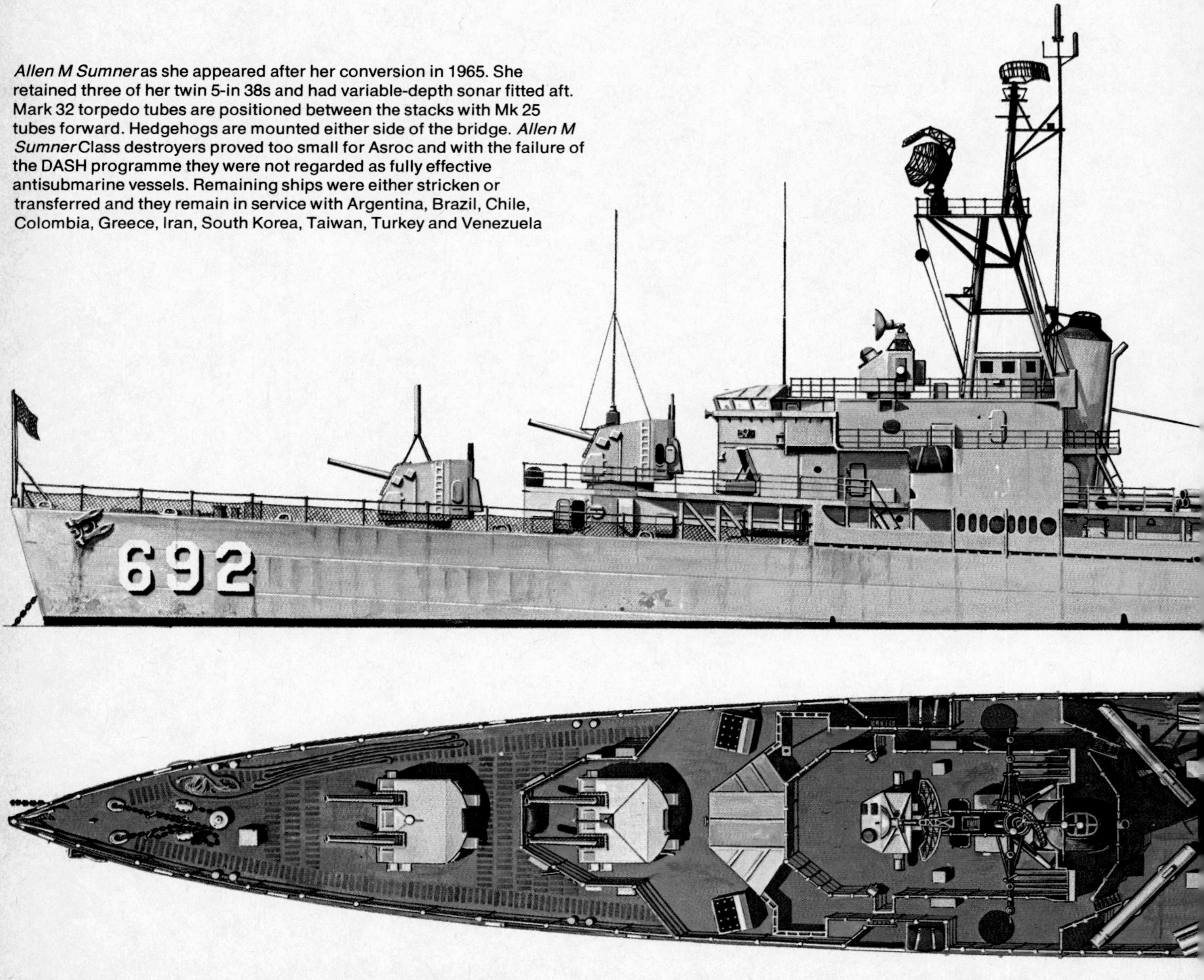

Allen M Sumner as she appeared after her conversion in 1965. She retained three of her twin 5-in 38s and had variable-depth sonar fitted aft. Mark 32 torpedo tubes are positioned between the stacks with Mk 25 tubes forward. Hedgehogs are mounted either side of the bridge. *Allen M Sumner* Class destroyers proved too small for Asroc and with the failure of the DASH programme they were not regarded as fully effective antisubmarine vessels. Remaining ships were either stricken or transferred and they remain in service with Argentina, Brazil, Chile, Colombia, Greece, Iran, South Korea, Taiwan, Turkey and Venezuela

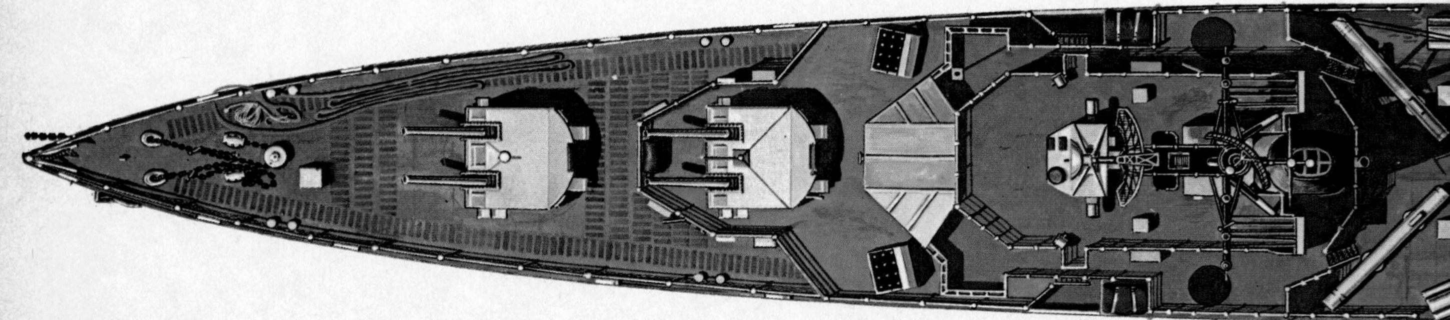

USS *Radford* (ex-*Fletcher* Class). She retained single 5-in guns and an A/S rocket launcher in B position. Hedgehog launchers are located forward of the bridge, but she carries no Asroc

The three ex-*Fletchers* were given a DASH hangar and flight deck aft and Mk 32 torpedo tubes amidships, but retained the Weapon Alfa rocket-launcher and Hedgehog mortars in B position which they had had as DDEs. However, they had the same funnels as the other FRAM ships. The *Sumners* and *Gearings* differed widely, some retaining all three 5-in (127-mm) twin mountings, others having only two. None had Asroc, and two did not have a DASH hangar and flight deck.

The FRAM programme was widely criticized as a waste of money, but as the lists show in all cases the life of the ships exceeded the planned extension. The ships were at least suited for front-line service, whereas before they were of little fighting value for modern warfare. The biggest criticism had, in fact, nothing to do with the ships, but affected the value of the FRAM Is. This was the decision to install the DASH drone system before the concept had been fully proven. When the DASH programme collapsed in 1969, after 416 drones out of 746 delivered had crashed, there was a bitter wrangle over who was to blame. To make matters worse the flight decks were not strong enough to take a manned helicopter, so there was no hope of providing any replacement. Thus in the decade when the Royal Navy and others were proving that antisubmarine escorts had to have a helicopter to function effectively, the escorts of the US Navy could not operate any type at all.

One of the group, *Frank E Evans* was cut in half by the Australian carrier *Melbourne* during an exercise on the night of June 2, 1969, in the South China Sea. The forward half sank but the after portion was towed to safety; it was written off and sunk as a target. *Bordelon* was scrapped after being in collision with the carrier *John F Kennedy*. The Turkish *Kocatepe* (ex-*Harwood*) was sunk in error by Turkish aircraft on July 22, 1974, during the attack on Cyprus. The ex-*Norris*, which had been transferred for spares, was commissioned in her place and renamed *Kocatepe*.

The specifications given below are for the ships following their FRAM conversions. For original specifications see entries under class names.

See also *Allen M Sumner*, Asroc, DASH, *Fletcher* and *Gearing*.

(FRAM I—*Gearings*) *Displacement:* 2425 tons (normal), 3512 tons (full load) *Dimensions and Machinery:* As built *Armament:* 2/4 5-in (127-mm)/38-cal dual purpose (1×2/2×2); 1 Asroc 8-barrelled missile launcher; 2 Hedgehogs; 6 12.75-in (32.4-cm) torpedo tubes (2×3) *Aircraft:* 2 DASH helicopters *Crew:* 274

(FRAM II—*Sumners* and *Fletchers*) *Displacement:* 2425 tons (normal), 3512 tons (full load) *Dimensions and Machinery:* As built *Armament:* 4/6 5-in (127-mm)/38-cal dual purpose (2×2/3×2); 2 Hedgehogs; 2 21-in (53-cm) Mk 25 torpedo tubes (not in all); 6 12.75-in (32.4-cm) Mk 32 torpedo tubes (2×3) *Aircraft:* 2 DASH helicopters (not in all)

(FRAM II—ex-*Allen M Sumner*) *Displacement:* 2200 tons (normal), 3300 tons (full load) *Dimensions and Machinery:* As built *Armament:* as FRAM II *Gearings*

(FRAM II—ex-*Fletcher*) *Displacement:* 2060 tons (normal), 2980 tons (full load) *Dimensions and Machinery:* As built *Armament:* 2 5-in (127-mm)/38-cal dual purpose; 1 Mk 108 A/S rocket-launcher; 2 Hedgehogs; 6 12.75-in (32.4-cm) torpedo tubes (2×3)

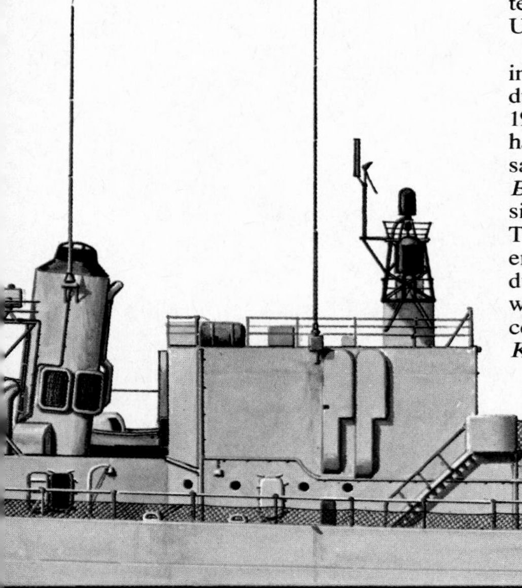

The French *Framée* Class destroyer *Pique*. Built at Granville-le Havre and launched on March 31, 1900, she served her career in the Mediterranean. In 1915-16 she operated off the Dardanelles and was then assigned to escort duties out of Brindisi. At the close of the First World War she was stationed off Provence and was stricken in 1921

No and name	launched	built
M4 *Framée*	21/10/1899	Nantes
M5 *Yatagan*	20/7/1900	Nantes
M6 *Pique*	31/3/1900	Granville-le Havre
M7 *Epée*	27/7/1900	Granville-le Havre

Musées de la Marine

Framée

French destroyer class, built 1897-1901. These ships were similar to the *Durandal* Class, but had four boilers as against two, which meant that the funnels were also doubled.

The machinery was not successful and as a result the trial speeds were disappointing. The acceptance trials were long and arduous, and they only made their designed speed of 26 knots with difficulty.

The prototype, *Framée*, was delivered by Chantiers de la Loire in February 1900 but did not complete trials for another four months; her sister *Yatagan* ran trials from May to October. *Pique* and *Epée* remained in the hands of their builders, Forges et Chantiers Mediterranée, for some months as well.

On the night of August 10-11, 1900, the brand new *Framée* was rammed and sunk by the battleship *Brennus* off Cape St Vincent. *Yatagan* spent all her time in the Channel, and by 1914 was on fishery protection. She was rammed and sunk by the British merchantman *Teviot* off Dieppe on the night of November 3, 1916, and her captain was drowned. *Pique* went to the Mediterranean and remained there throughout her career. She served at the Dardanelles in 1915-16 and then went to Brindisi for escort duties in the Adriatic. In 1918 she was stationed off the coast of Provence and was stricken in January 1921. *Epée* also spent most of her life in the Mediterranean, and was involved in a serious collision with torpedo boat *No 263* off Corsica in March 1907. In April 1915 she was transferred to Cherbourg to act as a divisional leader for submarines but she returned to Bizerta a year later. She was stricken in 1920 and sold for scrap in 1921.

In 1916 *Pique* was refitted with an enlarged bridge and the after torpedo tube was removed from the quarterdeck to amidships to make room for a high-angle 75-mm gun.

Displacement: 319 tonnes (normal), 348 tonnes (full load) *Length:* 58.2 m (190 ft 11½ in) oa *Beam:* 5.86 m (19 ft 2½ in) deck; 6.31 m (20 ft 8½ in) wl *Draught:* 3.02 m (9 ft 11½ in) mean *Machinery:* 2-shaft reciprocating, 5200 ihp (max)= 26 knots *Armament:* 2 65-mm (2.56-in) Model 1891 QF (2× 1); 6 47-mm (1.85-in) Model 1885 QF (6× 1); 2 38.1-cm (15-in) torpedo tubes; 1 75-mm (2.95-in) AA gun added 1916-17 *Crew:* 52

Français

French submarine class, built 1900-01. Two improved *Morse* type (Q.11-12) were ordered, almost identical in hull design, but built of steel, not bronze. *Français* was launched on January 29, 1901, and *Algerien* on April 25, 1901, both at Cherbourg arsenal.

The two boats were commissioned in the same year, and proved quite successful. *Algerien* proved the strength of her hull when she collided with the armoured cruiser *Kleber* while submerged. The submarine was damaged, but the cruiser had two of her propeller shafts badly bent.

Both craft were discarded in May 1914, being unsuitable for operational use.

Displacement: 147/160 tonnes (surfaced/submerged) *Length:* 36.78 m (120 ft 8 in) oa *Beam:* 2.75 m (9 ft) *Draught:* 2.87 m (9 ft 5 in) *Machinery:* 1-shaft electric motor, 307 shp= 10.1/8.3 knots (surfaced/submerged) *Armament:* 3 45-cm (17.7-in) torpedoes (1 bow tube, 2 drop-collars) *Crew:* 13

Frances Allied codename for Japanese bomber See **P1Y Ginga, Yokosuka**

Francesco Caracciolo

Italian battleship class, laid down in 1914-15 but never completed. The design was influenced by the British *Queen Elizabeth* Class, and the Tyneside Elswick Ordnance Works (part of Armstrong Whitworth) prepared the design of a 15-in (381-mm) gun similar to the 1912 Mark I pattern then under construction for the Royal Navy.

The first design for the new ships was drawn up in 1912, and four triple 15-in (381-mm) mountings were proposed. As this would have required an enormous jump to 35 000 tons the requirement was scaled down to nine 15-in (381-mm) on 29 000 tons. Both designs were rejected, for Italian industry could not provide such heavy triple mountings and the British parent company of the Pozzuoli gun foundry would not recommend such a drastic increase in complexity. By this time news of *Queen Elizabeth*'s high speed (25 knots) had leaked out, and so the design committee finally chose a ship of similar layout, with eight guns in twin mountings, but even higher speed. Whereas *Queen Elizabeth* needed a nominal 58 000 hp for 23 knots but could use overload to 70 000 hp, the Italian design started at 70 000 hp for 25 knots, and would have had a designed overload of 105 000 hp to give 28 knots.

A series of sketch designs show a good-looking ship with two funnels and two tripods, and the turrets unusually far apart. The hull was flush-decked and a 'spoon' bow was proposed.

All four ships were ordered in April 1914, and the name-ship was started six months later, while her sisters were laid down in the spring of 1915. But the steel shortage and lack of labour in the shipyards meant that construction slowed down, and when it stopped on all four in March 1916 only the

Name	builder
Francesco Caracciolo (ex-*Dandalo*)	Cantieri de Castellammare di Stabia
Francesco Morosini	Cantieri Orlando, Livorno
Cristoforo Colombo (ex-*Goffredo Mameli*)	Cantieri Ansaldo, Genoa
Marcantonio Colonna (ex-*Giuseppe Mazzini*)	Cantieri Odero, Genoa

Name	launched	built
Frankfurt (ex-*Ersatz Hela*)	3/1915	Kiel dockyard
Wiesbaden (ex-*Ersatz Gefion*)	1/1914	AG Vulcan, Stettin

(The prefix Ersatz, meaning substitute, was attached to names of ships designated as nominal replacements of existing vessels bearing the same name.)

Caracciolo was advanced. The *Colombo* was 5½% complete and hardly any work had been done on the other two. As about 9000 tons of material had been built into the hull of the *Caracciolo* it was decided to start work on her again in October 1919, and the hull was launched on May 12, 1920. Unfortunately Italy's finances were in a more parlous state than usual, and on October 25, 1920, she was sold to the Navigazione Generale Italiana for conversion to a cargo liner. A month later she was towed from La Spezia to Baia, near Naples, but the plans were subsequently abandoned as being uneconomic, and she was scrapped in 1921. The other three were stricken in January 1921 and scrapped.

The 15-in (381-mm) guns designed by Elswick were ordered from Pozzuoli, and 18 were completed before the ships were stopped. Apart from the ten kept back for the *Caracciolo*, the others were mounted in the following monitors: *Alfredo Cappellini* (2 guns from the *Morosini*); *Faa di Bruno* (2 guns from the *Colombo*); *Monte Santo*, ex-*Vella* (1 gun); *Monte Sabtino*, ex-*Tina* (1 gun); *Monte Cengio* (1 gun); *Monte Grappa* (1 gun); *Montello* (1 gun); *Monte Novegno* (1 gun).

The 15-in (381-mm)/40-cal Model 1914 was very similar to the British 15-in (381-mm)/42-cal Mk 1 and so was the mounting. The gun weighed 82 tonnes without breech-mechanism and the shell weighed 875 kg (1929 lb); the muzzle velocity was 700 m/sec (2296 ft/sec).

Displacement: 34 000 tonnes (designed normal) *Length:* 212.08 m (695 ft 9½ in) oa *Beam:* 29.6 m (97 ft 1½ in) *Draught:* 9.5 m (31 ft 2 in) *Machinery:* 4-shaft geared steam turbines, 105 000 shp= 28 knots *Protection:* 300 mm (11.8 in) belt, 51 mm (2 in) deck, 400 mm (15.75 in) conning tower and turrets *Armament:* 8 381-mm (15-in)/40-cal (4×2); 12 152-mm (6-in)/45-cal (12×1); 12 40-mm (2-pdr)/39-cal pom-poms (12×1) *Crew:* 1500 approx

Franchi

Italian submachine-gun. The firm of Luigi Franchi SpA, of Brescia, Italy, has a long record of manufacture of high-grade sporting guns. In the early 1950s the company designed a submachine-gun which was announced in 1956 as the LF56. This gun had a rectangular receiver of pressed steel and featured an 'overhung' bolt in which the bolt's main mass lay above the barrel and in front of the breech when the bolt was closed. A folding tubular metal butt was fitted, and a grip safety in the front edge of the butt was the only safety device. Some small, mainly cosmetic, changes were made and the gun was produced as the LF57, several thousand being bought by the Italian navy.

In 1962 a single-shot-only semiautomatic version with an extended barrel and flash-hider was produced. It is difficult to see what such a weapon might be good for. This must have occurred to others, since it never sold. The Franchi company have not, since then, produced any other military weapon designs.

(Model LF57) *Calibre:* 9 mm (0.354 in) Parabellum *Weight, loaded:* 4.05 kg (9 lb) *Length:* 68 cm (26.77 in) *Barrel length:* 20.5 cm (8.07 in) *Magazine:* 40-rd detachable box *Muzzle velocity:* 395-420 m/sec (1296-1378 ft/sec) *Rate of fire:* 500 rds/min

Frank Allied codename for Japanese fighter aircraft See **Ki-84 Hayate, Nakajima**

Frankfurt

German light cruiser class, built 1913-15. In 1912 a new design of light cruiser was drawn up, based on *Graudenz* but slightly shorter and beamier to allow a heavier weight of armament to be carried. In response to the enormous preponderance of gunpower in contemporary British light cruisers, the Marineamt finally abandoned the 105-mm (4.1-in) gun in favour of the much more effective 150-mm (5.9-in)/45-cal gun. They were the last prewar light cruisers to be laid down.

Both ships completed in August 1915 and joined the High Seas Fleet. At the Battle of Jutland *Frankfurt* was the flagship of the Second Scouting Group under Rear-Admiral Bödicker, and her sister was in the same squadron with the ex-Russian *Pillau* and *Elbing*. *Frankfurt* escaped with no damage but her sister took terrible punishment.

Wiesbaden and the rest of the Second Scouting Group went into action against the British cruiser *Chester* late in the afternoon of May 31, 1916, but after hitting the enemy several times they were in turn driven off by the guns of the battlecruisers *Invincible*, *Inflexible* and *Indomitable* as Rear-Admiral Hood led his 3rd Battle Cruiser Squadron into action. *Wiesbaden* was shattered by accurate 12-in (305-mm) salvoes and had her machinery disabled. She lay helpless in the path of the advancing British Grand Fleet, which was carrying out its deployment into the battle line. As each battleship passed by she indulged in leisurely target-practice against the wallowing hulk of *Wiesbaden*. In all 58 salvoes were fired at the cruiser, but she managed intermittent firing from the one or two guns still left working. Even the crippled British destroyer *Onslow*, capable of only 10 knots, closed to 3200 m (3500 yards) and hit her with a torpedo, but she remained afloat.

The ship was fired on again by British light cruisers, but this did not prevent her from achieving a final act of defiance. At about 1900 hrs, while the German battle fleet was wearily trying to find its way through the British line, she was able to hit the battleship *Marlborough* with a torpedo, inflicting sufficient damage to force her to fall out of line. The smouldering wreck of *Wiesbaden* finally sank later, at about 0245 hrs, but none of the 589 men aboard were seen again.

Frankfurt was scuttled in shallow water at Scapa Flow on June 21, 1919, but was raised a month later by the British. She was handed over to the United States, and on July 18, 1921, she was one of the target ships sunk off Cape Henry in General Billy Mitchell's famous exercise to demonstrate the value of aerial bombing against ships.

Displacement: 5180 tons (normal), 6601 tons (full load) *Length:* 145.3 m (476 ft 8 in) oa *Beam:* 13.9 m (45 ft 7 in) *Draught:* 6.06 m (19 ft 10½ in) max *Machinery:* 2-shaft steam turbines, 31 000 shp= 27.5 knots *Protection:* 60-18 mm (2.36-0.71 in) belt, 40-20 mm (1.57-0.79 in) deck, 100-20 mm (3.9-0.79 in) conning tower *Armament:* 8 150-mm (5.9-in)/45-cal (8×1); 4 52-mm (2-in)/55-cal AA (4×1), replaced by 2 88-mm (3.46-in)/45-cal AA (2×1); 4 50-cm (19.7-in) torpedo tubes (2 broadside above water, 2 broadside below water); provision for 120 mines *Crew:* 474

Franklin

US aircraft carrier, launched 1943. *Franklin* was the thirteenth vessel to carry a 'fleet carrier' designation (CV13), but only the twelfth to be built from the keel up as an aircraft carrier; CV1 (see *Langley*) was converted from a collier.

The eighth ship of the *Essex* Class to be constructed, *Franklin* was authorized in 1940 but not laid down until December 7, 1942—the first anniversary of Pearl Harbor—owing to a shortage of slipways of sufficient length. The Newport News Shipbuilding Company, with experience of four previous representatives of the class, surpassed itself by completing *Franklin* in less than 14 months, the US Navy commissioning her on January 31, 1944.

The process of working up the ship and her 90 aircraft strong Air Group 13 occupied the next five months and it was not until June 30 that *Franklin* left Eniwetok to join Task Group 58.2 for an Independence Day strike on the Bonin Islands. This was followed by a fortnight of strikes on the Marianas islands of Rota and Guam, preparing for the landings on the islands, a two-day strike on the Palau Islands and a transfer to TG 58.1 for another attack on the Bonins, on August 4.

This very busy opening month was rewarded by a 19-day break for rest and replenishment at Eniwetok. *Franklin*, with *Enterprise, Monterey* and *San Jacinto*, paid her third visit to the Bonins between August 31 and September 2; the group, less *San Jacinto*, was renumbered as TG 38.5 at Saipan on September 4. TG 38.4 supported the invasion of the Palaus from September 10, while the other three groups were away striking at the Philippines, and it was not until October 7 that *Franklin* and her consorts rejoined Task Force 58.

As a prelude to the invasion of Leyte, the American fast carriers attacked the Ryukus and Formosa from October 10 to 15. At dusk on October 13, *Franklin* was attacked by four Japanese torpedo bombers. She avoided the torpedoes, but one bomber hit the ship and slid across the deck, but caused very little damage. Two days later, she was hit, this time by a bomb which went through the deck-edge lift, killing three men but inflicting no serious damage. TG 38.4 attacked shipping in Manila Bay and airfields on Luzon on October 18 and 19, and afterward supported the Leyte invasion.

On October 24, *Franklin*'s aircraft joined in the follow-up to the battle of Surigao Strait, sinking a destroyer, and then turned north to participate in the strikes on the main Japanese fleet in the Sibuyan Sea, where they scored hits on the battleship *Musashi.* On the next day, at the battle of Cape Engano, bombers from *Franklin* stopped the carrier *Chiyoda* and finished off *Zuikaku.*

On October 27 and 28, *Franklin*'s group was extremely busy, defending the Leyte assault area and itself, but the carriers were not hit until October 30, when five Kamikazes broke through and hit both *Franklin* and *Belleau Wood* (which had replaced *Monterey*). *Franklin* lost 33 aircraft and suffered 116 casualties, of which 56 were fatal. Both carriers were severely damaged and withdrew, *Franklin* to Bremerton navy yard, Washington, where she was under repair until the beginning of February 1945.

When she rejoined Task Force 58 on March 15, 1945, *Franklin* was carrying 36 Marine Corps F4U Corsairs in addition to her own 32 Corsairs, six Hellcats and 30 TBM Avengers and SB2C Helldivers of Air Group 5. The marines were embarked for the forthcoming Okinawa assault, in which their ground-attack expertise was expected to play a major role.

TF 58's aircraft struck at Kyushu on March 18. The Japanese air forces reacted quickly but the slight damage sustained by three US Navy carriers was a small price to pay for the destruction of 380 enemy aircraft and the damage inflicted on many industrial installations. The next day began promisingly, with the first strike concentrating on the Kure navy yard and Kobe. As *Franklin* was preparing to fly off her second strike, she was hit by two 550-lb (250-kg) bombs dropped by a D4Y 'Judy' which had approached undetected. Two minutes later, at 0710 hrs, *Wasp* (CV 18) was hit by a conventional dive-bombing attack.

The two bombs which hit *Franklin* did not penetrate below the hangar deck, and the major immediate damage they caused was the destruction of the two inboard lifts, but the fires started were fed by the fuel of the 31 aircraft on deck—and those below in the hangar—and the detonation of the rockets and bombs which they were carrying. Casualties amounted to 724 killed and 265 wounded, but a large proportion of the dead were victims of the suffocating smoke which was drawn into the ventilation system from the blazing hangar. The machinery was undamaged but the compartments had to be abandoned due to the smoke and the ship was dead in the water three hours after the attack. The AA cruiser *Santa Fé* assisted the skeleton firefighting crews left aboard and the carrier was taken in tow by the heavy cruiser *Pittsburgh* at about noon. The fires were completely under control by early afternoon and 24 hours later she was able to proceed under her own steam at 15 knots. Two of her officers were subsequently awarded the Congressional Medal of Honor for their heroism on March 19.

Franklin proceeded to Pearl Harbor from the operational area and was there tidied up before going on to the New York navy yard for long-term repairs, involving virtual rebuilding above the hangar deck. *Wasp*, which suffered 370 casualties, also returned to the US for repairs, but in her case the damage was on a lesser scale and she was operational again before the end of the war. *Franklin* arrived at Brooklyn on April 25, 1945, and did not leave until well after the end of the war. She was never fully restored to service, and was decommissioned into reserve at Bayonne, New Jersey, on February 17, 1947. She was awarded Battle Stars for her participation in the Marianas, Palau, and Leyte campaigns and for the March 1945 strikes on Japan.

Redesignated CVS 13 in October 1952, indicating that she was now intended for antisubmarine support duties, *Franklin* remained out of commission even during the Korean War. In May 1959, she was reclassed as an aircraft transport (AVT8). Finally, on October 1, 1964, she was discarded and put up for sale for scrap.

Above: USS _Franklin_ hit by two bombs on March 18, 1945; she was severely damaged and was rocked by five hours of secondary explosions. _Below: Franklin_ in 1945, after emergency repairs

Displacement: 27 100 tons *Length:* 265.78 m (872 ft) oa *Beam:* 28.35 m (93 ft) *Draught:* 8.69 m (28 ft 6 in) *Machinery:* 4-shaft geared turbines, 150 000 shp= 33 knots *Armament:* 12 5-in (127-mm) (4×2; 4×1); 44-68 40-mm (1.57-in) AA guns *Aircraft:* 100 *Crew:* 3500

FRAS-1 Soviet antisubmarine rocket
See **SUW-N-1**

Freccia

Italian destroyer class, built 1929-32. These destroyers were the first in the world with single funnels, since the British *Fervent* and *Zephyr* in the 1890s. In 1928 the Odero firm of Sestri Ponente, near Genoa was asked to work out a new design, intermediate between the 1000-ton 'Turbine' and the 1900-ton 'Navigatori' type. The new destroyers had to try to achieve 38 knots, have sufficient endurance to enable them to accompany major warships, plus increased firepower.

This was a set of contradictory requirements on a 1200-ton hull, and it is hardly surprising that the 44 000-hp Belluzzo geared turbines could only produce a sea speed of 30 knots, especially as the normal displacement was finally 1690 tons. The lead-ship *Freccia* actually reached 39.43 knots on trials but her displacement was kept down to 1370 tons by leaving out the torpedo tubes and guns, and restricting the fuel and feedwater. None of her sisters got near this speed.

The armament was well laid out, a twin 120-mm (4.7-in) gun-mounting on the forecastle and another on the after deckhouse, with two sets of triple 53-cm (21-in) torpedo tubes amidships. The short forecastle was not ideal for high speed in rough weather, however, and the original AA armament of two 2-pdr pom-poms and twin 13.2-mm (0.52-in) machine-guns was far too weak. Little attempt was made to restrict topweight, with a large enclosed bridge structure surmounted by a director control tower and a lofty searchlight tower in addition to a secondary director aft, between the torpedo tubes.

Another problem was that the ships were only fully stable when carrying their full fuel load. The use of permanent ballast helped to cure the problem, but reduced the speed still further.

The class was fully employed on escort and patrol duties, and all became casualties. *Baleno* capsized after being severely damaged in action with British destroyers on April 16, 1941. *Fulmine* was sunk in action with British forces on November 9, 1941. *Lampo* sank in shallow water on April 16, 1941, after being set on fire by British destroyers (with *Baleno*). She was raised, only to be sunk by aircraft bombs on April 30, 1943. *Strale* ran aground near Cape Bon on June 21, 1942. *Folgore* was sunk by British forces on December 2, 1942, in the Sicilian Channel (the strait that lies between Sicily and Tunisia). *Saetta* was sunk by mine in the Sicilian Channel on February 3, 1943. *Freccia* was sunk by air attack in Genoa on August 8, 1943. *Dardo* was captured by German forces while refitting at Genoa in September 1943. Renamed *TA.31*, she was scuttled at Genoa on April 24, 1945.

Displacement: 1st Group—1225 tons (standard), 1690 tons (normal), 1890 tons (full load); 2nd Group—1650 tons (normal), 1920 tons (full load) *Length:* 94.3 m (309 ft 5 in) *Beam:* 1st Group—9.75 m (32 ft); 2nd Group—9.2 m (30 ft 2 in) *Draught:* 1st Group—3.15 m (10 ft 4 in); 2nd Group—3.3 m (10 ft 9 in) *Machinery:* 2-shaft geared steam turbines, 44 000 shp=30 knots (in light condition) *Armament:* (Original) 4 120-mm (4.7-in)/50-cal (2×2); 2 120-mm (4.7-in)/15-cal starshell guns (2×1); 2 40-mm (1.57-in)/39-cal (2×1); 4 13.2-mm (0.52-in) machine-guns (2×2); 6 53-cm (21-in) torpedo tubes (2×3); 54 mines; (Wartime) 4 120-mm (4.7-in)/50-cal; 6 20-mm (0.79-in)/65-cal (2×2, 2×1); 6 53-cm (21-in) torpedo tubes; (*Dardo* 1943) 4 120-mm (4.7-in)/50-cal; 8 37-mm (1.46-in)/54-cal AA (8×1); 12 20-mm (0.79-in)/65-cal AA (3×4); 3 53-cm (21-in) torpedo tubes (1×3) *Crew:* 183

Italian Navy

The Italian destroyer *Freccia*, built by Cantieri del Tirreno and lost at Genoa in 1943

Freccia, Fiat G.50

Italian fighter aircraft. Fiat's young designer Giuseppe Gabrielli produced his proposals for the G.50 single-seat monoplane prototype in 1936, at which time it was the most modern fighter design in Italy. Although a contemporary of the Spitfire and Hurricane, it did not have either the advanced qualities or the development potential of the British types and remained to the end extremely lightly armed. The Freccia (arrow) was the first all-metal monoplane with a retractable undercarriage to be evaluated by the Italian air force; the prototype flew for the first time on February 26, 1937, and proved light to handle, with a high degree of manoeuvrability, but somewhat lacking in both engine and fire power. Its powerplant was the rather cumbersome 840-hp Fiat A.74 RC 38 14-cylinder two-row radial, fitted with a supercharger and driving a Fiat-built Hamilton three-blade variable-pitch metal propeller. The armament comprised two 12.7-mm (0.5-in) Breda-SAFAT machine-guns mounted forward of the cockpit in the top of the fuselage, synchronized to fire through the propeller arc. The 150 rounds for each gun could be fired in single shots or in salvo.

Production was undertaken both by Fiat and CMASA, a subsidiary, and the first 12 were delivered to the Italian expeditionary forces in Spain in January 1939 towards the end of the civil war. Although too late to give a true indication of their potential under battle conditions, it was decided to continue with a further order for 200 aircraft. The first 45 production G.50s had an enclosed cockpit, but Italian pilots preferred the open variety, and after testing several designs, an open canopy with hinged, transparent side flaps was adopted as standard. Upon Italy's entry into the Second World War in June 1940, a total of 118 G.50s were in service: 97 with operational units and the other 21 awaiting either delivery or repair. The 51° Stormo CT at Ciampino was composed entirely of G.50s,

1st Group

Recognition letter	name	launched	built
DR (changed to DA 1939)	*Dardo*	9/1930	Odero-Terni-Orlando, Sestri
FR	*Freccia*	8/1930	C del Tirreno, Riva Trigoso
SA	*Saetta*	1/1932	C del Tirreno, Riva Trigoso
ST	*Strale*	3/1931	OTO, Sestri

2nd Group

Recognition letter	name	launched	built
BO	*Baleno*	3/1931	C Nav del Quarnaro, Fiume
FG	*Folgore*	4/1931	Off, e C Partenopei, Naples
FL	*Fulmine*	8/1931	C Navdel Quarnaro
LP	*Lampo*	7/1931	Off, e C Partenopei

The Fiat G.50*bis* substituted a semi-open cockpit for the original enclosed cockpit with sliding canopy. While the Freccia was the Regia Aeronautica's first all-metal monoplane with retractable undercarriage, it was somewhat underpowered and poorly armed with only two machine-guns in the forward fuselage

and G.50s in company with Fiat C.R.32s made up the 52° Stormo in Tuscany; they were used mainly as escorts during the early days of the war. A two-seat trainer version, also manufactured by CMASA, was produced. Designated G.50B, it had a second cockpit with dual controls added and the armament installation removed. One hundred and eight were produced, and gave satisfactory service at Regia Aeronautica training units.

Fiat G.50s also formed part of the 56° Stormo, based at Maldegem in Belgium, to assist the Luftwaffe during the Battle of Britain, but they achieved no great success in that theatre and most had been returned to Italy by April 1941. Better results were achieved by the 35 G.50s ordered by Finland in late 1939, although deliveries were initially sporadic due to German interference. However, after the start of the so-called 'continuation war' in Finland in June 1941, the Finnish G.50s gave excellent service until withdrawn from the front line in May 1944.

The Regia Aeronautica, meanwhile, utilized its G.50s in Greece, the Balkans, the Mediterranean and North Africa before they began to be replaced by the superior G.50*bis* The prototype of this was flown for the first time on September 9, 1940, and differed from the original aircraft in having improved fuselage contours, increased fuel capacity, more modern radio equipment, an enlarged rudder, and a modified canopy and armour protection for the pilot. A total of 421 G.50*bis* were built, and served mainly in North Africa (Libya) from late 1940 until December 1941. Nine were supplied to the Croatian air force. Some G.50*bis* were fitted with underwing racks at this time, to carry small bombs.

Several experimental variants were tested, including the G.50*bis*-A, which was an enlarged two-seat fighter-bomber with better armament and a bigger bombload, plus an arrester hook for service aboard the planned aircraft carriers *Aquila* and *Sparviero*. It flew for the first time on October 3, 1942, but after Italy's surrender all further development ceased and none was produced.

(G.50*bis*) *Span:* 11 m (36 ft 1 in) *Length:* 8.29 m (27 ft 2½ in) *Gross weight:* 2500 kg (5500 lb) *Maximum speed:* 486 km/h (302 mph)

IWM

A G.50 abandoned at Sidi Rezegh in North Africa. RAF Hawker Hurricanes are on the right

Freehand, Yakovlev

Soviet VTOL research aircraft. Displayed publicly at the Domodedovo, Moscow, flying display in July 1967, this single-seater appeared to be powered by two turbojets installed side by side in the belly, each discharging through a louvred and gridded swivelling nozzle. The nose was occupied by large lateral air ducts from a bifurcated pitot inlet, and the whole installation had much in common with that of today's Yak-36 Forger, though the latter is thought to have only a single main engine. Freehand had no lift jets, and pipes from the main engine served reaction-control nozzles at the tips of the wing, at the tail and on the end of an outsize nose boom. The wing, very similar to that of the Yak-36, was mounted in the mid-position directly above the engine nozzles. The vertical tail was sharply swept, and two ventral fins were fitted under the rear fuselage. A large surface under the nose, double-hinged to function as an airbrake, was also hinged at the rear, and was judged to reduce reingestion of hot gas in the low-level hovering mode.

Two Freehands took part at Domodedovo, one No 37 and the other No 38, the latter carrying two UV-16-57 rocket pods. Fitting the latter was considered chiefly a public relations exercise, but in fact Freehand could

The Yakovlev Freehand VTOL research aircraft, first seen in public in Moscow in July 1967

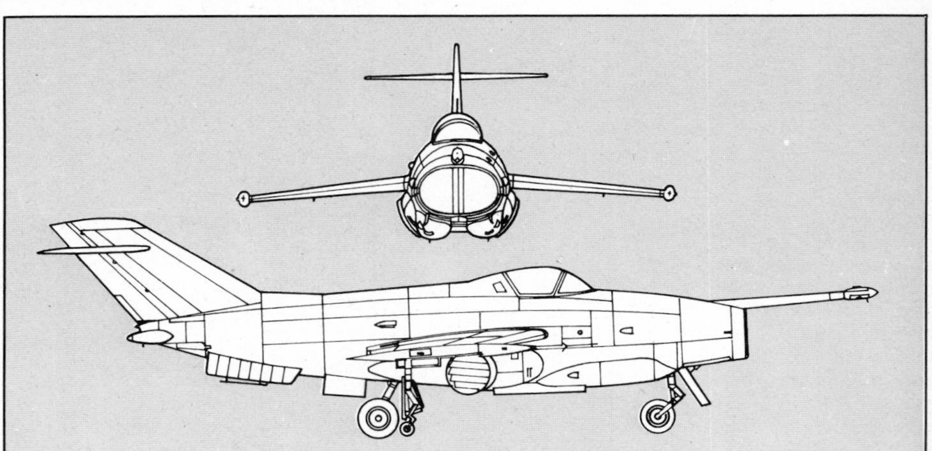

MiG-17 Fresco fighters in a practice scramble. Frescos were withdrawn from front-line service with the Soviet air force during the late 1960s

well have increased its value by carrying out research into weapon aiming and firing in wing- or jet-supported modes. There is no evidence to suggest that it was ever an operational type, though at least eight were built, and one went aboard the helicopter ASW cruiser *Moskva* where it conducted flying trials from an elevated platform not quite the same as those often used by Ka-25 helicopters.

Span: about 8 m (26 ft 3 in) *Length:* about 17.5 m (57 ft 5 in) *Gross weight:* about 6000 kg (13 300 lb) *Maximum speed:* about 800 km/h (500 mph)

Fresco, Mikoyan MiG-17

Soviet jet fighter-bomber. After the success with the MiG-15 Fagot (the replacement prototype flew on December 30, 1947), the Mikoyan design bureau set out to capitalize on its achievement by improving the transonic handling and generally updating the design. The air brakes on the MiG-15 had to be made to open automatically at Mach 0.92 to prevent the airframe being overstrained by buffeting, and a completely new wing was therefore adopted for what was to become the MiG-17. The prototype of the SI design flew in 1949, only nine months after the MiG-15 entered service with the Soviet air force, and before it had been blooded in Korea. The tendency of the MiG-15 to enter a spin caused by tip-stalling in high-speed combat manoeuvres was undoubtedly relayed to the design team so that modifications could be made to the new type.

The SI, developed at the time as the SD and SP versions of the MiG-15, embodied most of the fuselage of the former (better known as the MiG-15*bis*). The SD's forward and mid-fuselage section were married to a rear assembly lengthened by 90 cm (35 in) to give a greater fineness ratio. A fixed-incidence tailplane with greater sweepback angle was adopted, but the major change was in the use of a completely new wing; it was thinner and shorter than that of the MiG-15 and had greater sweepback, reaching a maximum of 45°. These alterations had the desired effect—the onset of compressibility effects was delayed—and in February 1950 the new aircraft exceeded the speed of sound.

The MiG-17 was preferred to the Yak-50 and entered service with the Soviet air force in its Fresco-A form during 1952. Its powerplant was a Klimov VK-1 turbojet producing 2700 kg (5950 lb) of thrust, the same as in the MiG -15*bis*, and the armament was similar: one 37-mm (1.46-in) N-37 cannon and a pair of 23-mm (0.90-in) NR-23s, aimed with the aid of a simple gyro gunsight. Air-to-surface armament could also be carried in the form of four UV-8-57 pods each containing eight 5.5-cm (2.16-in) S-5 rockets, two 21-cm (8.26-in) rockets, two 250-kg (551-lb) bombs or 240-litre (53-Imp gal) drop tanks. The use of steel underwing beams allowed two rocket pods or bombs to be carried inboard, with drop tanks on the outboard pylons.

Fresco-B was the MiG-17P fitted with an S-band 'Izumrud' (Emerald) radar, known as Scan Fix in the West, with the main dish mounted on the intake splitter and the ranging element housed above in the lip. The fuselage was lengthened by 127 mm (5 in) and the cockpit glazing was modified to cater for additional displays.

Both initial variants were soon replaced by Fresco-C and -D, the MiG-17F and -17PF respectively. The original engine was replaced by a VK-1F fitted with an afterburner and giving a maximum thrust of 3380 kg (7451 lb). The fuselage was cut back to expose the end of the afterburner nozzle, and the air brakes were modified. The latter had consistently given trouble; those on the new variants were larger than their predecessors, mounted in a different position on the fuselage and operated by external jacks. Armament for the two uprated MiG-17s was standardized on three NR-23s with 100 rounds each, and the MiG-17F was built under licence in Poland as the LIM-5P and in China as the F-4; the earlier model had been constructed as the LIM-5 and the Czech S.104.

The MiG-17PF Fresco-D entered service in 1955 and was fitted with progressively improved versions of Izumrud/Scan Fix, operating in X-band as well as the original S-band, and in the MiG-17PFU Fresco-E variant the gun armament was replaced by four beam-riding AA-1 Alkali air-to-air missiles carried on underwing pylons projecting forward of the leading edge. Some MiG-17s were fitted out for reconnaissance, with cameras in the forward fuselage and only two guns, and the type has increasingly been used for ground attack as it was replaced in the interception role.

Some Polish LIM-5Ps were modified to LIM-5M standard by fitting additional fuel tanks and a twin-wheel main undercarriage with low-pressure tyres which retracted into a larger wing centre section built of reinforced plastics. A relatively small number were converted, but many others were upgraded to LIM-6 standard by introducing a braking parachute, rocket-assisted takeoff units and additional stores pylons. The LIM-6, together with the LIM-6*bis* having modified ordnance racks and the reconnaissance LIM-6R, remained in Polish service until replaced by the Su-20 Fitter-C.

More than 9000 MiG-17s were built. The production lines in the USSR were closed in 1958, but the type was exported more widely than any other Soviet military aircraft. The Fresco was withdrawn from Soviet air force service in the late 1960s but soldiers on in many parts of the world, typical ground-attack weapons comprising 250-kg (551-lb) bombs, UV-16-57 rocket pods and S-24 rockets.

(MiG-17F) *Span:* 9.63 m (31 ft 7¼ in) *Length:* 11.09 m (36 ft 4½ in) *Gross weight:* 6070 kg (13 380 lb) *Maximum speed:* Mach 0.985

Fret

Dutch destroyer class, built 1909-14. Eight four-funnelled destroyers were built to a Yarrow design for service in the East Indies. They resembled contemporary British destroyers, with a high forecastle and two single 45-cm (17.7-in) torpedo tubes on the centreline but the gun armament was heavier. Two Krupp 75-mm (2.95-in) quickfirers were mounted side by side on the forecastle, one on a 'bandstand' between the tubes, and the other aft.

Fret and *Wolf* were launched in 1910, *Jakhals* and *Bulhond* in 1911, *Hermelijn* and *Lynx* in 1913—all of them constructed by the Royal de Schelde yard, Flushing. *Panter* and *Vos* were built by Fijenoord at Rotterdam and launched in 1913. All reached their

Bur. Mar. Hist. v.d. Marinestaf

***Hermelijn,* a *Fret* Class destroyer built by the Royal de Schelde yard and launched in 1913**

designed speed of 30 knots on trials. They were unusual in carrying both coal (130 tons) and oil fuel (11 tons).

The ships were scrapped in the late 1920s, the first to go being *Fret* and *Wolf*.

Displacement: 510 tons (normal) *Length:* 70.1 m (230 ft) oa *Beam:* 6.7 m (22 ft) *Draught:* 2.05 m (6 ft 8¾ in) (normal) *Machinery:* 2-shaft steam turbines, 8500 shp=30 knots *Armament:* 4 75-mm (2.95-in)/55-cal (4×1); 4 machine-guns (4×1); 2 45-cm (17.7-in) torpedo tubes (2×1) *Crew:* 84

Friant

French protected cruiser class, built 1891-98. Four were laid down between 1891 and 1893, with a heavy armament of six 164.7-mm (6.5-in) guns on a relatively small hull. They were intended for service in European waters rather than commerce-raiding; this was an outright contradiction of the doctrines expressed by the *Jeune Ecole*, and was another example of the erratic changes of policy by successive Ministers of Marine.

The ships were not an outstanding success, although well regarded outside France on account of their alleged superiority in gunpower and speed. It was held, for example, that an encounter between *Chasseloup-Laubat* and one of the British *Apollo* Class cruisers must result in the British ship's annihilation. In theory the French ship had the great advantage of being able to fire three of her 164.7-mm (6.5-in) guns ahead or astern, but in practice the beam guns in their heavy sponsons could not have fired dead ahead without causing severe damage from blast. Nor did the snout bow and the excessive tumblehome of the hull make for good seakeeping, and it is unlikely that she would have been able to make effective use of the guns she had. The forecastle gun was badly placed for spray interference as well.

Chasseloup-Laubat was disarmed in 1913, and during the First World War she was stationed at Corfu to act as a distilling ship. *Friant* was stationed in Newfoundland in 1914 on fishery protection, and was sent to the Mediterranean to join the Special Division. In 1915-16 she was with the Moroccan Division, and in 1918 she went to Mudros to act as depot ship for the 3rd Submarine Flotilla. In 1920 she was stricken.

Du Chayla landed troops at Casablanca in 1907, and from the outbreak of war in 1914 she was stationed in the Western Atlantic. In 1916-18 she transferred to the Red Sea Division, patrolling between Suez and Socotra. In 1917 she and her sister *Cassard* were hunting German raiders in the Indian Ocean, but in 1918 her armament was reduced to two 164.7-mm (6.5-in), four 75-mm (2.95-in) and four 47-mm (1.85-in) guns (the 164.7-mm guns had been given higher elevation to increase their range). Just before the Armistice in 1918 she was involved in the final clearing of Turkish forces from the Lebanon, and in 1919 *du Chayla* was stationed in the Red Sea. She was stricken in 1923.

Cassard joined the Special Division in the

Name	launched	builder
Chasseloup-Laubat	1893	Cherbourg arsenal
Friant	1893	Brest arsenal
du Chayla	1895	Cherbourg arsenal
Cassard	1896	Cherbourg arsenal

The French protected cruiser *Friant.* She served in the Mediterranean and Levant during the First World War and was stricken in 1924

Musées de la Marine

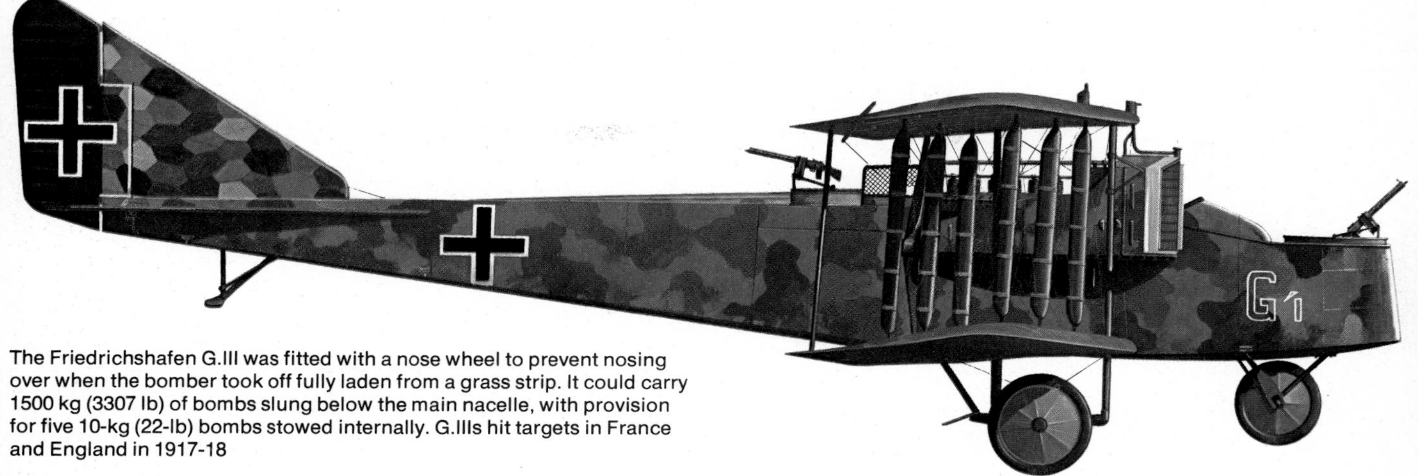

The Friedrichshafen G.III was fitted with a nose wheel to prevent nosing over when the bomber took off fully laden from a grass strip. It could carry 1500 kg (3307 lb) of bombs slung below the main nacelle, with provision for five 10-kg (22-lb) bombs stowed internally. G.IIIs hit targets in France and England in 1917-18

Western Mediterranean in August 1914, like *Friant*, and also went to the Moroccan Division. She served with *du Chayla* in the Indian Ocean in 1917 and then in the Red Sea, and saw her last service on the Syrian Station in 1921-22. Her armament was removed in 1922-23 when she was attached to the gunnery school as a hulk, and in 1924 she was stricken.

By French standards they were good-looking ships, with three unevenly spaced funnels and a flush deck. The most conspicuous feature was the pair of massive sponsons for the guns in the waist, and the high sponsons on either side of the forecastle and quarterdeck for the 100-mm (3.9-in) guns. Like many French ships they had conspicuous square ports instead of the more usual round scuttles or portholes. In 1918 the *Friant* had only one funnel.

Displacement: 3800-4000 tons (normal) *Length:* 100 m (328 ft) (*Friant*) 95 m (311 ft 8 in) pp *Beam:* 13 m (42 ft 8 in) *Draught:* 6.4 m (21 ft) *Protection:* 80 mm (3.15 in) deck; 30 mm (1.18 in) gun shields; 100 mm (3.9 in) conning tower *Machinery:* 2-shaft reciprocating, 10 000 ihp= 19 knots *Armament:* 6 164.7-mm (6.5-in)/45-cal Model 1891 (6×1); 4 100-mm (3.9-in) (4×1); 10 47-mm (1.85-in) (10×1); 2 45-cm (17.7-in) torpedo tubes (above water, beam) *Crew:* 385

Friedrichshafen

German bomber. A pre-1914 aeronautical manufacturer, the Flugzeugbau Friedrichshafen GmbH Manzell und Warnemunde produced a wide variety of aeroplane design throughout 1914-18, including a long line of successful marine aircraft, tiny single-seat scouts, and huge bombers. In the latter category, the firm was an early entrant in the design field, producing its G.I twin-engined biplane in 1915. Powered by twin 150-hp Benz Bz III engines driving pusher propellers, the G.I carried a three-man crew, and provided its makers with invaluable practical experience in the relatively new field of large aircraft design. The G.II appeared in 1916—a pleasing design with slightly shorter wings and a single fin/rudder tail unit (as opposed to the biplane tail of the G.I). Power came from twin 200-hp Benz Bz IV engines mounted between the wings and driving pusher propellers. Successfully passing its official trials, the G.II went into limited production.

IWM

A captured Friedrichshafen G.II bomber in French hands at Villacoublay airfield June 21, 1918

The firm's next design was the G.III bomber, a twin-engined scaled-up version of the G.II which saw much operational service from early 1917. Its wings of increased span incorporated three bays outboard of the motors. The undercarriage comprised two pairs of wheels, with a fifth wheel immediately under the nose gunner's cockpit—the latter assisting any heavily-loaded takeoff, but mainly preventing a nose-over landing on the crude runways of the period. Construction of the G.III was a typical contemporary mixture of wood, plywood and steel tubing, and the three-man crew consisted of a pilot and a 'bombing officer' in a side-by-side cockpit, with two cockpits mounting guns in the nose and mid-fuselage connected by an internal passageway for the third crew member. Capable of lifting a 1500-kg (3310 lb) bombload, the main weight of bombs was carried externally below the main nacelle, but internal racks, each for five 10-kg (22-lb) bombs, were located either side of the communicating passage aft of the pilot's cockpit.

For the final 18 months of the First World War, Friedrichshafen G.IIIs, in company with the better-known Gotha G.V bombers, formed the real strength of German heavy bomber units, particularly on the Western Front in France. Used mainly in long-distance night raids, G.IIIs are known to have attacked such principal targets as Paris, and are believed to have participated in some of the well-publicized attacks against England. An improved variant was the G.IIIa, built under licence by the Daimler works. This differed from the G.III only in minor structural changes to the tail unit and wing-tip configuration.

In 1918 came the G.IV, in size almost as large as the G.III, but with several significant differences in general design. The former front gunner's cockpit was dispensed with, leaving the main fuselage somewhat snub-nosed, while the usual twin 260-hp Mercedes engines now drove tractor propellers. Compound tail surfaces, as in the G.IIIa, were employed. One or two examples may have seen limited operational trials, but this is unconfirmed.

Friedrichshafen's only other large bomber design was the N.1, a mammoth single-engined biplane which was built in 1917. Virtually a scaled-up two-seater, the N.1 employed markedly sweptback wings and a composite undercarriage. The sole power came from a 260-hp Mercedes D IVa engine in the nose, resulting in the pilot's cockpit being located almost halfway back along the narrow fuselage, with a consequent hopeless forward view for landing and takeoff. Yet another large Friedrichshafen aircraft was the 1918 FF60, a four-engined triplane float-

German sailors manhandle a Friedrichshafen FF 29a floatplane onto wheeled trolleys prior to recovering it from a coastal patrol during the early months of the First World War. The FF 29a differed from the 29 only by modified tail surfaces and floats and both aircraft were unarmed except for a small bomb load which was sometimes carried. Powered by a 120 hp Mercedes D II engine only a small quantity were built from November 1914 before being supplanted by larger Friedrichshafen types with longer range and better armament

IWM

Koninklijke Marine

The Dutch destroyer *Drenthe*, a *Friesland* Class vessel launched in March 1955 at Amsterdam

plane, intended as a naval patrol and torpedo carrier but never fully developed due to the Armistice in November 1918.

Span: (G.II) 20.3 m (66 ft 7¼ in); (G.III) 23.7 m (77 ft 9 in); (G.IV) 22.6 m (74 ft 1½ in) *Length:* (G.II) 11.05 m (36 ft 3 in); (G.III) 12.8 m (42 ft); (G.IV) 12 m (39 ft 4½ in) *Endurance:* 5 hrs *Powerplants:* (G.I) 2 150-hp Benz Bz III; (G.II) 2 200-hp Benz Bz IV; (G.III; G.IIIa; G.IV) 2 260-hp Mercedes D IVa *Armament:* Bombload up to 1496 kg (3300 lb); (G.I; II; III) 1 Parabellum machine-gun in nose; (G.II; III; IV) 1 Parabellum machine-gun in rear *Maximum speed:* (G.III) 135 km/h (84 mph)

Friesland

Dutch destroyer class, built 1951-58. Eight ships of an enlarged 'Holland' design or 47B type were authorized between 1951 and 1955. They resembled the British *Daring* Class (the Netherlands Corps of Constructors was receiving considerable technical assistance from the British at the time) in having the forefunnel incorporated in a lattice mast. They also resembled the British *Daring* Class in layout, with a twin gun-mounting forward and aft, but had two antisubmarine rocket-launchers in B position.

The main difference between these ships and the earlier Type 47A *Holland* Class is in the armament. The two twin 120-mm (4.7-in) Bofors dual-purpose gun mountings and the 375-mm (14.76-in) rocket-launchers were as before, but the secondary armament was increased to six single 40-mm (1.57-in) AA guns, two on B deck, two between the funnels and two between the mainmast and the after 120-mm (4.7-in) gunhouse. Eight antisubmarine torpedo tubes were also to be mounted, four single tubes on either side amidships. The basic outfit of radar remained the same, a big air-warning search antenna on a short lattice mast aft, a tactical (surface and target-indication) one on the foremast and fire-control sets for the 120-mm (4.7-in) and 40-mm (1.57-in) guns.

The ships changed little in the course of 20 years, but the torpedo tubes were only mounted in *Overijssel* and *Utrecht* in 1960-61; after a year or two in service they were removed, and were never mounted in the rest of the class. The two 40-mm (1.57-in) guns in B position were also removed. The class are reported to have armour, but considering the displacement this cannot mean more than splinterproof plating, and is probably on the waterline and deck over the machinery, to prevent splinters from putting the turbines out of action. Plating thick enough to keep out even a 76-mm (3-in) shell would not be feasible without a severe reduction of speed. By the late 1970s the class was nearing the end of its effective life, and the ships had proved expensive to man. They were planned to be replaced by the 'Standard' or *Kortenaer* Class frigates, due to enter service from late 1978.

See also *Holland*.

No	name	launched	builder
D.812	*Friesland*	2/1953	Nederlandse Dok, Amsterdam
D.813	*Groningen*	1/1954	Nederlandse Dok, Amsterdam
D.814	*Limburg*	9/1955	Royal de Schelde, Flushing
D.815	*Overijssel*	8/1955	Wilton-Fijenoord, Schiedam
D.816	*Drenthe*	3/1955	Nederlandse Dok, Amsterdam
D.817	*Utrecht*	6/1956	Royal de Schelde, Flushing
D.818	*Rotterdam*	1/1956	Rotterdam Dry Dock Co
D.819	*Amsterdam*	8/1956	Nederlandse Dok, Amsterdam

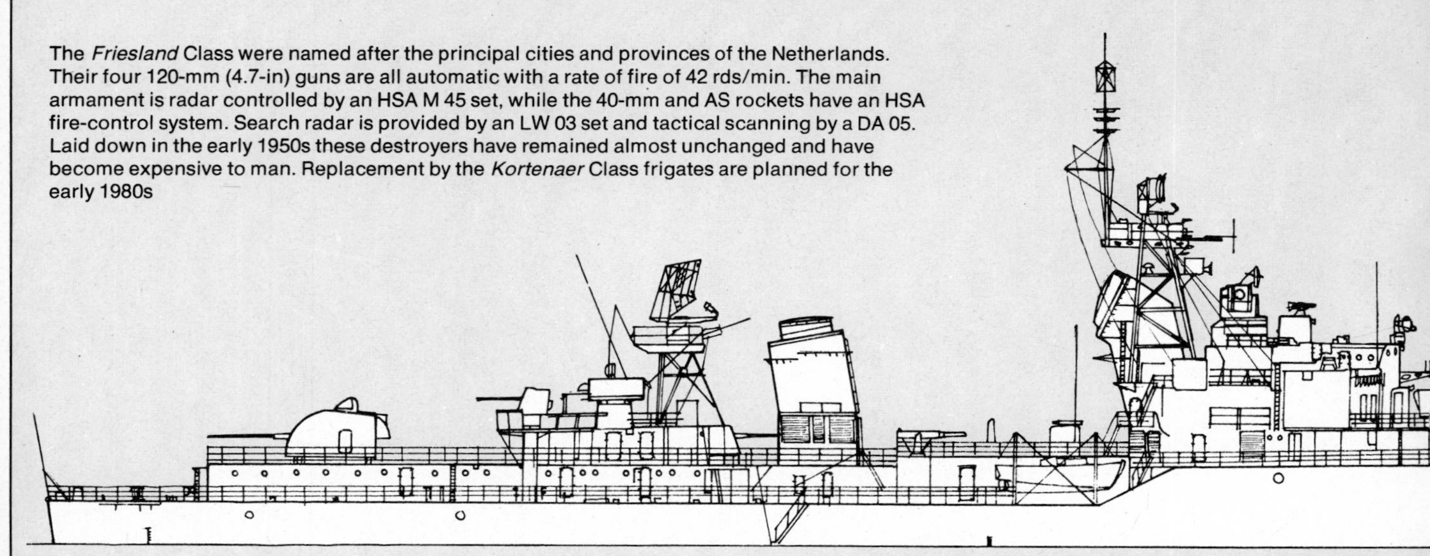
The *Friesland* Class were named after the principal cities and provinces of the Netherlands. Their four 120-mm (4.7-in) guns are all automatic with a rate of fire of 42 rds/min. The main armament is radar controlled by an HSA M 45 set, while the 40-mm and AS rockets have an HSA fire-control system. Search radar is provided by an LW 03 set and tactical scanning by a DA 05. Laid down in the early 1950s these destroyers have remained almost unchanged and have become expensive to man. Replacement by the *Kortenaer* Class frigates are planned for the early 1980s

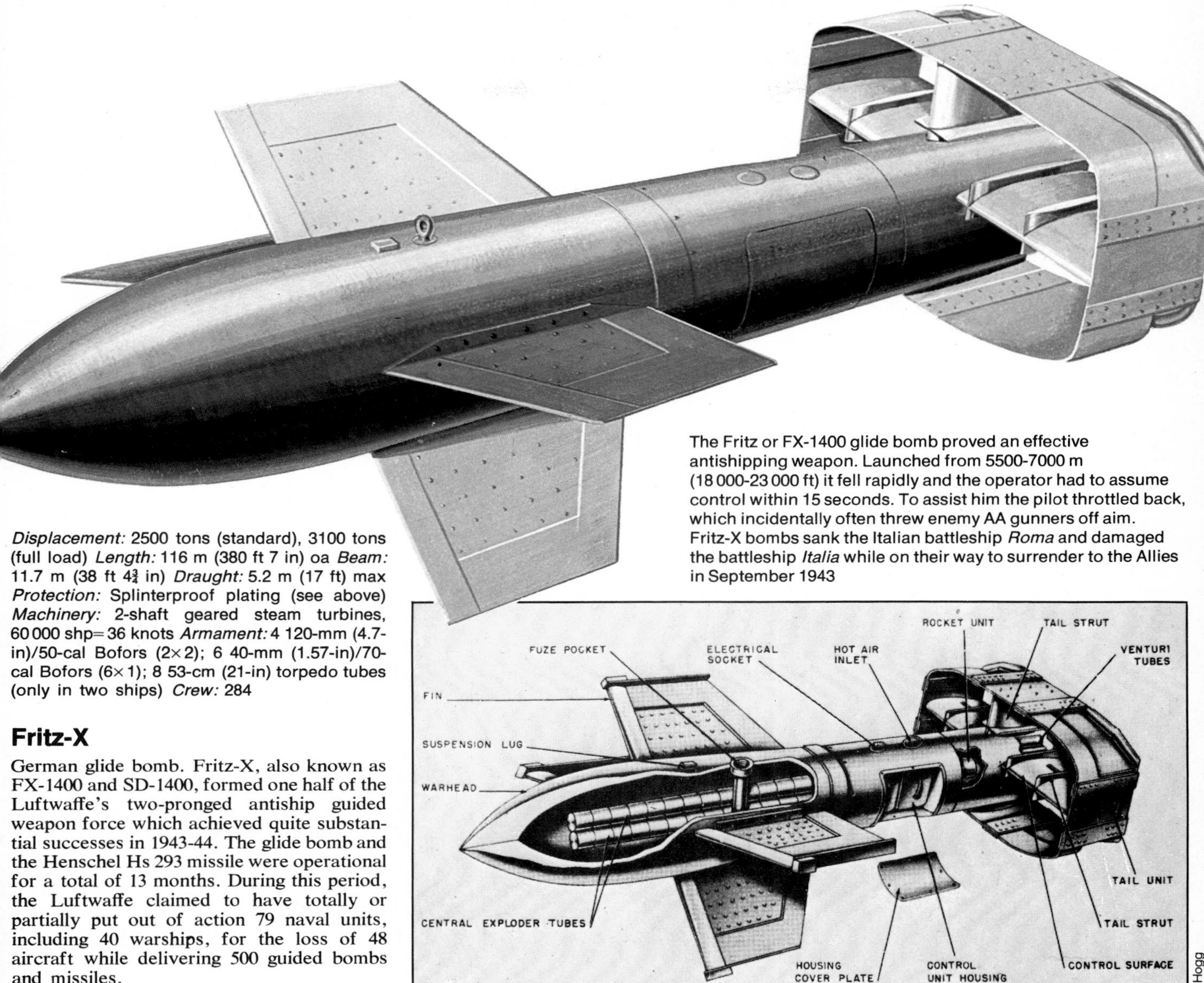

The Fritz or FX-1400 glide bomb proved an effective antishipping weapon. Launched from 5500-7000 m (18 000-23 000 ft) it fell rapidly and the operator had to assume control within 15 seconds. To assist him the pilot throttled back, which incidentally often threw enemy AA gunners off aim. Fritz-X bombs sank the Italian battleship *Roma* and damaged the battleship *Italia* while on their way to surrender to the Allies in September 1943

Displacement: 2500 tons (standard), 3100 tons (full load) *Length:* 116 m (380 ft 7 in) oa *Beam:* 11.7 m (38 ft 4¾ in) *Draught:* 5.2 m (17 ft) max *Protection:* Splinterproof plating (see above) *Machinery:* 2-shaft geared steam turbines, 60 000 shp=36 knots *Armament:* 4 120-mm (4.7-in)/50-cal Bofors (2×2); 6 40-mm (1.57-in)/70-cal Bofors (6×1); 8 53-cm (21-in) torpedo tubes (only in two ships) *Crew:* 284

Fritz-X

German glide bomb. Fritz-X, also known as FX-1400 and SD-1400, formed one half of the Luftwaffe's two-pronged antiship guided weapon force which achieved quite substantial successes in 1943-44. The glide bomb and the Henschel Hs 293 missile were operational for a total of 13 months. During this period, the Luftwaffe claimed to have totally or partially put out of action 79 naval units, including 40 warships, for the loss of 48 aircraft while delivering 500 guided bombs and missiles.

The Luftwaffe was one of the first air forces to grapple with the problem of hitting moving ships. Its experiences during the Spanish Civil War showed that bombing from level flight was unacceptably inaccurate and dive-bombing, while producing better results, was unprofitable against heavily armed targets. The first practical guided bomb was built by Max Kramer in 1939, when he fitted radio-controlled spoilers to the tail fins of a 250-kg (550-lb) weapon. In 1940 Kramer transferred his attention to the 1400-kg (3100-lb) Fritz armour-piercing bomb, but initial trials were unsuccessful, mainly because of the high terminal velocity reached and difficulties with optical tracking However, a new high-speed wind tunnel became available the following year, and development at Peenemünde proceeded smoothly. Bad weather prevented high-altitude tracking, but trials were transferred to Foggia in Italy in March 1942 and were completed in four weeks.

Fritz-X was based on the standard SD-1400 armour-piercing bomb with the addition of four wings and a 12-sided tail unit. The latter contained the receiver portion of the Strassburg-Kehl FuG 203 radio control link, stabilizing gyros and four fins. The weapon was intended to arm the He 177 Greif heavy bomber, but delays led to it being deployed on Do 217K-2s. The latter aircraft could carry two of the bombs under the wings, with an auxiliary fuel tank installed in the bomb bay, but was often limited to a single weapon to avoid a crippling reduction in range.

Fritz-X was dropped from a height of 5500-7000 m (18 050-22 970 ft) and could pierce 130 mm (5.1 in) of armour plating when delivered from this altitude. The launch aircraft dropped the bomb at a range of some 5 km (3.1 miles) while in straight and level flight, the operator then assuming control by means of a joystick. Flares were fitted at the rear of the weapon to aid sighting, and the operator was required to assume control within 15 seconds of release, the launch aircraft being throttled back so that the bomb remained in sight. Drop time from 7000 m (22 970 ft) was 42 seconds, dive brakes limiting the speed to 290 m/sec (950 ft/sec). The four fins were fitted with radio-controlled spoilers which allowed the operator to correct the trajectory over a maximum of 500 m (1640 ft) in the range and 350 m (1150 ft) in azimuth.

Operational training began in March 1943, and on September 9 of that year Fritz-X scored its most famous victory. Do 217s of III/KG 100 operating from Marseilles-Istres sank the battleship *Roma* and damaged the battleship *Italia* (ex-*Littorio*), when the Italian fleet was en route for Malta to surrender to the Allies. Further successes were scored during the Salerno landings, but at the end of 1943 the Fritz-X units based around the Mediterranean were withdrawn to re-equip with the He 177 and Fw 200C Condor. The Hs 293 missile had proved more manoeuvrable and Fritz-X was never deployed again.

Hitler was told that the successes in the Mediterranean had been achieved by conventional bombing. Adolf Galland, in charge of the Luftwaffe's fighter force, did not want effort to be transferred back to bomber production and, therefore, misled both Hitler and Goering. Fritz-X and the Hs 293 had been intended for use against the Russian fleet and North Sea supply convoys, but Hitler overruled this plan and demanded that the weapons be used to attack North Atlantic convoys. The shortage of long-range aircraft made this impracticable, and half-hearted missions against the D-Day landings marked the end of the Hs 293's use as well. Fritz-X was at one time planned to build at a rate of 750 a month, but only 1386 were produced in all from April 1943 to December 1944, of which 602 were used operationally and for training.

Length: 3.25 m (10 ft 8 in) *Span:* 1.35 m (4 ft 5 in) *Diameter:* 56 cm (22 in) *Weight:* 1570 kg (3460 lb)

Frog

Soviet rockets. Frog (Free Rocket, Over Ground) is the NATO codename for this series of Soviet surface-to-surface bombardment rockets for tactical use, generally similar to the American Honest John in both appearance and employment.

Frog 1 appeared in the middle 1950s and was a spin-stabilized rocket using a single-stage solid propellant motor. A conventional high-explosive warhead was used, and the rocket was transported and fired from a special tracked amphibious launcher derived from the Josef Stalin III tank chassis. The rocket was carried inside a tubular casing which could be elevated to act as the launcher tube and which contained heating elements to maintain the solid propellant at optimum temperature.

Frog 2 was a similar rocket which appeared shortly after Frog 1. The principal change was in the warhead which was now of bulbous shape instead of being cylindrical and the same diameter as the rocket motor. This gave the warhead greater capacity and also gave space for the incorporation of a nuclear device. The transport vehicle was now lighter and more mobile, being derived from the PT76 amphibious tank, and the rocket was carried in an open-frame launching rack, which suggested that the problem with temperature and the solid propellant motor had been overcome.

Frog 3 and Frog 4 appeared in the early 1960s. The transport vehicle was the same but the rocket had been lengthened to accommodate a two-stage solid fuel motor which improved the range by a considerable amount. Frog 3 had the bulbous warhead of Frog 2, while Frog 4 reverted to using a cylindrical warhead which, to most obser-

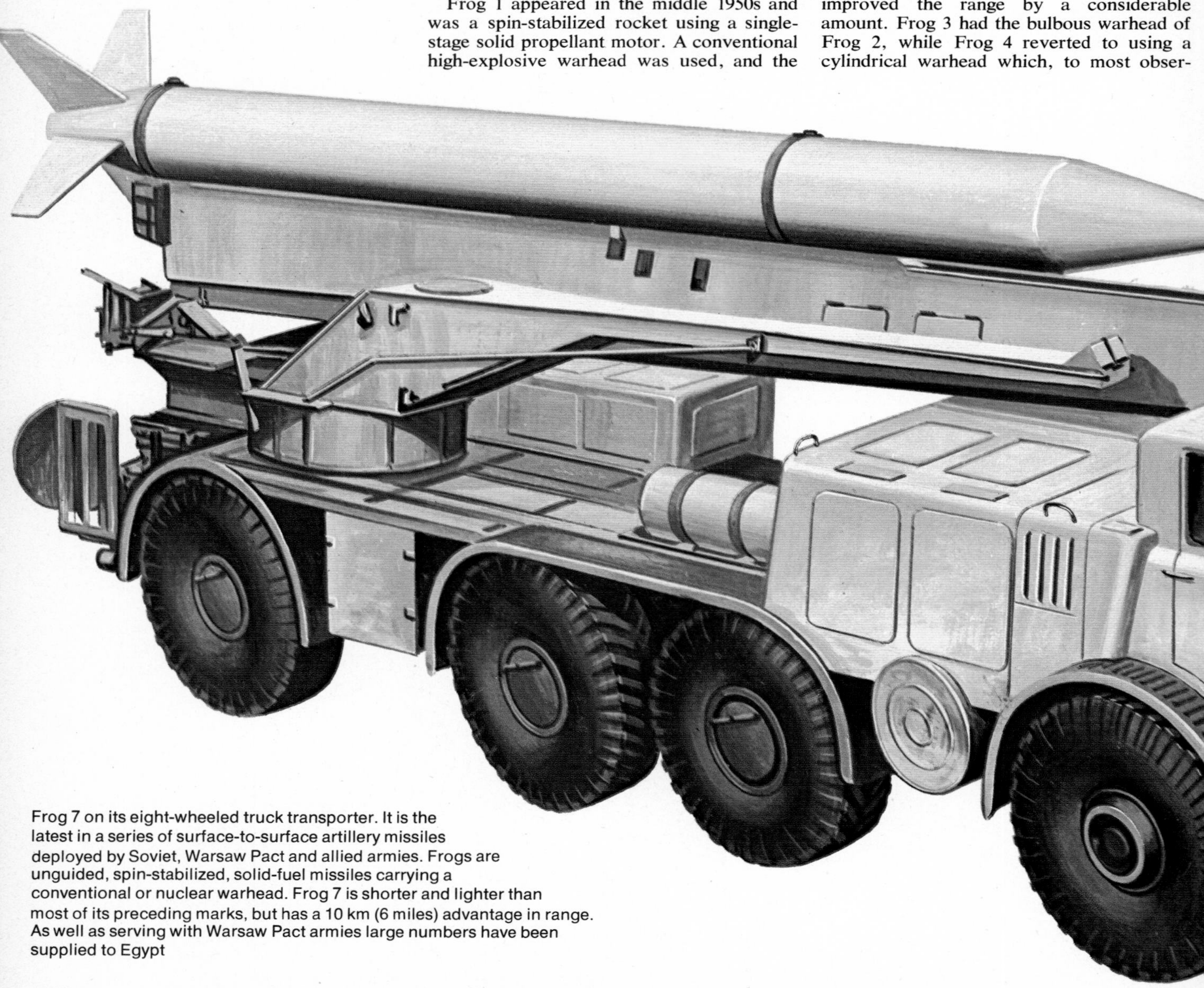

Frog 7 on its eight-wheeled truck transporter. It is the latest in a series of surface-to-surface artillery missiles deployed by Soviet, Warsaw Pact and allied armies. Frogs are unguided, spin-stabilized, solid-fuel missiles carrying a conventional or nuclear warhead. Frog 7 is shorter and lighter than most of its preceding marks, but has a 10 km (6 miles) advantage in range. As well as serving with Warsaw Pact armies large numbers have been supplied to Egypt

The operating crew of a Frog 7 missile run to the mobile launcher during a training exercise in the Soviet Union. The launcher, based on a ZIL-135 eight-wheeled truck, has a small crane for loading new missiles onto the launcher rail, two extra Frog 7s can be carried

vers, suggested improvements in the design of nuclear components.

Frog 5 came along in 1964 and was essentially the motor of Frog 3 with the warhead of Frog 2. It was rarely seen and may have been a trial device. Frog 6 was a training vehicle with dummy rocket.

Frog 7, a completely new design, appeared in 1967. The rocket reverted to single-stage construction and the warhead was cylindrical and sharply tapered. The transporter was, for the first time, wheeled instead of tracked, and based on the ZIL-135 eight-wheeled truck chassis. The rocket was carried on a girder-rail launcher and two more rockets could be carried on the vehicle, one at each side of the launcher rail. Frog 5 and 7 were in service together; Frog 5 was attached to armoured formations, while Frog 7 accompanied infantry units. Both Frog 5 and Frog 7 were believed to be continuing in service in the late 1970s.

Frommer Hungarian small arms
See **Fegyvergyar**

Type	length (m/ft)	diameter (cm/in)	weight (kg/lb)	range (km/miles)	carrier	carrier weight (tonnes)
Frog 1	10.2/33.5	850/33.5	3200/7055	25/15.5	JS111	36
Frog 2	9/29.5	600/23.6	2400/5291	27/16.8	PT76	15
Frog 3	10.5/34.4	530/20.9	2200/4850	40/24.9	PT76	15
Frog 4	10.2/33.5	400/15.7	2300/5071	45/28	PT76	15
Frog 5	10.4/34.1	400/15.7	3000/6614	50/31.1	PT76	15
Frog 7	9/29.5	600/23.6	2032/4480	60/37.3	ZIL-135	12

Frunze

Russian destroyer built 1911-15 as *Bistry.* One of a group of the modified *Novik* or *Azard* Class built at the Metal Works, Cape Kherson in the Black Sea. She was one of the ships refitted and incorporated into the new Red Fleet after the civil war in 1922. Under the new grouping she was called Type II, and apart from additions to her antiaircraft armament remained much as she had been in 1915-17. No alterations were made to her as she was lost only three months after Germany's attack on Russia, being sunk by bombers east of Tendra Island on September 21, 1941.

See also *Azard.*

Displacement: 1100 tons (normal), 1300 tons (full load) *Length:* 93 m (305 ft 1½ in) oa *Beam:* 9.3 m (30 ft 6 in) *Draught:* 2.8 m (9 ft 2¼ in) *Machinery:* 2-shaft steam turbines, 29 800 shp=25 knots *Armament:* 4 102-mm (4-in) (4×1); 1 75-mm (2.95-in) AA; 1 37-mm (1.46-in) AA; 2 machine-guns (2×1); 9 45-cm (17.7-in) torpedo tubes (3×3); 60 mines *Crew:* 160

FS-T2, Mitsubishi Prototype Japanese jet fighter aircraft See **F-1**

FU, Vought

US fighter. In January 1927 the Chance Vought company produced a single-seat fighter version of its mass-produced VO-1 shipboard observation aircraft. A two-bay biplane, the VO-1 was not entirely suitable as the basis for a competitive fighter, and with only the same engine as before, the 200-hp Wright R-1790 Whirlwind, performance was inadequate. Nevertheless, 20 FU-1 fighters were built for the US Navy, most of them being central-float seaplanes (at least two were fitted with wheels for airfield use).

Despite being pleasant to fly, the FU was really only suitable for training. In their first year, ending in the winter 1928-29, the FU-1s equipped fighter squadron VF-2B aboard the carrier *Langley.* Thereafter the 18 that survived were converted into FU-2 trainers, still with a fixed Marlin machine-gun. They remained in use as trainers and general-purpose aircraft into the 1930s.

Span: 10.46 m (34 ft 4 in) *Length:* 7.44 m (24 ft 5 in) *Gross weight:* 1093 kg (2400 lb) *Maximum speed:* 236 km/h (147 mph)

Fubuki

Japanese destroyer class, completed between 1928 and 1933. The *Fubuki* Class initiated a completely new pattern in destroyer design. Planned as part of an overall programme designed to provide Japan with the most modern fleet afloat after the First World War, they were to be heavily armed with a high radius of action and high speed. As such they would be used in conjunction with the new cruisers and battleships Japan then had under construction (*Aoba, Furutaka, Kaga* and *Amagi*).

The initial design was for a 2000-ton destroyer armed with a 127-mm (5-in) gun being developed, two of new triple 61-cm (24-in) torpedo tubes (first fitted to *Mutsuki*) and with a speed of 40 knots.

Because of the Washington Treaty limitations on warship construction the design had to be recast resulting in a 1680-ton destroyer armed with six 127-mm (5-in) guns in twin mounts, nine 61-cm (24-in) torpedo tubes in triple launchers and with a speed of 35 knots. The radius of action was set at 8046 km (5000 miles) at 14 knots.

As well as the armament the basic design of the new class differed from other destroyers then afloat. Previous Japanese destroyers had mounted the forward torpedo tube in a break in the forecastle in front of the bridge. The operation of these tubes had suffered in heavy weather and in the *Fubuki* Class the first set of tubes was mounted high on the superstructure between the two funnels, the other two sets being aft of the funnels. The 127-mm (5-in) guns were far in advance of their time, being mounted in totally enclosed lightly armoured splinter and gas-proof turrets.

The design also provided an extra deck on the forecastle to aid with the dispersal of water from around A gun. This was further assisted by a pronounced flare which ran from the bows right aft to the first funnel. The bridge was also much larger and higher than in earlier designs and was totally enclosed to provide the officers with a degree of comfort in the rough weather experienced in the Pacific.

A total of 24 destroyers in three groups were completed between June 1928 and March 1933. The difference between the groups affected the armament and machinery rather than the basic design. Destroyers of the second and third groups carried the 127-mm (5-in) guns in a new mounting permitting a maximum elevation of 75°, the first destroyers in the world to carry a dual-purpose armament. The second and third groups also incorporated a streamlined ventilator round the funnels rather than the large conspicuous cowl of the first group.

The third group of destroyers to be com-

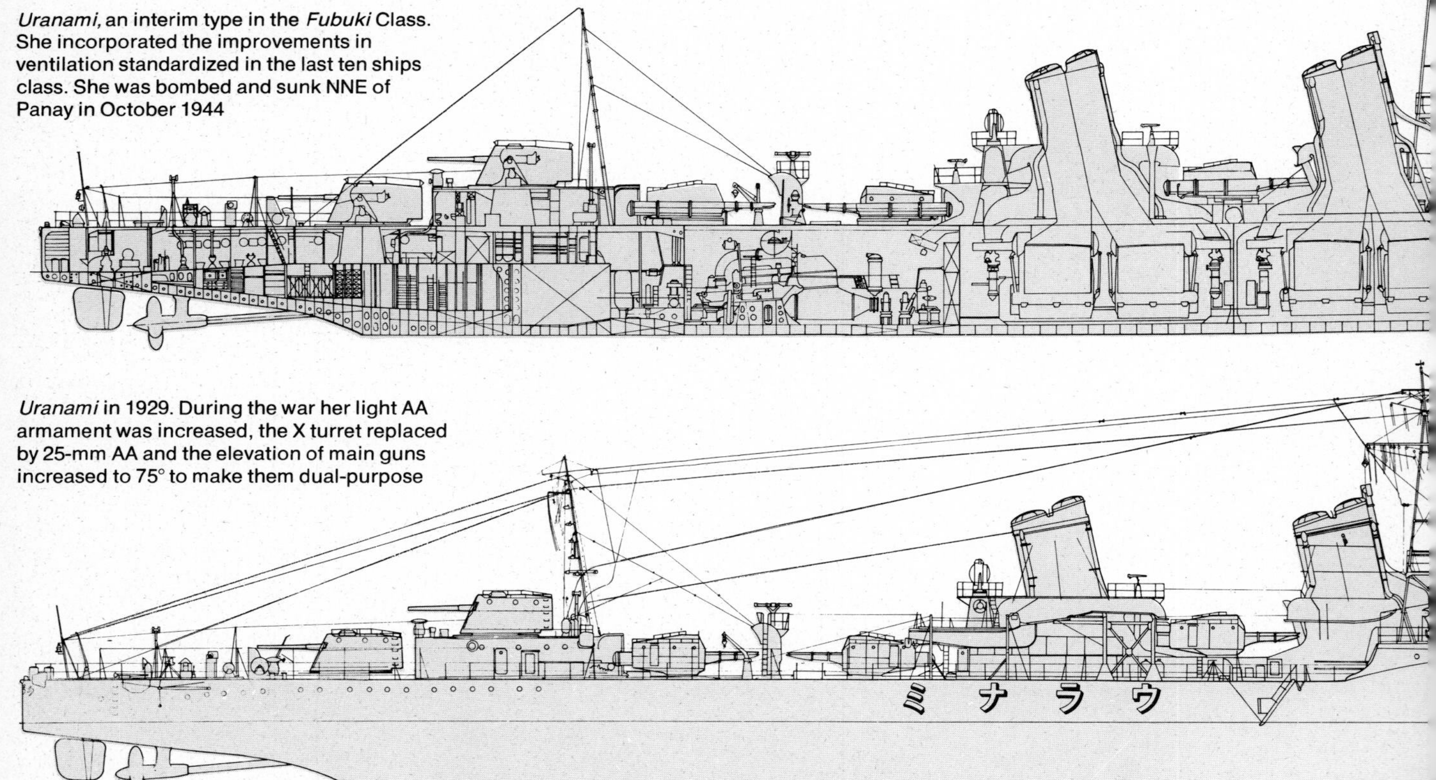

Uranami, an interim type in the *Fubuki* Class. She incorporated the improvements in ventilation standardized in the last ten ships class. She was bombed and sunk NNE of Panay in October 1944

Uranami in 1929. During the war her light AA armament was increased, the X turret replaced by 25-mm AA and the elevation of main guns increased to 75° to make them dual-purpose

pleted was fitted with much larger boilers, and only three were carried instead of the four of earlier groups. This resulted in the third group being equipped with a very narrow funnel forward in comparison with the large funnel of the earlier groups. The torpedo tubes of the third group were also housed in a distinctive splinterproof turret and the earlier destroyers were similarly fitted at a later date.

When completed the displacement was much greater than as designed, and following the capsizing of the torpedo boat *Tomozuru* in March 1934 and typhoon damage suffered by many Japanese warships in September 1935, the *Fubuki*s were found to suffer from instability and structural weaknesses.

The class was modified to correct these faults between 1935-38. They served with distinction throughout the war but only *Hibiki* and *Ushio* survived. Eight were sunk by submarines, seven through air attack, two by mines, four in action with surface ships. *Miyuki* was lost in a collision in 1934. During the war X turret was removed, the AA armament considerably increased and radar added.

Fubuki (Group I), *Hatsuyuki* (I), *Shikinami* (II), *Yugri* (II), *Sazanami* (II), *Hibiki* (III)—built Maizura navy yard
Shinonome (I), *Uranami* (I), *Asagiri* (II), *Oboro* (II), *Akatsuki* (III)—built Sasebo navy yard
Usugumo (I), *Amagiri* (II)—built Ishikawajima
Shirakumo (I), *Murakumo* (I), *Ayanami* (II), *Akebono* (II), *Inazuma* (III)—built Fujinagata
Isonami (I), *Miyuki* (I), *Sagiri* (II), *Ushio* (II), *Ikazuchi* (III)—built Uraga
Shirayuki (I)—built Yokohama

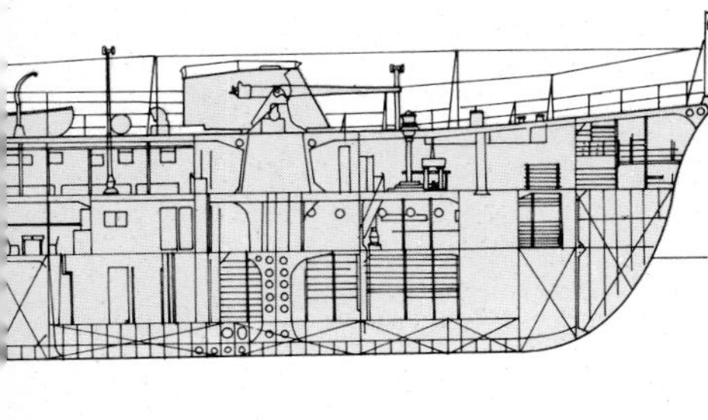

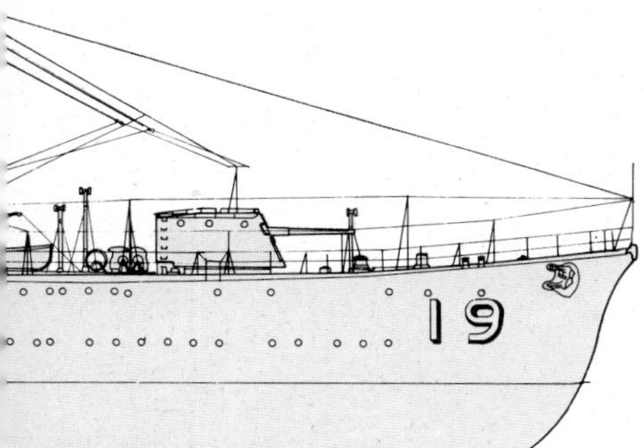

The Japanese battleship *Fuji* dressed overall in 1897, the year she was completed in England

Displacement: 1750 tons *Length:* 118.5 m (388 ft 9 in) oa *Beam:* 10.36 m (34 ft) *Draught:* 3.2 m (10 ft 6 in) mean *Machinery:* 2-shaft Kanpon geared turbines 50 000 shp=38 knots *Armament:* 6 127-mm (5-in)/50-cal (3×2) guns; 2 13-mm (0.51-in) (2×1) guns; 9 61-cm (24-in) (3×3) torpedo tubes; 18 torpedoes; 18 depth charges *Crew:* 197

FUG

Hungarian reconnaissance and scout car. FUG stands for Felerito Uszó Gepkocsi (amphibious reconnaissance vehicle). The FUG-65 is also used by the Czechoslovakian army who call it the OT-65. The vehicle has a welded steel hull, four-wheel drive, and is propelled in water by the usual water-jet system from two jet units in the rear of the hull. Two smaller wheels are partly concealed beneath the armour on each side, and these can be lowered to give additional support when operating in rough country. The vehicle has limited use as a personnel carrier, since only three men, in addition to the crew, can be carried.

There are two versions. The 65A has a fixed superstructure with firing ports and mounts a 14.5-mm (0.57-in) and a 7.62-mm (0.3-in) machine-gun on simple pivots. The 65B has a small turret which mounts a 23-mm (0.9-in) cannon and a 7.62-mm (0.3-in) machine-gun. The Czech version is frequently seen with a Tarasnice recoilless gun mounted alongside the turret. A newer version, the FUG-70, first seen in 1970, dispenses with the belly wheels and has a slightly lengthened hull, enabling it to carry six passengers.

Weight: 7650 kg (16 865 lb) *Length:* 5.75 m (18 ft 10 in) *Width:* 2.35 m (7 ft 8½ in) *Height:* 2.31 m (7 ft 7 in) *Armament:* 1 14.5-mm (0.57-in); 1 7.62-mm (0.3-in); or 1 23-mm (0.9-in) and 1 7.62-mm (0.3-in) mg *Engines:* Csepel D414 4-cylinder diesel, 100 bhp at 2300 rpm *Speed:* 87 km/h (54 mph) *Range:* 500 km (310 miles) *Crew:* 3

Fuji

Japanese battleship class, completed 1897. During the early 1890s the political climate between China and Japan worsened. As war became imminent, Japan embarked on an ambitious plan to build up her fleet to counter the Chinese navy. The Chinese had two German-built battleships available, and to match these Japan ordered two battleships from Britain to a design prepared by G C Macrow. However, before the vessels were completed, the war had been fought and won.

The basic design of *Fuji* and *Yashima* was similar to that of the British *Royal Sovereign* Class but the armament was greatly improved. Since the completion of the British ships, Elswick had perfected a new 12-in (305-mm) weapon, the most powerful gun in the world at that time. It was mounted on *Fuji*, instead of the 13.5-in (343-mm) gun of the *Royal Sovereigns*. The gun fired a 385-kg (850-lb) shell every 1⅓ minutes. It had a much higher muzzle velocity than that of the 13.5-in (343-mm), with a corresponding increase in range, and was also much lighter. The weight saved was used to give extra armour protection to the gun mounting.

The other major difference between the British and Japanese ships lay in the secondary armament. In *Fuji* and *Yashima* only four of the 6-in (152-mm) guns were in casemates, the remainder being in splinterproof shields on the upper deck. There was some compensation for sacrificing armour protection on these weapons, for they commanded a good field of fire. In addition, they were not subject to flooding, a fault from which casemated guns suffered, resulting in them often being unusable in heavy weather.

Yashima differed from *Fuji* in having the deadwood aft cut away, which reduced her length somewhat and resulted in a lighter displacement. The feature was not completely successful, for although the ship had a smaller turning circle than *Fuji*, it resulted in the straining of certain hull members.

During 1901 both ships had all but four of the old 3-pdr (47-mm) guns replaced by 16 12-pdrs. *Yashima* sank in tow on May 15, 1904, after striking a mine off Port Arthur in the Russo-Japanese war. In 1910 *Fuji* was reboilered and her funnels lowered. Being obsolete, she was rerated as a coast defence ship and was completely disarmed and immobilized in 1922-23 under the terms of the Washington Treaty. The hulk was surrendered at the end of the war and what

MOD

A Fairey Fulmar II equipped with airborne radar for night interception. Night fighters covered Russian convoys during the winter of 1944-45

was left of her finally scrapped in 1948.

Fuji was laid down at Thames Iron Works, August 1, 1894, and completed on August 17, 1897; *Yashima* was laid down at Armstrongs, Elswick, on December 28, 1894, and completed September 9, 1897.

Displacement: 12 533 tons (normal); *Yashima* 12 320 tons (normal) *Length:* 125.57 m (412 ft) oa *Beam:* 22.25 m (73 ft) *Yashima* 22.48 m (73 ft 9 in) *Draught:* 8.07 m (26 ft 5¾ in) *Machinery:* 2-shaft vertical triple-expansion, 10 000 ihp=18 knots *Protection:* 457-355 mm (18-14 in) belt; 63 mm (2½ in) decks; 356 mm (14 in) barbettes; 152 mm (6 in) casemates *Armament:* 4 12-in (305-mm)/40-cal (2×2) guns; 10 6-in (152-mm)/40-cal (10×1) guns; 20 3-pdr (47-mm) guns; 4 2½-pdr (42-mm) guns; 5 18-in (46-cm) fixed torpedo tubes *Crew:* 600

Fulmar, Fairey

British carrier-based fighter aircraft, first flew 1940. There was no prototype as such for the Fulmar, which was evolved in 1939 from an existing type, the P.4/34 lightweight development of the Fairey Battle day bomber. The urgent need by the Fleet Air Arm (FAA) for a new fighter led to a rapid trials programme, beginning on January 4, 1940, with the maiden flight of N1854, the first production Fulmar, of which 250 were ordered. The Fulmar I was an all-metal cantilever monoplane, with folding wings for carrier stowage; the semimonocoque fuselage housed the deck arrester gear and catapult points, and space was provided for an inflatable dinghy.

The pilot's cockpit was separated from that of the observer/navigator, and both were enclosed by perspex canopies following the contours of the fuselage. The wide-track undercarriage retracted inwards towards the wing roots. The powerplant for all except two early Fulmar I aircraft was the 1080-hp Rolls-Royce Merlin VIII engine. Due to the additional weight of a second crew member, and the special equipment required for carrier operation, the Fulmar did not achieve the same rate of climb or airspeed as its land-based counterparts—although this was not necessarily required by the Royal Navy. Armament was very similar to the best in the RAF, consisting of eight 0.303-in (7.7-mm) Browning machine-guns—four in each wing—with twice the ammunition capacity of the Spitfire and Hurricane. The lack of a rear defensive gun was one of the Fulmar's principal deficiencies, and some crews unofficially

Fulmars warm up on the deck of *Illustrious*, while *Valiant* has a practice shoot with her 15-in main armament during a wartime exercise

IWM

IWM

A Fulmar takes off on a reconnaissance patrol. Fairey Fulmars saw action in the Mediterranean and operated as night intruders from Malta in 1941

fitted an additional gun of their own choice in the rear cockpit.

Deliveries of the Fulmar I began in June 1940, to 806 Squadron, and it became operational aboard the aircraft carrier *Illustrious* about two months later. At this time, Fairey had plans for the development of the Fulmar II, to be powered by the 1300-hp Merlin 30, and with weight reductions brought about by the use of lighter constructional materials. This enabled the Fulmar II to carry the originally-intended bombload in the form of a single 113.4-kg (250-lb) or 227-kg (500-lb) bomb beneath the fuselage (the Mk I being limited to eight 9-kg [20-lb] or 11.3-kg [25-lb] bombs under the wings).

Orders for 350 Fulmar IIs were placed during the autumn of 1940, bringing the total number on order to 600. With conversions to Fulmar II beginning on the Mk I production line, the eventual result was that well over 400 were completed as Mk IIs. Ammunition capacity of the Fulmar II was eventually increased from 750 to 1000 rounds per gun but, despite this, the aircraft's fighting ability was still disappointing. Nevertheless, although short on speed and manoeuvrability, it served with no fewer than 14 FAA squadrons, accounting for more than 100 enemy aircraft and playing a useful role until the appearance of more advanced types such as the Seafire and Firefly. During the summer of 1941, four 0.5-in (12.7-mm) machine-guns were fitted to one Fulmar. Firing trials proved satisfactory, and the last 100 aircraft were adapted for such an armament, but not all were so equipped due to an insufficient supply of the heavier guns. Fulmars were used quite successfully as convoy escorts during the mid-war years, and about 100 were converted into makeshift night fighters. In 1943 they were gradually withdrawn from front-line service and reassigned to training duties.

(Fulmar II) *Span:* 14.13 m (46 ft 4½ in) *Length:* 12.24 m (40 ft 2 in) *Gross weight:* 4695 kg (10 350 lb) *Maximum speed:* 417 km/h (259 mph)

Fulmine

Italian destroyer built 1897-1900. This was the first Italian destroyer of *controtorpidiniera,* and she was designed by Engineer Inspector-General Ernesto Marinez. His model was the British 30-knot destroyer *Bat,* built by Palmers at Jarrow.

MOD

A Fulmar II, powered by a 1300-hp Merlin 30 12-cylinder engine, photographed in April 1942

Fulmine was laid down at the Odero yard at Sestri, near Genoa in July 1897; she was launched on December 4, 1898, and commissioned in October 1900. As built she had five 6-pdr (57-mm) guns and three torpedo tubes. The disposition of the guns was similar to British destroyers, but the torpedo tubes were quite different, with two singles sited abreast of the forward funnel and one tube right aft. The gun armament was soon changed to a 76-mm (3-in) gun forward, two 57-mm (2.24-in) guns sited amidships, and one on the after conning tower. In 1906 the after torpedo tube was removed.

The ship had an uneventful career, but in 1911-12 she took part in the war against Turkey, during which she was part of the squadron blockading the coast of Tripolitania. She was then attached to the Naval Academy at Livorno, but at the end of 1915 she was sent to Maddalena as guardship, and escorted shipping in the Tyrrhenian Sea. On August 30, 1918, she collided with the destroyer *Corazziere* in rough weather, and both ships were badly damaged. She was disarmed as soon as the war ended and was discarded in May 1921.

She was a most uneconomical steamer, making only 1290 km (800 miles) at 15 knots, and although it was originally hoped to reach 30 knots, her actual speed was much less. By 1915 she was only capable of 20 knots.

Displacement: 298 tonnes (normal), 342 tonnes (full load) *Length:* 62.17 m (204 ft) oa *Beam:* 6.41 m (21 ft) *Draught:* 2.3 m (7 ft 6½ in) *Machinery:* 2-shaft triple-expansion reciprocating, 4800 ihp= 26.5 knots *Armament:* (1900-1906) 1 76-mm (3-in)/40-cal QF; 3 57-mm (2.24-in)/43-cal QF (3×1); 3 35.6-cm (14-in) torpedo tubes (3×1) *Crew:* 47

Fumitsuki

Japanese destroyer, launched 1926. *Fumitsuki* was one of the 12 destroyers of the *Mutsuki* Class ordered under the 1923 new reinforcement programme, and which entered service between 1925-27. With two earlier classes—altogether 36 destroyers—they formed the 'Minekaze' group all built to basically the same design, but differing in details as regards internal layout and armament.

When the *Mutsuki* Class was ordered the requirement was for a much heavier armament to match foreign designs. At the time of the design the Japanese had just completed development work on a new 61-cm (24-in) torpedo and its launcher, and it was decided to test the weapon in an operational environment aboard the new destroyers. A new triple launcher had also been recently built and tested and the *Mutsuki* Class were fitted with two of these triple mounts, one in the break in the forecastle in front of the bridge, and the other in front of the after superstructure.

The design of the *Mutsuki* Class also differed in its bow configuration from previous classes. In order to improve seaworthiness and performance generally in their warships, the Japanese had recently been carrying out tank tests with models fitted with various bow designs. As a result of the tests the *Mutsukis* were fitted with a 'swan-neck' bow with a pronounced flare and a turtleback forecastle to disperse quickly any shipped water. It was found that the new bow configuration created less resistance to the passage of the ship through the water thus adding several knots to the vessel's speed.

On completion the ships were given numbers, but were renamed in August 1928. Between 1941-42, the ships were rearmed, X gun and the mount between the funnels being removed and ten 25-mm (1-in) added. The minesweeping gear was replaced with antisubmarine equipment consisting of four depth-charge throwers and 36 depth charges. The torpedo tubes and associated fire-control equipment were housed in conspicuous splinterproof turrets. These alterations increased the tonnage to 1590 tons and reduced the speed to 34 knots. Surviving units received further additions to their light AA guns during the war.

Mutsuki, Mikatsuki—built Sasebo Navy Yard
Kisaragi, Kikutsuki—built Maizuru Navy Yard
Yayoi, Minatsuki, Mochitsuki—built Uraga
Uzuki, Nagatsuki—built Ishikawajima
Satsuki, Fumitsuki, Yuzuki—built Fujinagate

Displacement: 1313 tons *Length:* 102.41 m (336 ft) oa *Beam:* 9.14 m (30 ft) *Draught:* 3 m (9 ft 8 in) mean *Machinery:* 2-shaft Parsons geared turbines, 35 500 shp=37 knots *Armament:* 4 120-mm (4.7-in)/45-cal (4×1) guns; 2 7.7-mm (0.303-in) (2×1) guns; 6 61-cm (24-in) (2×3) torpedo tubes; 10 torpedoes; 16 mines *Crew:* 150

Sopwith Pup fighters clustered on the forward deck of HMS *Furious* during pre-flight checks

Funryu

Japanese series of air-to-surface and surface-to-air missiles. The Funryu (Raging Dragon) missiles and test vehicles were developed late in the Second World War, when the Japanese were forced to concentrate on defensive weapons to counter Allied air and naval attacks. The Japanese Naval Technical Research Unit developed surface-to-air rockets with solid-propellant motors and was also responsible for the Funryu series.

Funryu 1, using a fuselage built by the Yokosuka dockyard, and a Mitsubishi solid-propellant rocket motor, was an experimental radio-controlled antiship missile which was abandoned at the development stage, largely because of problems with the powerplant. The other weapons in the Funryu series were for surface-to-air roles.

Funryu 2 was an experimental gyro-stabilized SAM with cruciform wings and tail surfaces. The solid-propellant rocket motor produced 2400 kg (5300 lb) of thrust for 3½ seconds, accelerating the weapon to its maximum speed of 845 km/h (525 mph). Flight trials are thought to have been reasonably successful, although the weapon's maximum effective altitude of 5000 m (16 400 ft) would not have allowed it to intercept high-flying B-29 Superfortress bombers.

Funryu 3 was based on its predecessor but was powered by a liquid-propellant motor and was unsuccessful. The last in the series, Funryu 4, was intended to enter series production, and a prototype was under construction when the war ended. The weapon would have used radar command guidance, the target and missile being tracked by separate radars while a primitive ground-based computer generated steering commands for transmission to the round in flight. The Toko Ro.2 (KR10) bifuel rocket motor produced 1500 kg (3300 lb) of thrust, and since this was less than the launch weight of 1900 kg (4200 lb) it is assumed that boosters were used during the initial stage of flight. Funryu 4 had an operational ceiling of 15 000 m (49 212 ft) and a range of 30 km (18.6 miles), and it is likely that the weapon—like its German counterparts—could have presented a serious threat to the Allied bomber offensive if it had been available earlier.

(Funryu 4) *Length:* 3.96 m (13 ft) *Span:* 1.67 m (5 ft 5 in) *Diameter:* 61 cm (24 in) *Speed:* 1100 km/h (683 mph) *Warhead:* 200 kg (440 lb)

A Swordfish torpedo bomber takes off from HMS *Furious* on a reconnaissance patrol. *Furious* served with the Home Fleet during the Second World War, but between August 1942 and January 1943 she operated out of Gibraltar with Force H. In September 1944 her aircraft attacked the German battleships *Tirpitz* sheltering in Kaa Fjord, Norway. *Furious* was sold for scrap in 1948

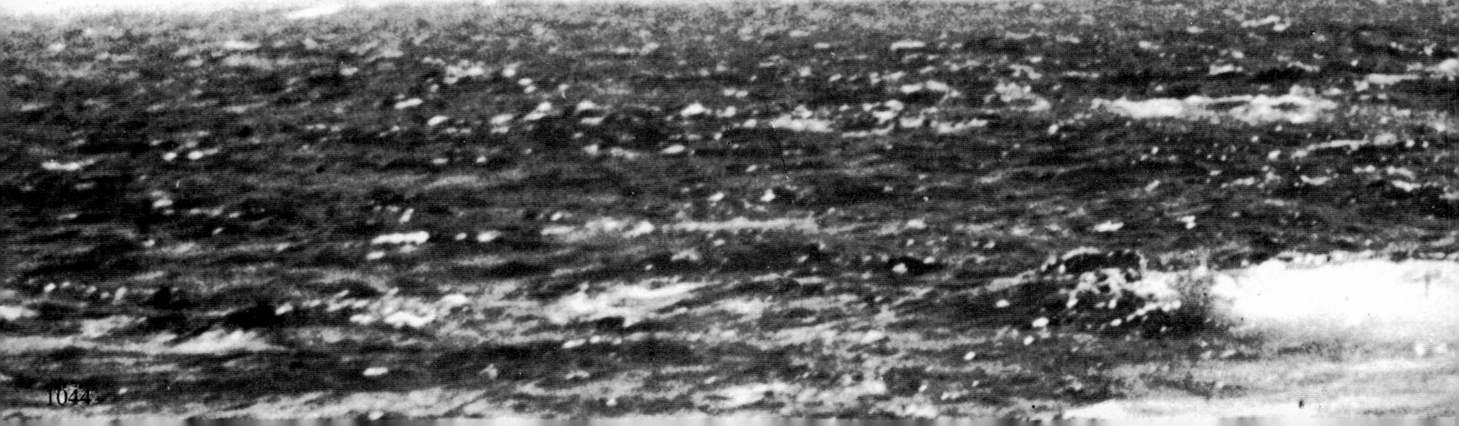

IWM

Furious as a seaplane carrier in 1917. She retained an 18-in gun aft, but a hangar, workshops and store rooms replaced that installed in the bows

Furious

British aircraft carrier. *Furious* was laid down in June 1915 as the third of the *Courageous* Class light battlecruisers. However while under construction her design was altered to provide an armament of two 18-in (460-mm) (2×1) and 11 5.5-in (140-mm) guns (11×1) in place of the original four 15-in (381-mm) (2×2) and 16 4-in (102-mm) (4×3, 4×1). The ship was launched on August 18, 1916, but a few months later it was decided that she should be further altered for service as a fleet seaplane carrier. This decision was largely a result of the realization that the existing seaplane carriers were too slow to operate effectively with the Grand Fleet. As *Furious* was nearing completion, with an ideal speed although of limited value in her original configuration, she was a perfect choice for such a role.

The design was recast early in 1917, the forward 18-in (460-mm) mounting being omitted and a hangar, store rooms and workshops added to the forecastle, above which a flying-off deck, 69.4 m (228 ft) long and 15.2 m (50

IWM

ft) wide, was constructed between the bridge and the stem. The hangar could accommodate eight aircraft (four reconnaissance and four fighters) which were lifted onto the flight deck by derricks through a large hatch in the hangar roof.

The ship was completed in this form in June 1917 and joined the Grand Fleet the following month. Her single 18-in (460-mm) gun was the largest ever mounted in a British ship, and fired a shell of 1633 kg (3600 lb); the turret was of generally similar design to the twin 15-in (381-mm) and had a revolving weight of 827 tons. In spite of its power, the gun would have been of no use in a fleet action, because of the impossibility of accurate fire control with a single slow-firing weapon.

Although operating as part of the fleet, *Furious* also served as an experimental vessel in the development of naval aviation. If the ship's aircraft were seaplanes, they were recovered from the sea; if they were wheeled, they had to be ditched or landed ashore. The former operation occupied valuable time, and the latter meant that aircraft could only be launched once. In August 1917, a possible answer to these problems was found when Squadron Commander Dunning successfully landed his Sopwith Pup on the flying-off deck by flying past the ship's superstructure and sideslipping onto the deck. This method was too dangerous, and on his third landing Dunning went over the side and was drowned. This event brought an end to these experiments, but the advantages of being able to 'land-on' were considerable and it was subsequently decided to build a second flight deck specifically for this purpose over the after section of the ship. The necessary refit, carried out between November 1917 and March 1918, involved the removal of the second 18-in (460-mm) gun-mounting and constructing a 21.3 m × 11.5 m (70 ft × 38 ft) hangar over the after part of the ship above which was constructed a 91.4-m (300-ft) landing-on deck connected to the flying-off deck by a narrow gangway on each side of the superstructure. An electric-powered lift replaced the hatchway and derricks which served the forward hangar and a similar installation was provided for the after hangar. She could now carry 16 aircraft all of which were wheeled machines.

During 1918, *Furious* continued her service with the Grand Fleet, during which time experimental work was mainly concentrated on improving and developing landing techniques and equipment. It soon became clear that the new deck was not completely successful as aircraft attempting to land-on were seriously affected by the air turbulence created by the superstructure and funnel gases. Even so, many successful landings were made and she was to prove herself in the operational role. On July 19, 1918, she launched seven Sopwith Camels which attacked the Zeppelin base at Tondern near the Elbe Estuary. The aircraft bombed and set alight the Zeppelin sheds and destroyed the naval Zeppelins L54 and L60.

After the war, *Furious* joined the Atlantic Fleet, but spent some months in the Baltic before being placed in reserve at Rosyth in November 1919. For a while her fate hung in the balance, but following the Washington Conference of 1921, it was decided that she should be reconstructed to incorporate the latest ideas and developments in naval aviation. The principal feature was a full-length flight deck. She was taken in hand at Devonport in June 1922 and completed in September 1925, during which time her original superstructure was removed and the forward and after hangars connected together to provide a single 167.6-m (550-ft) hangar. Above this a second hangar 158.5 m (520 ft) long was added, opening out at its forward end onto the original flying-off deck (now shortened to 60.9 m [200 ft] and renamed the slip deck) and above that the new main flight deck, 175.5 m (576 ft) long and 28 m (91 ft 6 in) wide. The funnels were trunked aft to exhaust through vents in the after end of the flight deck or, when flying was in progress, through vents in the ship's side. No island superstructure was provided, navigating and air control positions being accommodated under the forward end of the flight deck on each side and a retractable navigating hut on the centreline which was lowered into the flight deck when flying was in progress. To compensate for the loss of stability involved in adding so much topweight, narrow bulges were added on each side of the hull. Four 4-in (102-mm) AA guns were mounted on the slip deck, but these were removed by 1927, two being repositioned on the quarterdeck.

In 1932, the quarterdeck was raised flush with the forecastle deck and the 4-in (102-mm) AA guns were again rearranged to provide two on the slip deck (which was no longer used) and one on the quarterdeck. At the same time, two eight-barrel pom-pom mountings were added on the slip deck and aircraft arrestor wires fitted on the flight deck. During a major refit in 1938-39 her 5.5-in (140-mm) and 4-in (102-mm) guns were removed and replaced by six twin 4-in (102-mm) dual purpose gun-mountings. A small island superstructure was added on the starboard side which carried an aircraft homing beacon on a short mast and an AA director and control positions, but was not intended for navigation. An eight-barrelled pom-pom mounting was fitted abaft this island and a second AA director on the slip deck. Subsequent war modifications included the addition of a fourth pom-pom mounting forward of the island, 22 20-mm (0.79-in) guns and surface, air and gunnery radar sets.

The majority of *Furious*'s war service was with the Home Fleet, but she transferred to the Mediterranean on several occasions and during August 1942-January 1943 operated with Force H out of Gibraltar. Her Mediterranean service included ferrying aircraft to Malta, in 1941, the Malta convoy 'Pedestal' in August 1942, and covering the North Africa landings in November 1942. In home waters she covered Atlantic and Soviet convoys, but she was most active off the Norwegian coast. In 1940, she had taken part in the Norwegian campaign, providing air cover for the fleet and air reconnaissance and ground attack for the army. Subsequently, her aircraft carried out shipping strikes in Norwegian waters during July-October 1940, July-August 1941, and April-September 1944. The latter period included air attacks on the battleship *Tirpitz* at Kaa Fjord in September 1944. She was sold for scrap in 1948. Of the seven carriers in service with the Royal Navy in 1939, only *Furious* and *Argus* (which was employed mainly on training duties) survived the Second World War.

See also *Courageous*.

An aerial view of *Furious* with her elevators lowered and her hull painted in dazzle camouflage

IWM

Displacement: (1917) 19100 tons (normal), 22400 tons (full load); (1925) 22450 tons (standard), 27150 tons (full load) *Length:* 239.64 m (786 ft 3 in) *Beam:* 26.82 m (88 ft); (1925) 27.43 m (90 ft) across bulges *Draught:* (1917) 6.55 m (21 ft 6 in); (1925) 7.31 m (24 ft) *Machinery:* 4-shaft geared steam turbines, 90000 shp=31.5 knots (30 knots, 1925) *Protection:* 76 mm (3 in) sides; 25 mm (1 in) deck *Armament:* (1917) 1 18-in (460-mm); 11 5.5-in (140-mm) (11×1); 4 3-in (76-mm) AA (4×1); 2 53-cm (21-in) torpedo tubes (submerged); (1925) 10 5.5-in (140-mm) (10×1); 4 4-in (102-mm) AA (4×1) *Aircraft:* (1917) 8; (1918) 16; (1925) 36; (1939) 33 *Crew:* (1917) 745; (1925) 1918 (including 325 Fleet Air Arm)

Fürrer

Swiss machine-gun. Colonel Adolf Fürrer, of the Swiss army, was Director of the Eidgenossische Waffenfabrik Bern, the

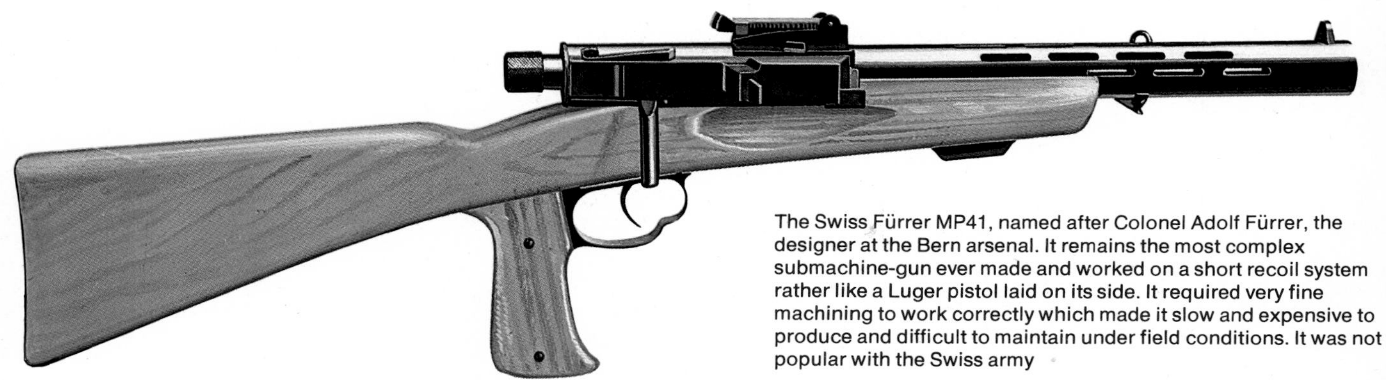

The Swiss Fürrer MP41, named after Colonel Adolf Fürrer, the designer at the Bern arsenal. It remains the most complex submachine-gun ever made and worked on a short recoil system rather like a Luger pistol laid on its side. It required very fine machining to work correctly which made it slow and expensive to produce and difficult to maintain under field conditions. It was not popular with the Swiss army

Swiss government arsenal, from 1921 to 1940. In addition to superintending production of various service weapons, he was in charge of design and produced a brace of the most complicated and expensive service weapons in history. They would probably never have survived the test of combat had they been put to it.

During the early 1920s, the Bern factory was making the Parabellum (Luger) pistol for the Swiss army, and it seems probable that having the machinery to make the Luger toggle joint, Fürrer decided to exploit it further. His Model 25 machine-gun, therefore, utilized the Luger toggle lock, laid on its side and covered by a metal casing on the left of the gun. The magazine passed in from the right side. There were some slight modifications to the toggle, and one major innovation was to arrange the design so that it incorporated a form of differential recoil. After the bolt had closed on a fresh round, and while the barrel and bolt unit was still running forward, the sear was tripped and the gun fired, so that the recoil had to arrest the movement of the mass and then reverse it. This reduced the recoil blow by more than 50% and made the Model 25 very pleasant to fire, but the care needed in manufacture, plus the delicacy of the toggle lock, made the gun an extremely expensive one and it is doubtful if the mechanism would have survived the dirt and dust of an actual combat environment. However, it survived in service until the 1950s.

In May 1940, the Swiss army took a look at their submachine-gun holdings and discovered that they owned only about 450 guns made up of six different models in five different calibres; and only ten of these weapons fired standard Swiss service ammunition. In view of the political climate, something had to be done, and the army ordered 100 submachine-guns from Bern and 50 from SIG, for trials. Realizing that six months would go by in testing, before production for service would get under way, the army plunged in and ordered the Fürrer design to go into immediate production, without waiting for tests. Needless to say, Fürrer's design used the same sideways toggle lock as did his machine-gun, and proved to be the most expensive and difficult submachine-gun to manufacture in military history. It was April 1942 before the first 92 test guns were delivered. After tests and some modification, production began in January 1943, a total of 4800 being made in the ensuing year. By comparison, in that same year the Erma company in Germany delivered 234 000 MP40 submachine-guns to the German army and the British were turning out 20 000 Sten guns a month from one factory alone.

(Light machine-gun Model 25) *Calibre:* 7.5 mm (0.29 in) *Weight:* 10.61 kg (23 lb 6 oz) *Length:* 116 cm (45.6 in) *Barrel:* 58.5 cm (23.03 in) *Magazine:* 30-round box *Muzzle velocity:* 746 m/sec (2450 ft/sec) *Rate of fire:* 450 rds/min

(Submachine-gun MP41/44) *Calibre:* 9 mm (0.35 in) Parabellum *Weight:* 5.19 kg (11 lb 7 oz) *Length:* 77.5 cm (30.5 in) *Barrel:* 25 cm (9.84 in) *Magazine:* 40-round box *Rate of fire:* 900 rds/min

Fürst Bismarck

German armoured cruiser built 1896-1900. As *Ersatz Leipzig* she was to be a 1st Class cruiser, but she was in fact the first cruiser with an armoured belt built for the Reichsmarine. (The prefix *'Ersatz'*, meaning 'substitute', was attached to names of ships designated as nominal replacements of existing vessels bearing the same name.) She was launched at Kiel dockyard on September 25, 1897, and entered service in April 1900.

The design proved most successful, and the ship was manoeuvrable, a good seaboat and a reliable steamer. Her main drawback was vibration at high speed. Between 1910 and 1915 she was modernized, with lighter masts. The midships 150-mm (5.9-in) guns were removed and the positions plated in.

The early years of *Fürst Bismarck* were spent overseas as flagship of the East Asia Squadron, but she returned home in 1909. In 1915 she was relegated to coast defence, but in 1916 she was disarmed and hulked as a training ship for engineers at Kiel. She was stricken on June 17, 1919, and sold to a shipowner for conversion to a merchant ship, but this was not practicable so the scheme was abandoned and she was eventually scrapped in 1920.

Displacement: 10 690 tons (normal), 11 461 tons (full load) *Length:* 127 m (416 ft 8 in) oa *Beam:* 20.4 m (67 ft) *Draught:* 8.46 m (27 ft 9 in) max *Machinery:* 3-shaft triple-expansion steam, 13 500 ihp= 18 knots *Protection:* 203-101 mm (8-4 in) belt; 51 mm (2 in) deck; 203 mm (8 in) conning tower and turrets *Armament:* 4 240-mm (9.4-in)/40-cal (2×2); 12 150-mm (5.9-in)/40-cal (12×1), reduced to 10 by 1919; 10 88-mm (3.46-in)/30-cal (10×1); 4 machine-guns; 6 45-cm (17.7-in) torpedo tubes (1 bow below water, 1 stern, 4 beam above water) *Crew:* 621 (plus 76 as flagship)

Furutaka

Japanese cruiser class, completed 1926. In the early 1920s, the Japanese designed a new class of 7000-ton light cruiser incorporating many of the novel features experimentally tried with great success in the *Yubari*. These features were important to Japanese warship design. Restricted by the 1921 Washington Treaty, Japan was determined to build up the most powerful navy in the Pacific.

Much of the design was based around the use of newly-developed lightweight materials and design techniques in which the armour protection formed part of the hull strength members—the armour plates being built into the hull side at an angle. Powerful machinery was installed to give the vessels a high speed, this being assisted by the new 'swan-neck' bow shape adopted and the pronounced sheer and flare forward for quickly dispersing water. This sleekness and generally low profile (spoilt by the bridge structure) was not adopted by other navies until some years later. The towering bridge (common to all Japanese warships of the period and often referred to as a 'pagoda structure') was a contributing factor to a certain instability which was suffered by many Japanese warships built under naval treaty limitations.

By making great use of light materials and keeping the weight of various items of equipment to a minimum, the Japanese reasoned that the new cruisers would be able to mount a powerful armament of six 200-mm (7.9-in) guns. No other light cruiser in the world mounted such heavy guns. The arrangement of the guns was a compromise, however, for they had to be mounted singly on the keel line fore and aft (three forward and three aft) and because of weight restrictions could only be mounted with light splinter shields rather than in armoured turrets. In this respect, the ships were not as powerful as they at first appeared. The ships were also given a powerful torpedo armament, 12 new 61-cm (24-in) weapons being in fixed broadside firing positions aft of the boiler room. A flying-off platform for aircraft was sited abaft the after funnel and behind this a single 200-mm (7.9-in) gun. The remaining two 200-mm guns were superimposed in X and Y positions. The three forward guns were sited in front of the bridge, the middle gun superfiring over the other two.

When the vessels were completed in 1926 it was discovered that the actual displacement exceeded the designed figure by 1100 tons. Soon after completion, the flying-off platform was replaced by a catapult.

Between 1936-39, both ships were extensively modernized when bulges were added and weight generally redistributed in an effort to overcome stability problems. The ships were rearmed with six twin 200-mm (7.9-in) gun turrets and the fixed torpedo tubes replaced by two quadruple trainable mounts abreast the catapult. In addition the 76-mm (3-in) AA guns were replaced by 120-mm (4.7-in) and an extra seaplane carried. During reconstruction, the ships were reboilered and the bridge rebuilt to a larger design. With the alterations, displacement rose to 9150 tons and speed was reduced to 33 knots.

By the start of the war the ships had been fitted with four twin 20-mm (0.79-in) around the after funnel and two twin 13-mm (0.51-in) on the bridge. Both vessels were lost in 1942.

Furutaka was laid down at Mitsubishi on December 5, 1922, and completed March 31, 1926; *Kako* was laid down at Kawasaki on November 11, 1922, and completed July 20, 1926.

(As built) *Displacement:* 7100 tons *Length:* 184.70 m (606 ft) oa *Beam:* 16.5 m (54 ft) *Draught:* 5.48 m (18 ft) mean *Machinery:* 4-shaft geared turbines 102 000 shp=34.5 knots *Protection:* 76 mm (3 in) belt; 35 mm (1.37 in) deck *Armament:* 6 200-mm (7.9-in)/50-cal (6×1) guns; 4 76-mm (3-in)/40-cal (4×1) guns; 12 61-cm (24-in) fixed (2×2) torpedo tubes; 1 aircraft *Crew:* 604

(As modernized) *Displacement:* 9000 tons *Beam:* 17.6 m (57 ft 9 in) *Machinery:* 108 456 shp=33.5 knots *Armament:* 6 203-mm (8-in)/50-cal (3×2) guns; 4 120-mm (4.7-in)/45-cal (4×1) guns; 4 13-mm (0.51-in) (4×1) guns; 8 61-cm (24-in) rotating (2×4) torpedo tubes; 2 aircraft *Crew:* 625

The North American FJ-1 Fury naval fighter which first flew at Inglewood on November 27, 1946

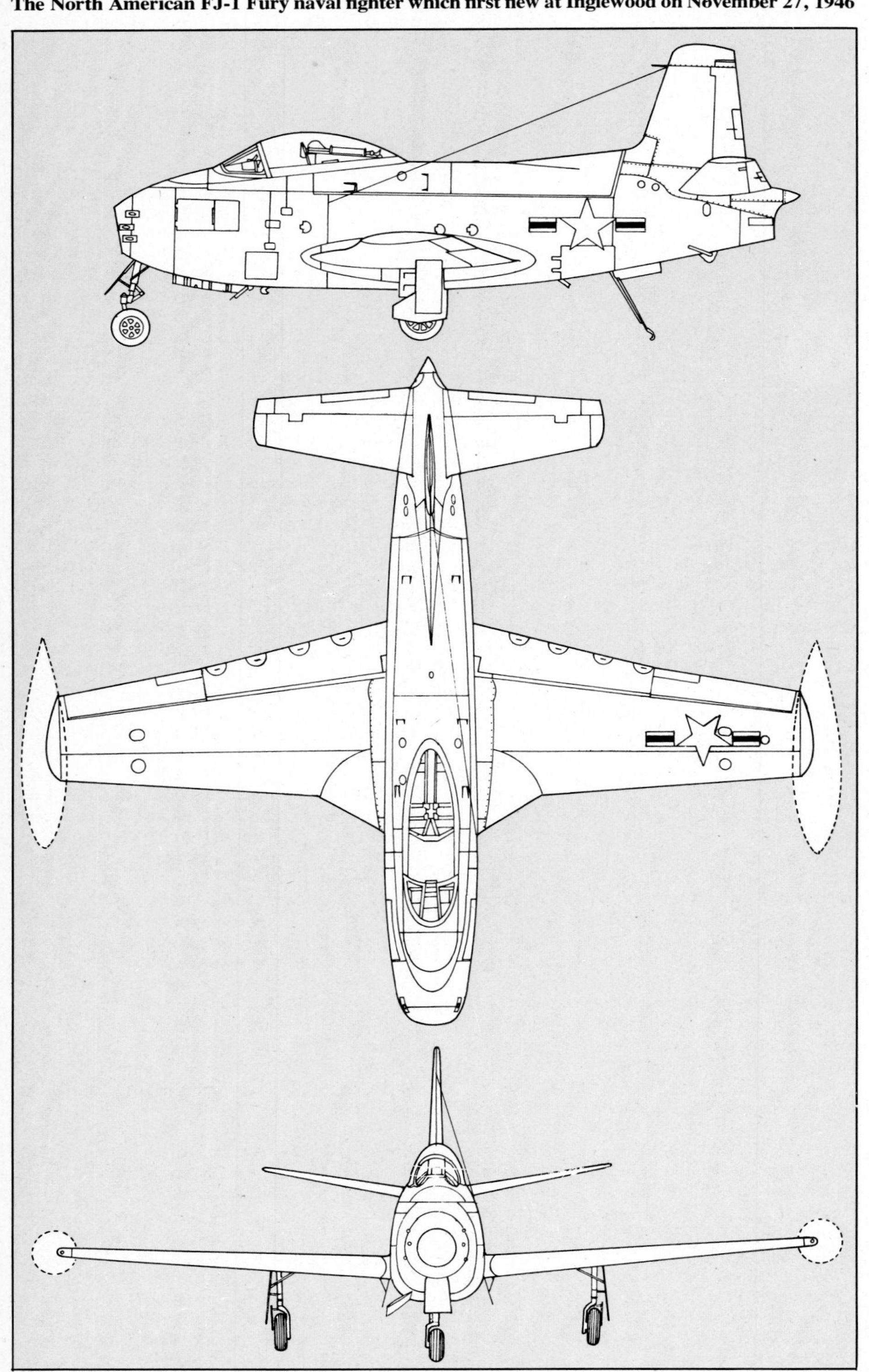

Fury, FJ North American

US naval fighter and attack aircraft. In the summer of 1944 North American Aviation completed the project design for a jet fighter using a wing based on that of the P-51 but with a completely new fuselage with a 'straight through' jet duct from a nose inlet. Two designs were prepared, the second being a longer and heavier aircraft for the USAAF (this was later delayed and finally emerged as the XP-86, the first of the sweptwing Sabre family). The original proposal became the NA-134, ordered by the US Navy as the three XFJ-1 prototypes with the name Fury on January 1, 1945. The Navy became aware of German sweptwing data in the summer of 1945 but, unlike the USAAF, decided not to incorporate it in the new jet fighter. (The first unconventional-wing aircraft to be planned for carrier duty were the Chance Vought F7U Cutlass and Douglas F4D Skyray.)

Like the same company's XB-45 four-jet bomber, the XFJ-1 was little more than jet propulsion applied to an advanced traditional airframe, with a laminar wing similar in profile to the P-51. The first flight was made at Inglewood on November 27, 1946, the engine being the 1733 kg (3820 lb) thrust General Electric J35-2 (TG-180) axial. By this time Inglewood was building 100 production FJ-1 Furies, with the Allison J35-2, virtually the same engine but rerated at 1814 kg (4000 lb) thrust, and with full carrier equipment and six 0.5-in (12.7-mm) guns. Features included small dive brakes above and below the non-folding wings, tip tanks, a primitive ejection seat and a 'kneeling' nose gear for stacking in a tight nose-to-tail line below decks. Designated NA-141, this batch was cut to 30 in 1948 and served only with VF-5A, soon restyled VF-51, between November 1947 and May 1949. In 1948 VF-51 became the first jet unit to complete a seagoing tour of duty, aboard USS *Boxer*, the first carrier landing having been on March 10, 1948.

Though the original Fury was no better than several other fighters of the day, the Air Force clearly had made a major advance with the F-86 Sabre, and despite the Cutlass, Skyray and even the later McDonnell Demon the Navy decided to order a naval version of the Sabre in 1950. Confusingly, it decided to designate this FJ-2, instead of F2J, and to perpetuate the name Fury, thereby making

Hawker Siddeley

A Hawker Fury II. The Fury served with the RAF and five other countries during the early 1930s

funds easier to obtain by suggesting that the type was a mere improved FJ-1 instead of a totally new aircraft. The first of the new Fury prototypes flew on December 27, 1951. It was essentially an F-86E with four 20-mm (0.79-in) M-2 guns, an A-frame arrester hook, catapult hooks and a lengthened nose leg, the General Electric J47-13 engine remaining. Type number was NA-185. Two NA-179 specially built XFJ-2 prototypes followed.

Carrier qualification was outstanding, and the Columbus, Ohio, factory (previously a Curtiss-Wright facility) constructed 300 of the much-refined FJ-2 production type, with 2722-kg (6000-lb) thrust J47-2 engine, modified power-folding wings, wider-track landing gear and APG-30 radar gunsight. Production was assigned lower priority than the F-86F, and when the Korean war ended orders were cut to 200; all were delivered in the first nine months of 1954. All served with shore-based Marine fighter squadrons, with bomb racks and, from 1955, the new Sidewinder AAM.

In March 1952 Columbus received the go-ahead on an improved Fury with the British Sapphire engine, built by Wright and Buick as the J65-2 at 3538-kg (7800-lb) thrust, fed by an enlarged duct which made the fuselage deeper. The first to fly was a rebuilt FJ-2, designated NA-196 XFJ-3, on July 3, 1953. On December 11, 1953, the first of 389 production FJ-3 (NA-194) Furies took to the air, and the navy later added 214 NA-215 models with the W-4D engine, but cut this back to an extra 149 only, for a total of 538. The last FJ-3 flew in August 1956. This excellent fighter/bomber equipped 17 navy and four marine squadrons, and VF-21 in January 1956 became the first combat unit to embark aboard the super carrier *Forrestal.* (The first FJ-3 unit at sea was VF-173, aboard *Bennington*, in May 1955.)

From August 1956 a total of 80 FJ-3s were converted to fire Sidewinders as the FJ-3M, while later others were rebuilt as drone targets and as drone (RPV) directors. The FJ-3D controlled the Regulus I ship-launched cruise missile, while the FJ-3D2 was parent aircraft to F9F-6K and KDA target aircraft. By 1959 surviving FJ-3s were being rebuilt with a long-chord wing, without slats, with integral wing fuel tanks and either three or four weapon pylons. In 1962 the new designations became DF-1C, DF-1D and MF-1C.

In 1953 Columbus, which from the start had a competent and aggressive design and project staff, proposed a completely reengineered Fury with much enhanced capability. This was soon accepted, and a rebuilt FJ-3 styled NA-208 and with the Navy designation XFJ-4, flew on October 16, 1953. Hardly any part was common to earlier Furies. The wing was much broader and thinner, with mid-span ailerons and full integral tankage, inboard high-lift flaps and small fences on a fixed leading edge. The very deep reprofiled fuselage combined with the wing to increase internal fuel capacity by 50%, and with the four underwing pylons all loaded the gross weight was increased by the same proportion compared with the original FJ-2. The tail was thinner, and the vertical surface taller, and much of the engineering was that of the F-100C then in production at the Ohio factory. Main gears had levered suspension and further widened track, and the result was a superior carrier-based attack aircraft.

Production FJ-4 (NA-209) Furys flowed from February 1955, the engine being the 3493-kg (7700-lb) thrust J65-16A. The first batch of 150, completed in March 1957, were followed by 222 FJ-4B (71 followed by 151 improved NA-244) which finally closed out production of Sabres and Furys in the United States in May 1958. The FJ-4B had a stiffer wing with six pylons, LABS (Low-Altitude Bombing System) for nuclear toss-delivery, extra air brakes on the rear fuselage and other changes. It was entirely configured as an attack bomber, and among its claims to fame was clearance to fire the ASM-N-7 Bullpup in January 1957, one of the first aircraft in use with air-to-surface guided missiles since Hitler's Luftwaffe.

Five Bullpups could be carried, with the radio-command guidance pod on the sixth pylon. In the revised Department of Defense numbering scheme the FJ-4 became the F-1E, and the FJ-4B the AF-1E. The AF equipped nine navy and three marine corps attack squadrons, before being progressively transferred to the reserve in 1962-65. A little-known research programme involved mixed-power trials using two FJ-4 Furys with North American hydrogen-peroxide rockets mounted in a fuselage extension above the normal jetpipe, and with nose extensions housing instrumentation.

(FJ-4B/AF-1E) *Span:* 11.9 m (39 ft 1 in) *Length:* 11.2 m (36 ft 9 in) *Gross weight:* 11 793 kg (26 000 lb) *Maximum speed:* 1150 km/h (715 mph)

Fury, Hawker

British fighter aircraft. To meet the requirements of Air Ministry Specification F.20/27, Sydney Camm of Hawker designed a single-seat fighter biplane, which flew for the first time in August 1928 powered by a 450-hp Bristol Jupiter VII radial engine. It was also tested with a 520-hp Bristol Mercury VI powerplant, also a radial, and the satisfactory results inspired the design of the Hornet prototype, which utilized the 420-hp Rolls-Royce F.XIA V-type engine. This was changed for a 480-hp F.XIS when it was sent for service trials. Registered J9682, the Hornet was purchased by the Air Ministry in September 1929 and renamed Fury I; 21 were ordered initially for the RAF in August 1930, the total eventually reaching 118 aircraft.

Officially, the Fury was constructed under Specification 13/30, though it would be more accurate to say that the specification was written round the Fury. The fighter had a standard tubular metal airframe of rectangular section, fairing into an oval; the forward fuselage was metal-skinned and the rear portion fabric-covered. The staggered, unequal-span wings had ailerons on the upper mainplane only, and the wooden two-blade propeller was driven by a supercharged 525-hp Rolls-Royce Kestrel IIS engine, the developed version of the F.XI. Standard armament comprised two synchronized Vickers 0.303-in (7.7-mm) machine-guns in the nose, and racks for light bombs could be fitted beneath the lower wings.

The first production Fury I flew on March 25, 1931. No 43 Squadron received 16 aircraft in May 1931, and Nos 1 and 25 Squadrons were equipped from orders placed during that year. The Fury had an exceptionally rapid rate of climb, 3048 m (10 000 ft) in $4\frac{1}{4}$ minutes, was highly manoeuvrable, and was the first intercepter with the RAF capable of achieving a level speed of more than 322 km/h (200 mph).

A private-venture prototype (G-ABSE), built by Hawker for various trials purposes, made its first flight on April 13, 1932, and was developed as the Intermediate Fury. From this was evolved the High Speed Fury, also a private venture, flown for the first time on May 3, 1933, and subsequently fitted with various Rolls-Royce Kestrel or Goshawk engines. After evaluation, Specification 6/35 was issued to cover the production of 23 similar aircraft, with 640-hp Kestrel VI engines, as Fury IIs for the RAF. General Aircraft was given an order for 75 of this version, but this was not completely fulfilled, though it included a few Fury IIs for South Africa. Fury IIs entered RAF service (with No 25 Squadron) in early 1937, but the five squadrons equipped with the Mk II had begun phasing them out by January 1939. However, 16 Fury Is and 48 Fury IIs were still serving, with RAF training units, at the beginning of the Second World War.

Variants of the Fury I, with assorted power

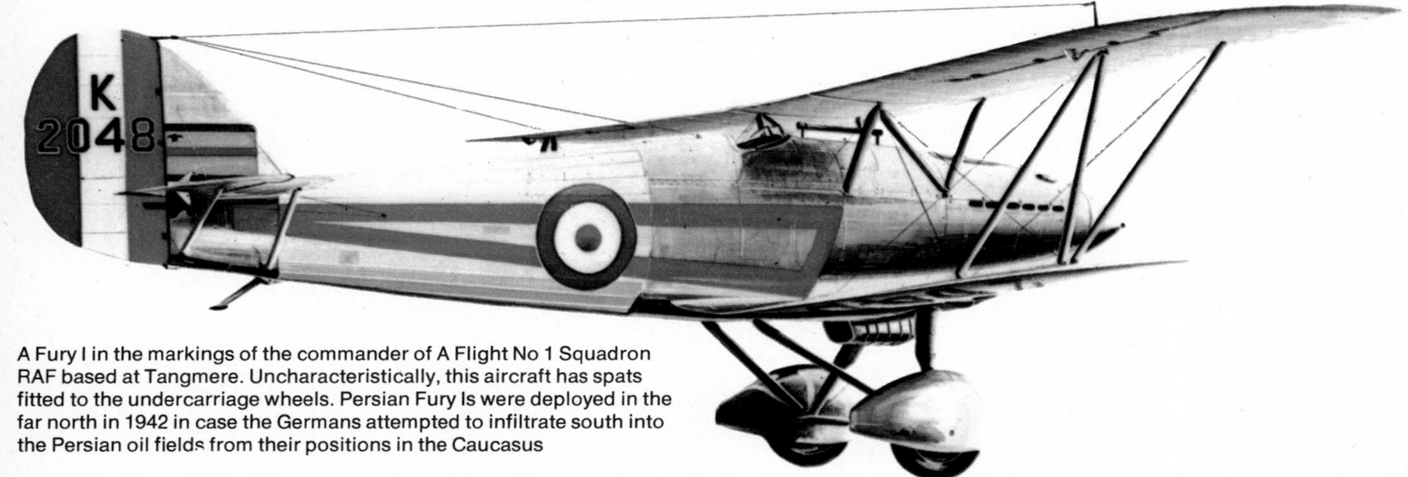

A Fury I in the markings of the commander of A Flight No 1 Squadron RAF based at Tangmere. Uncharacteristically, this aircraft has spats fitted to the undercarriage wheels. Persian Fury Is were deployed in the far north in 1942 in case the Germans attempted to infiltrate south into the Persian oil fields from their positions in the Caucasus

plants, were exported to Persia (16), Spain (3), Norway (1) and Yugoslavia (6); and of the Fury II to Persia (6), Portugal (3) and Yugoslavia (10). These foreign models were armed with various calibre machine-guns of Colt, Mauser or Spandau manufacture, and those supplied to Yugoslavia could carry two additional machine-guns beneath the lower wings.

(Fury I) *Span:* 9.14 m (30 ft) *Length:* 8.13 m (26 ft 8 in) *Gross weight:* 1583 kg (3490 lb) *Maximum speed:* 333 km/h (207 mph)

Fury, Hawker British monoplane fighter aircraft See **Sea Fury**

Fuso

Japanese battleship class, completed between 1915 and 1917. *Fuso* and her sister ship *Yamashiro* were ordered under the emergency expansion programme of 1911-12, designed to build up the Japanese fleet to one of the most powerful and largest battleships in the world when completed and the weight of their broadside was unequalled until the completion of the 16-in (406-mm) gunned *Nagato.*

During the early 1920s both ships were refitted when the tripod foremasts had various structures housing command posts added to it. The forefunnels were fitted with a distinctive cap to deflect smoke away from these command centres. In addition, *Yamashiro* had a searchlight platform fitted round the after funnel, a feature lacking on *Fuso.*

In April 1930, *Fuso* entered dockyard to undergo modernization. Being unable to embark on construction of new battleship types, Japan, like Britain, America and Italy, was forced to modernize her old craft. *Fuso* was the first Japanese ship to undergo such work and set the pattern for the modernization of the rest of the Japanese fleet. *Yamashiro* underwent a similar modernization which commenced in December 1930, and both ships rejoined the fleet early in 1935.

Under the modernization, the ships were completely reboilered and reengined, six oil-fired boilers replacing the original 24 mixed-firing boilers. The reduction in the number of boilers meant a great saving in space and entailed the removal of the forward boiler-room and funnel. The new turbines increased the horsepower from 40 000 to 75 000.

The armament was also updated during the modernization, the elevation of the 14-in (356-mm) guns being increased from 30° to 43° and that of the secondary armament from 15° to 30°; the 3-in (76-mm) guns were replaced by 5-in (127-mm) AA and the torpedo tubes removed. Both ships were fitted with aircraft handling facilities—*Fuso* carrying a catapult on a turret which was resited so that the guns could only bear on a forward arc. In *Yamashiro,* the catapult was sited aft on the quarterdeck. A new towering bridge structure replaced the tripod foremast making the two ships among the ugliest in the Japanese fleet.

All these alterations created problems of stability in *Fuso* and four months after initial completion of the refit in May 1933 she had to reenter dock to have her bulges widened to provide a remedy. She reemerged in February 1935. *Yamashiro* was not so advanced with her modernization and the bulges were added while she was still in dockyard hands.

Being obsolete, and the modernization not proving wholly successful, the two battleships were mainly employed on training and second-line duties during the war. Following the heavy carrier losses at Midway, plans were formulated to convert them to hybrid carriers like the *Ise,* but the loss of pilots at the battle of the Mariannas in June 1944 caused the idea to be abandoned.

Few additions were made to the AA armament during the war and the two ships received radar only a few weeks before the battle of Leyte Gulf on October 25, 1944, when they were both sunk.

Fuso was laid down at Kure navy yard on March 11, 1912, and completed November 8, 1915; *Yamashiro* was laid down at Yokosuka navy yard on November 20, 1913, and completed March 31, 1917.

(As built) *Displacement:* 29 330 tons *Length:* 205.13 m (673 ft) oa *Beam:* 28.65 m (94 ft) *Draught:* 8.61 m (28 ft 3 in) *Machinery:* 4-shaft Curtiss geared turbines, 40 000 shp= 22.5 knots *Protection:* 305-102 mm (12-4 in) belt; 63 mm (2.48 in) decks; 305 mm (12 in) turrets *Armament:* 12 356-mm (14-in)/45-cal (6×2) guns; 16 152-mm (6-in)/50-cal (16×1) guns; 4 76-mm (3-in) AA guns; 6 53-cm (21-in) fixed torpedo tubes *Crew:* 1193

(As modernized) *Displacement:* 34 700 tons, (*Yamashiro*) 34 500 tons *Length:* 212.75 m (698 ft) oa *Beam:* 33.07 m (108 ft 6 in) *Draught:* 9.67 m (31 ft 9 in) *Machinery:* 4-shaft Kanpon geared turbines, 75 000 shp= 24.75 knots *Protection:* 178 mm (7 in) decks *Armament:* 12 356-mm (14-in)/45-cal (6×2) guns; 14 152-mm (6-in)/50-cal (14×1) guns; 8 127-mm (5-in)/50-cal guns; 16 25-mm (1-in) AA guns; 3 aircraft *Crew:* 1396

The Japanese battleship *Fuso,* steaming off the Bungo Strait during refit trials in 1933

COI

FV 432 APCs at Warminster in an experimental camouflage scheme

COI

APC familiarization training with the Royal Regiment of Wales

FV 432

British armoured personnel carrier. It entered British Army service in 1963 and is currently in use. Development took place during the late 1950s and the first model was built by GKN-Sankey in 1963 and production continued until 1971. It was originally known as Trojan, but this name fell into disuse.

The FV 432 is simply an armoured steel box on tracks, very similar to several others of the class, such as the American M113. Due to the steel armour it is not inherently amphibious, but can be swum by means of erecting a flotation screen carried on the roof. The driver is seated at the front, with the engine on his left, and a single rear door gives access to the body of the vehicle in which ten fully-equipped infantrymen can ride. There are no weapons ports, however, so that the passengers cannot fight from the vehicle. Armament is limited to a GP machine-gun operated through a hatch in the roof by the vehicle commander.

The basic FV 432 chassis has formed the basis for a number of specialized vehicles. FV 433 is Abbot, the 105-mm (4.13-in) self-propelled gun; FV 434 is a mobile recovery and fitter's vehicle for use by REME and carries a hydraulic crane; FV 438 carries two Swingfire antitank missile launchers, with another 14 missiles inside the hull; FV 439 is a communications vehicle developed for use by the Royal Corps of Signals.

The basic FV 432 has also been adapted to various roles, although without a change in designation. It is used, for example, to carry FACE (field artillery computer equipment) system in artillery batteries and to act as the battery command post vehicle. The 81-mm (3.18-in) infantry mortar has been mounted inside on a rotating baseplate, firing through the roof hatch; the ZB 298 surveillance radar can be mounted on the roof, as can the Green

An FV 432 at the School of Infantry, Warminster, crewed by the Royal Irish Rangers. It is fitted with a Fox type armoured car turret mounting a 30-mm Rarden cannon for local defence

MOD

FV 432

A British Army FV 432 adapted for an ambulance role in service in Germany in 1976. The ambulance version can take four stretchers or seated wounded with an attendant. The FV 432 can also be used for mortar fire location radar, and as a mobile mount for antitank weapons and the 81-mm (3.19-in) mortar. Despite its wide employment within the British Army there have been no foreign customers due to the wide use of the American M116 APC. The FV 432 can swim using flotation screens and can operate in an NBC environment. As an APC it takes a commander, driver and a ten-man section and entered service in 1964

MOD

02EA21

COI

Riflemen of the Royal Green Jackets deploy from their 432. The number on the side shows that they are in 1 Section, No 1 Platoon of A Company

Below: Camouflaged Royal Irish Rangers prepare to fire an 81-mm mortar from their FV 432

COI

Archer and Cymbeline mortar-locating radars. It can tow the Barmine layer, mount a Carl Gustav 84-mm (3.30-in) recoilless gun, and carry stretchers. There is almost no end to its versatility. In spite of this, however, it has never been adopted by any other army than the British, largely because of the competitive price of the American M113.

Weight: 15 026 kg (33 128 lb) *Length:* 5.25 m (17 ft 3 in) *Width:* 2.79 m (9 ft 2 in) *Height:* 1.88 m (6 ft 2 in) *Armour:* 12-6 mm (0.47-0.24 in) *Armament:* 7.62-mm (0.30-in) general purpose mg *Powerplant:* Rolls-Royce K-60 6-cylinder multi-fuel, 240 bhp at 3750 rpm *Speed:* 51.5 km/h (32 mph) *Range:* 580 km (360 miles) *Crew:* 2 plus 10 passengers

Fw 189, Focke-Wulf

German tactical reconnaissance and army cooperation aircraft. The Fw 189, which was to become one of the most useful and ubiquitous reconnaissance aircraft employed by the Luftwaffe during the Second World War, had its origins in a February 1937 specification from the Reichsluftfahrtministerium (RLM, the German aviation ministry) for a three-seat short-range tactical reconnaissance type to succeed the parasol-winged Henschel Hs 126.

To meet this specification, Focke-Wulf's team under the leadership of Kurt Tank evolved a then-radical twin-boom design of which the first prototype, the Fw 189 V1 (registration D-OPVN), made its maiden flight in July 1938. A 430-hp Argus As 410 12-cylinder air-cooled inverted V-type engine

An Fw 189 in service on the Eastern Front where the type was nicknamed *das Fliegende Auge* (the flying eye). Fw 189s were used for short- and long-range reconnaissance, liaison, casevac and ground support from 1938 until 1944

was installed at the front of each slender tail boom, driving a two-blade propeller, and mounted on the centre-section of the wing, between the booms, was an extremely well-glazed nacelle accommodating the three-man crew. Each tail boom terminated in a single fin and rudder, bridged by a centrally-mounted tailplane. No armament was fitted to the Fw 189 V1, but the second prototype (D-OVHD), which flew in August 1938, was armed with a 7.9-mm (0.311-in) MG 17 machine-gun in each wing root and three 7.9-mm MG 15 guns: one each in the nose, a dorsal blister, and the tailcone of the nacelle. The V3 (D-ORMH) was unarmed, but had the definitive 450-hp As 410A-1 engines intended for production aircraft.

The Fw 189 V4 fourth prototype was representative of the Fw 189A production configuration, but it was actually the Fw 189B, based on the V5, that was first to be ordered into production by the RLM in 1939. The Fw 189B (three B-0s and ten B-1s) was built as an unarmed, dual-control five-seat trainer, its modified nacelle lacking the nose and tailcone glazing of the A-series prototypes.

Production of the Fw 189A finally got under way in the spring of 1940, a batch of ten preproduction Fw 189A-0s for service trials being followed by the first series version, the Fw 189A-1. This began to reach Luftwaffe units in late 1940 and early 1941, and eventually equipped at least nine Aufklärungsgruppen (long-range reconnaissance wings) and 15 Nahaufklärungsgruppen (short-range reconnaissance wings), most of them on the Eastern Front. Known variously as the *Uhu* (owl), or as *das Fliegende Auge* (the flying eye) of the Wehrmacht, the Fw 189A performed invaluable service in many theatres of war. It had first-class handling qualities, could give a good account of itself in combat, and could withstand a remarkable amount of battle damage for such an (apparently) slightly-built aeroplane.

Production Fw 189A-1s carried an armament similar to that of the second prototype, except that the nose machine-gun was deleted. The second production version, the Fw 189A-2, differed in having 7.9-mm (0.311-in) MG 81Z (twin MG 81) guns in the dorsal and tailcone positions, instead of the MG 15s. The Fw 189A-4 (the Fw 189A-3 was an unarmed trainer) was a ground-support development of the A-2, having ventral armour-plating and 20-mm (0.79-in) MG FF cannon instead of MG 17s in the wing roots. All except the A-3 could carry four 50-kg (110-lb) bombs on racks under the outer wings. The Fw 189A-1/Trop was a hot climate version for service in the Mediterranean and North African theatres; the A-1/U2 and A-1/U3 were two special one-off conversions for a VIP transport role; the single Fw 189E was another A-1, converted to 700-hp French Gnome-Rhône 14M radial engines; and many A-types were, in their later years, used for such secondary duties as liaison and casualty evacuation. Some even had a short spell as night fighters with I/NJG 100. Slovakia, a nominally-independent republic which came into being following the Nazi dismemberment of Czechoslovakia, received 14 Fw 189A-1s, and Hungary about 30 A-2s.

Production ended in August 1944, by which time a total of 864 Fw 189s had been completed. Of these, 310 were produced by the SNCA du Sud-Ouest at Bordeaux-Mérignac during 1942-44 and 337 Fw 189As by the Aero factory in Czechoslovakia between 1941-43. The French total comprised 293 Fw 189As plus 17 examples of the Fw 189F-1, a version of the A-2 with 580-hp Argus As 411MA-1 engines. Focke-Wulf's total of 217 included six prototypes, 198 Fw 189As and 13 Fw 189Bs. The sixth prototype (V6) and the modified first prototype (V1b) were used to flight-test a very much smaller, well-armoured two-seat nacelle intended for the proposed Fw 189C assault version; other projects that did not come to fruition were the twin-float Fw 189D and the 950-hp As 402-engined Fw 189G.

(Fw 189A-2) *Span:* 18.40 m (60 ft 4½ in) *Length:* 12 m (39 ft 4½ in) *Gross weight:* 3950 kg (8710 lb) *Maximum speed:* 350 km/h (217 mph)

An Fw 189A, powered by two Argus As.410 A-1 engines, is warmed up during pre-flight checks

Fw 190, Focke-Wulf

German fighter. In many ways the most advanced fighter to take part in the Second World War, the Fw 190 was an outstanding example of modern aeronautical engineering at the time of its design in 1938. It was noteworthy for extremely clever structure and packaging, the advanced installation of the powerful radial engine, the almost totally electrical nature of the secondary power systems and the remarkably small overall size.

Kurt Tank, technical director of Focke-Wulf Flugzeugbau (aircraft factory) at Bremen, was invited to propose a new fighter design to the German Air Ministry Technische Amt (technical dept) in April 1938, not because there was any urgency but because a second type to back up the Bf 109 was deemed prudent. (In fact, the Messerschmitt fighter was to exhibit increasing shortcomings and faults, but remained in ever-increasing production up to the final Nazi collapse.)

Tank personally convinced the officials of the suitability of using a large air-cooled radial engine, one major factor being the existence of the BMW 139, promising powers well beyond the capacity of the leading liquid-cooled units, the DB 601 and Jumo 211. Focke-Wulf was awarded an order for three prototype Fw 190 V-series (*Versuchs*)

An Fw 190A-1, one of the 100 aircraft sent to Luftwaffe units for front-line evaluation. Trials showed that the engine overheated during running up and most takeoffs were aborted when the engines seized up. Focke-Wulf blamed BMW, and BMW blamed the designers

John Batchelor Collection

or trial aircraft in June 1938. Tank himself sketched the original basic configuration, a shape reminiscent of the Hughes racer with a very small wing, slim body, and extremely tall, wide-track landing gears. Detailed engineering design was headed by R Blaser, who imprinted his brilliance on every part of the aircraft. Never before had so much been packed into so compact a fighter.

The only obvious shortcoming was that the close-coupled engine and cockpit precluded fuselage armament, and also risked unbearably high cockpit temperatures, and the latter were borne out on the first flight on June 1, 1939. But by this time BMW had succeeded in getting permission to drop the BMW 139 in favour of a more advanced radial, the BMW 801. This was of slightly larger swept volume, and though heavier and longer than the 139 promised eventually to yield some 2000 hp. The Fw 190 was therefore grossly reengineered to take the new engine. In June 1939 it was decided to fly the Fw 190 V2 with the original engine, scrap the next two aircraft in an agreed preproduction batch of 40, and build the V5 as a BMW 801-powered machine with a different forward fuselage.

Cutaway BMW 801C 14-cylinder two-row radial air-cooled engine, rated at 1600 hp for takeoff, and 1380 hp at 4600 m (15 100 ft). The engine mounting was a steel tubular welded construction and the hollow circular mounting ring acted as the hydraulic fluid reservoir

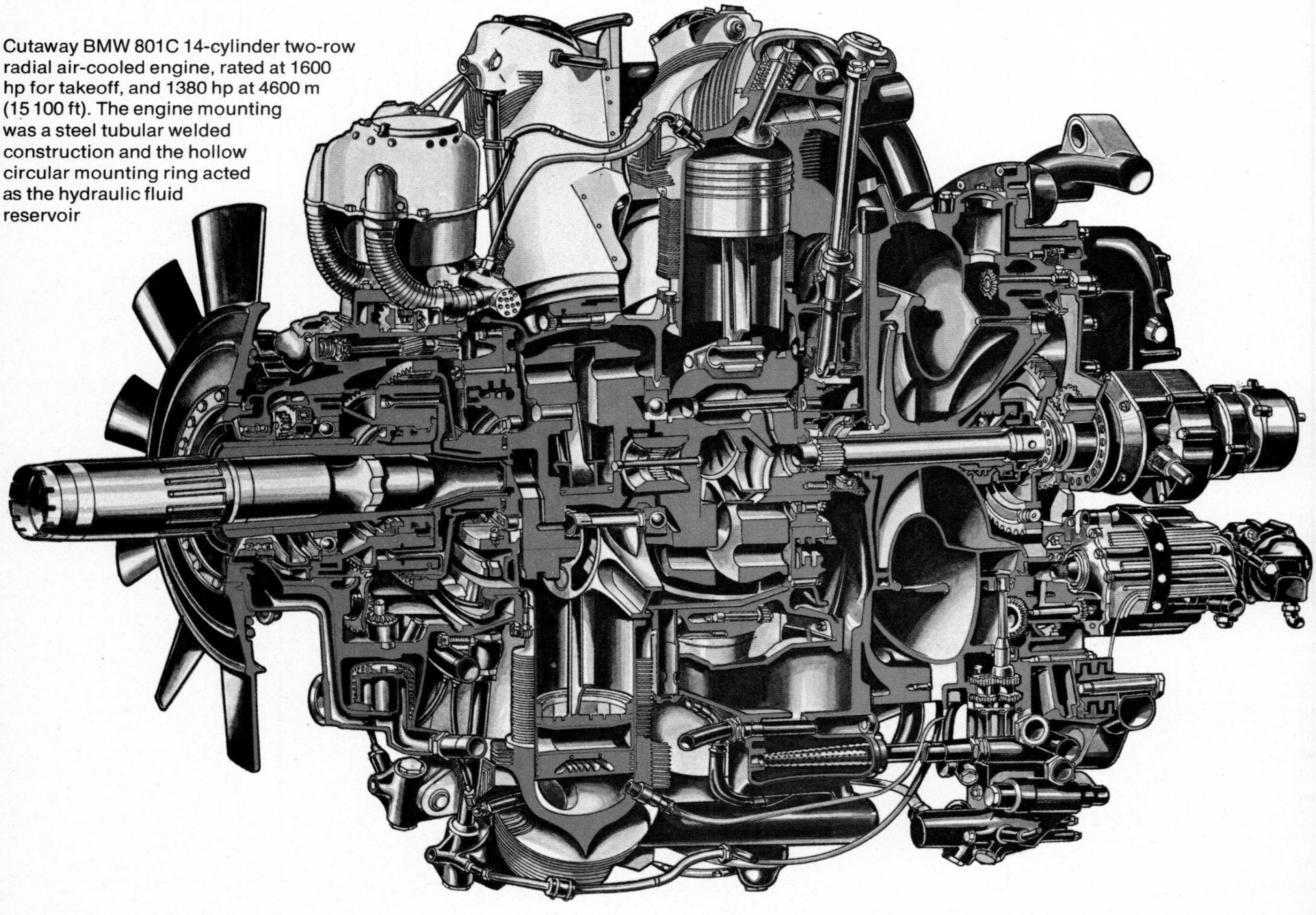

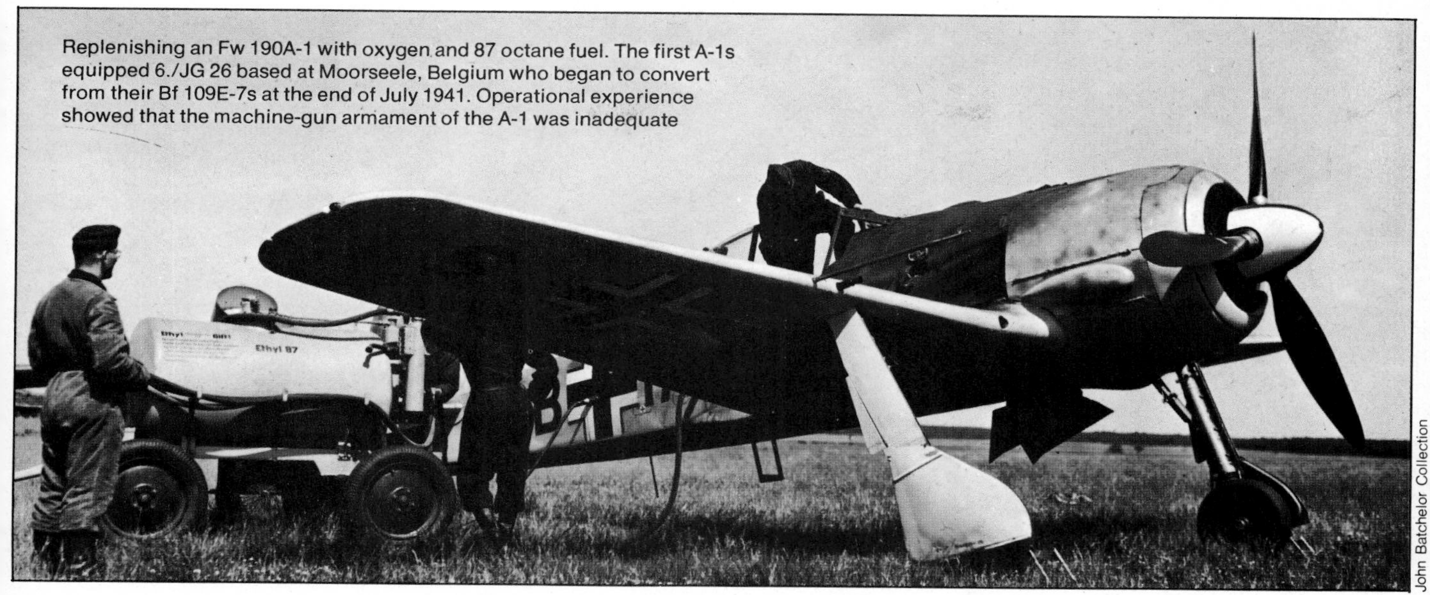

Replenishing an Fw 190A-1 with oxygen and 87 octane fuel. The first A-1s equipped 6./JG 26 based at Moorseele, Belgium who began to convert from their Bf 109E-7s at the end of July 1941. Operational experience showed that the machine-gun armament of the A-1 was inadequate

John Batchelor Collection

Early flight trials with Fw 190 V1 showed superb handling, but the advanced engine installation with ducted VDM propeller spinner lacked the ten-blade cooling fan and this overheated the engine as well as the cockpit. With the V2, flown on October 31, 1939, two MG 17 machine-guns were added to the wing roots, and the engine installation eventually had the cooling fan geared up from the propeller shaft, plus a normal air inlet flowing around a small spinner. Much larger changes were seen in V5, flown in April 1940, which apart from the definitive BMW 801 engine had a restressed airframe for considerably increased weights, a smaller and rearranged cockpit moved considerably further back over the trailing edge of the wing, changed main landing gears raked sharply forward with the wheels housed in swept-forward wing roots (with fairing doors moved from the legs to the belly) and several other alterations. An advantage of moving the cockpit back was that guns could be installed in the top decking, but the view for taxiing was made worse than before, though it was still acceptable.

An even more fundamental factor was that the bigger engine, and other changes, had substantially raised the weight; in fact the Fw 190 was ever afterward generally heavier than either a Bf 109 or a Merlin-Spitfire, though it was exceptionally small and compact. Tank decided as early as May 1939 to increase the size of the wing, which had always been more appropriate to a racer than a dogfighter. In about October 1940 this wing, with area raised from 16 to 18.3 sq m (161 to 197 sq ft) was flown on V5, and became standard. The Fw 190A-0 preproduction batch that followed had the 1600-hp BMW 801C engine and four 7.92-mm (0.312-in) MG 17 machine-guns. Deliveries to Rechlin and other test centres began in February 1941, and II/JG 26 (a wing of the group selected to be first with the new fighter) assisted in unearthing problems and refining operational procedures.

Focke-Wulf had named the new fighter *Die Würger* (shrike, or butcher-bird), but this did not catch on. But its outstanding qualities led to urgency in getting it into production, and while Focke-Wulf established a production line at Marienburg, Arado at Warnemünde and Ago at Oschersleben also tooled-up for production. But initial operational evaluation by II/JG 26 at Le Bourget (Paris) and Maldeghem (Belgium) was a disaster, hardly any flight being completed without overheating and engine-seizure and most not even getting airborne. An official investigation recommended that the Fw 190 should be cancelled; but all that was needed was more cooperative effort between Focke-Wulf and BMW. Within a month the situation was dramatically improved.

Delivery of the four-MG 17 Fw 190A-1 was followed by the A-2 from Arado in August 1941. Many A-1 were given two 20-mm (0.79-in) MG FF cannon outboard of the landing gear, most as a modification, while the A-2 had two of the new 20-mm (0.79-in) Mauser MG 151 cannon instead of MG 17s in the wing roots. This formidable armament combined with outstanding all-round performance and manoeuvrability to make the 190 the greatest air-superiority aircraft in the sky in 1941. One of its first major actions, with JG 26, was air cover for *Scharnhorst, Gneisenau* and other ships on February 12, 1942. JG 26 annihilated 825 Squadron's Swordfish, the one-sidedness of the encounter being made ironic by the fact that the Fw 190 was itself destined to carry full-size torpedoes. Against the Spitfire V it established immediate supremacy, the British fighter being outclassed in every respect except turn radius, where the rivals were closely comparable. But the early-model Fw 190 gave the RAF the largest combat shock in its entire history. The superiority of the German fighter was accentuated by the fact that it was virtually unknown (at first intelligence decided the Luftwaffe must be using captured French Curtiss Hawk 75s!) even though it had been flying well before the war. Throughout 1942 the Fw 190 was a bogey man which, among other things, so distorted the Spitfire programme that the carefully designed Mk VIII was delayed while 5665 Mk IXs were hastily put together as an interim measure. This was solely because of the scare caused by the Focke-Wulf.

By 1942 production was centred on the A-

The Fw 190A-4 began to appear in mid-1942. It has a Methanol Water MW 50 power boost

John Batchelor Collection

John Batchelor Collection

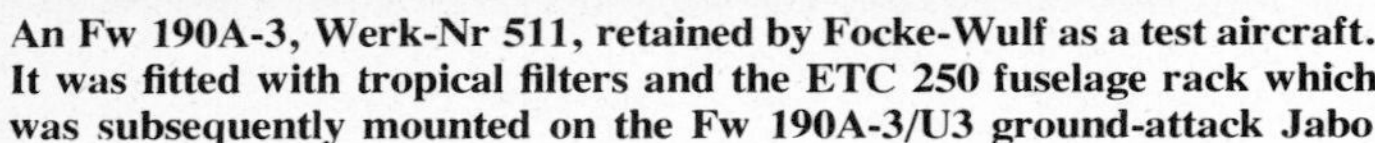

An Fw 190A-3, Werk-Nr 511, retained by Focke-Wulf as a test aircraft. It was fitted with tropical filters and the ETC 250 fuselage rack which was subsequently mounted on the Fw 190A-3/U3 ground-attack Jabo

3, with many changes and introducing the first of a fantastic variety of external armament options which made the Fw 190 the most versatile fighter of the war. Later, on June 23, 1942, Oberleutnant Arnim Faber, adjutant of III/JG 2, achieved an unsought place in history by mistaking his bearings in a dogfight over the Bristol Channel and making a perfect landing at RAF Pembrey in South Wales, thereby giving the RAF what was probably its most welcome prize and enabling a thorough and sobering flight evaluation to be made. Dissecting the Fw 190 if anything increased the respect in which it was held. Likewise on the Eastern Front a growing force of Focke-Wulfs battled with Soviet fighters and soon became highly regarded by the Russian designer Yakovlev, who judged large fighters such as the Typhoon, P-47 and F4U to be mistakes. In fact, the Fw 190 was not exactly small and light in the Soviet style, but compact; it seldom turned the scales at under 4000 kg (8800 lb) and nearly all had a laden weight of around 4900 kg (10 800 lb), much of which was accounted for by the heavy armament, equipment, armour and external tanks or ordnance.

In the summer of 1942 the A-4 introduced methanol/water (MW 50) injection for brief bursts of power up to 2100 hp, and new radio resulted in a changed aerial mast on the fin. One subtype, the A-4/R6 (R being the suffix for field-modification kits), was first to carry the 21-cm (8.27-in) WGr 21 rocket tubes which did more than anything else to break up the B-17 formation of the disastrous first raid on Schweinfurt on October 14, 1943. The American target had been a ball-bearing works, and precisely six months earlier a British ball-bearing factory at Chelmsford had been destroyed by Jabo (fighter/bomber) Fw 190A-4/U8 aircraft of SKG 10, each racing in at low level with four SC50 or one SC250 in one of the more damaging of hundreds of 'tip and run' attacks by the nimble Fw 190 on southern England. So successful was the Jabo 190 that special versions were developed for this duty, and these gradually supplanted the Ju 87 and all other Luftwaffe attack aircraft for almost every kind of battlefield mission. Very small numbers (for example, five of the A-5/U2) were built as night fighters, and used by Major Hajo Herrmann's famed Wilde Sau free-ranging JG 300 wing, followed by JG 301 and 302, but suffered high attrition in brief careers.

By 1943 the variations were too numerous to describe in detail, but new armament included the 13-mm (0.51-in) MG 131 in the top decking of the fuselage (making a shallow bulge from windscreen to engine) and various wing arrangements of 20-mm (0.79-in) and 30-mm (1.18-in) cannon. From the A-5 the length was increased, and the most numerous of all Fw 190 versions, the A-8, even included a tandem trainer version, supplemented by the Fw 190S series high-speed communications transport. Other new features included turbocharged engines, various reconnaissance installations, Doppelreiter overwing drop tanks, torpedoes, spin-stabilized rockets,

The Fw 190A-3 of 7 Staffel JG 2 'Richthofen' piloted by Oblt Arnim Faber which landed accidentally at RAF Pembrey on June 23, 1942

IWM

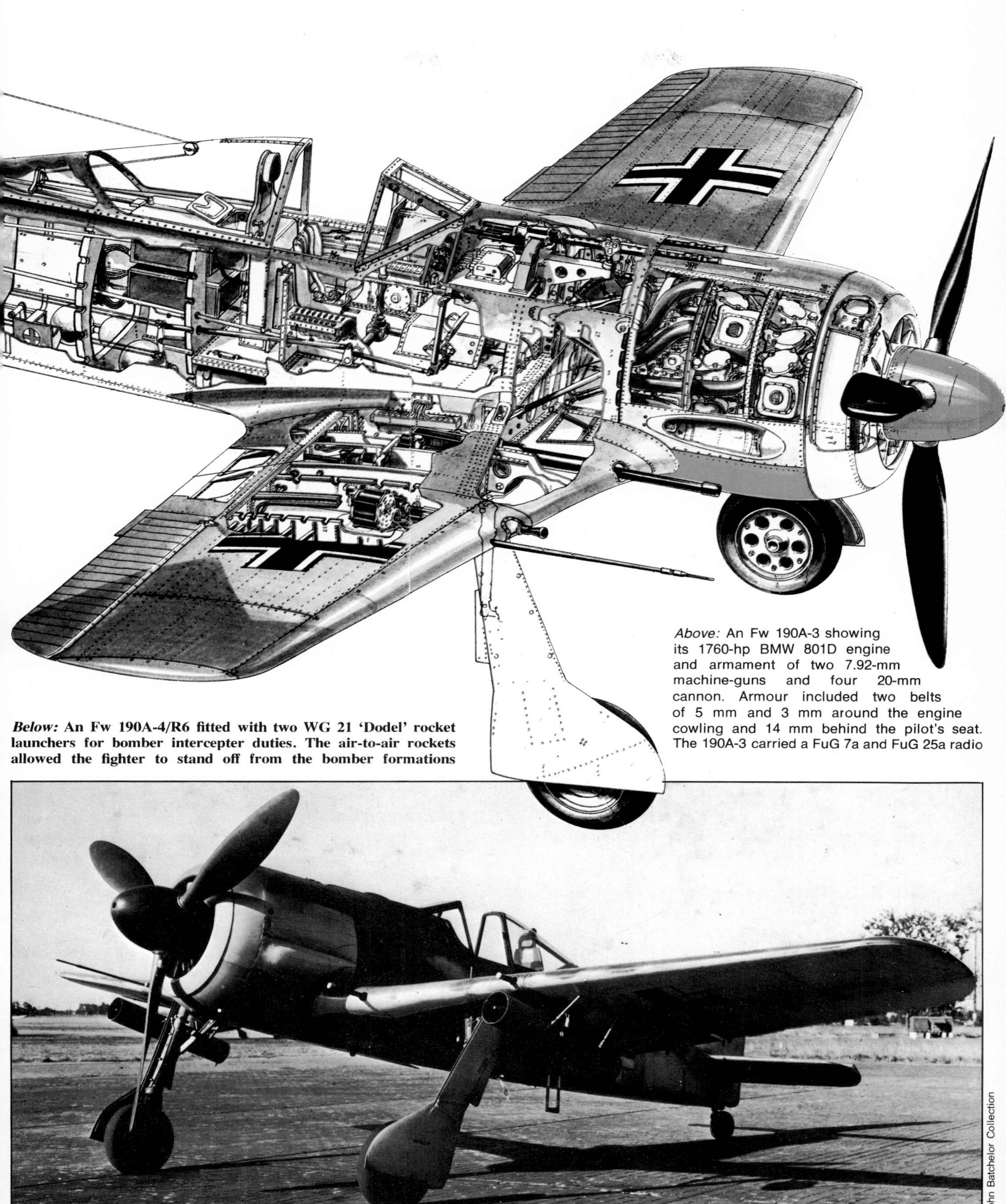

Above: An Fw 190A-3 showing its 1760-hp BMW 801D engine and armament of two 7.92-mm machine-guns and four 20-mm cannon. Armour included two belts of 5 mm and 3 mm around the engine cowling and 14 mm behind the pilot's seat. The 190A-3 carried a FuG 7a and FuG 25a radio

***Below:* An Fw 190A-4/R6 fitted with two WG 21 'Dodel' rocket launchers for bomber intercepter duties. The air-to-air rockets allowed the fighter to stand off from the bomber formations**

John Batchelor Collection

The assembly line for German Fw 190A-0 Focke-Wulf fighters in the winter of 1941. The aircraft in the foreground has just been fitted with its propeller

Fw 190, Focke-Wulf

John Batchelor Collection

Above: **Factory checks on the Focke-Wulf Fw 190A-0 fighter engine, in this picture probably the pre-production BMW 801C-0 power plant**

John Batchelor Collection

Above: **Part of the airframe of the fifth model of the Fw 190A-0 showing the fuselage-mounted 7.92-mm MG 17 machine-guns**

John Batchelor Collection

Above: **The twin 13-mm MG 131 machine-guns mounted in the fuselage of the Fw 190A-8.** ***Right:*** **The Fw 190 V8, a large-wing version of an Fw 190A-0 (Werk-Nr 0022) fitted with eight SC 50 bombs on fuselage and wing racks during weapons trials. A number of Fw 190A-1s were retrofitted with large wings after these trials**

John Batchelor Collection

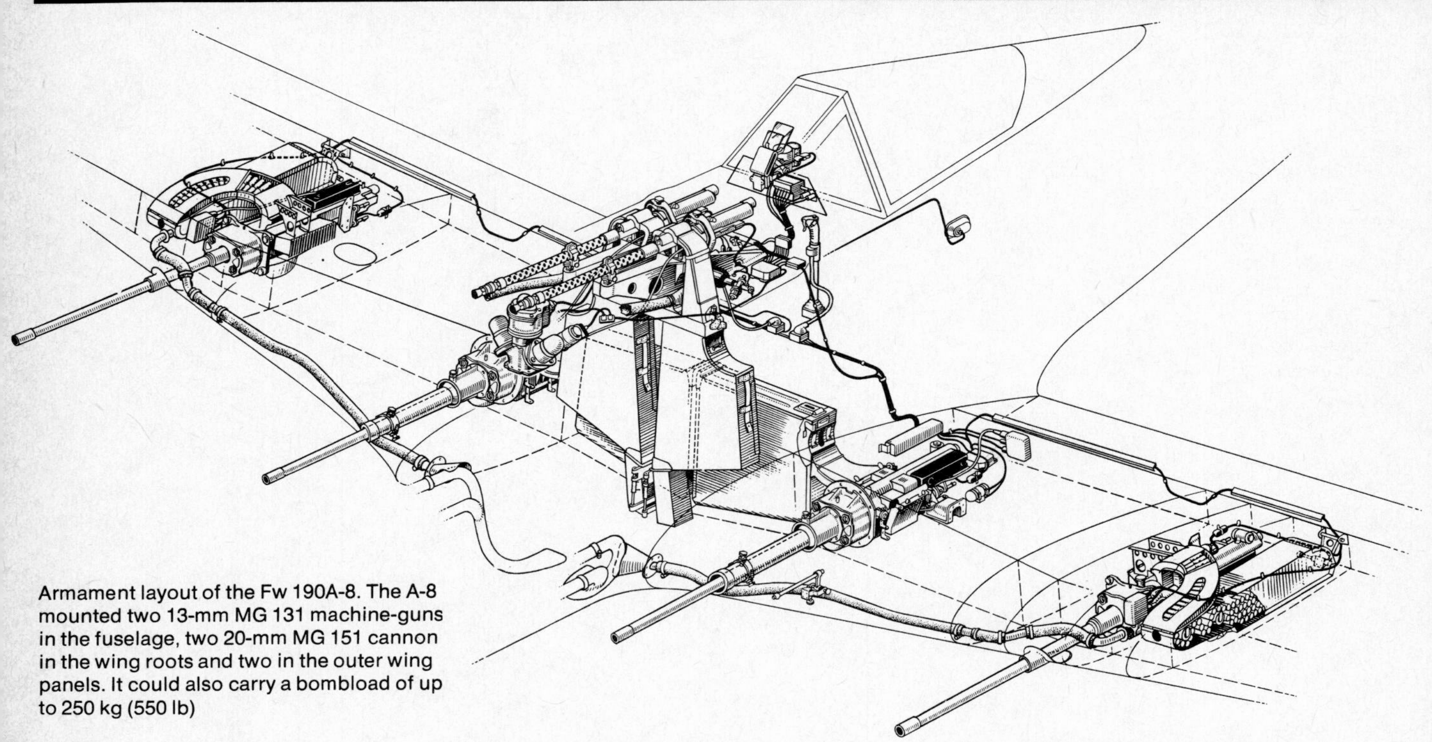

Armament layout of the Fw 190A-8. The A-8 mounted two 13-mm MG 131 machine-guns in the fuselage, two 20-mm MG 151 cannon in the wing roots and two in the outer wing panels. It could also carry a bombload of up to 250 kg (550 lb)

recoilless guns (firing horizontally or almost vertically), heavy underwing cannon, the X-4 wire-guided air-to-air missile and armoured leading edges for ramming.

Two important families placed in production in early 1943 were the F-series Schlachtflugzeug (tactical attack and close-support) and G-series Jabo-Rei (long-range bomber). By the end of 1943 these were the most important Luftwaffe attack aircraft in Italy and on the Soviet front, progressively re-equipping all except one of the former Stukagruppen and carrying out every kind of front-line sortie as well as providing for air-superiority fighting (a task for which the under-gunned G was not suited). On the Eastern Front a variety of special weapon installations were tested against armour, including the Zellendusche SG 116 (three 30-mm [1.18-in] barrels), HF/15 (five 15-mm [0.59-in] barrels under each wing), Panzerschreck 88-mm (3.46-in) rockets, Panzerblitz (eight longer-range rockets), WGr 28 (special hollow-charge rockets) and Förstersonde SG 113A, consisting of two pairs of 77-mm (3.03-in) recoilless guns mounted vertically in the wings, triggered by a tank's magnetic field. Other late-war installations included the Kurt SB 800RS roller-drum bomb, Hagelkorn (Hailstone) Bv 246 guided glide-bomb with slender concrete-coated wings, and the various BT (Bomben-Torpedo) antishipping weapons. None of these saw as much action as the various bombs of weights seemingly fantastic for so small a fighter, which included the Luftwaffe's largest conventional weapon, the SC 1800 of 1800 kg (3970 lb). No other fighter of the Second World War went into action with such massive weapons, and the SC 1800 needed special tires, and a long (and tricky) takeoff. On March 7, 1945, NSG 20 (night attack wing) used SC 1800 bombs against the vital Remagen bridge. Various Fw 190s, including the A-8 and F-8, were used as the piloted upper component of Mistel composite attack aircraft, to be described later.

In 1941 Tank and the air ministry had discussed ways of improving high-altitude performance. Tank pushed use of the liquid-cooled DB 603 (an engine developed after the 190 was designed), and in 1942-43 numerous prototypes flew with this engine, nearly all having circular ring-cowls and the coolant radiator variously under the engine or under the rear fuselage. Many had pressure cabins, and the majority a four-bladed propeller with broad blades. Rather gradually a vast experience of extremely fast high-altitude flight was built up which, via the Fw 190B and C series, resulted in the definitive model, the long-nosed Fw 190D ('Dora'). The engine was not to be the Daimler-Benz at all, but the fast-revving Jumo 213, the A-1 version of which was rated at 1776 hp (2240 with MW 50 injection) and could deliver 1880 hp at 4750 m (15 500 ft) and almost twice the power of the original 1939 BMW radial at twice this altitude. To counter the length of the nose, an extra section was added to the rear fuselage, and in all production D-versions the area of the fin and rudder was increased. Most examples had a bulged canopy giving better rear view. By October 1944 the 'Dora 9' (Fw

Fw 190A-8 cockpit key

1	Volume control and FT (communications) -ZF homing switch	13	IFF camera unit (FuG 25a)	28	Engine ventilation flap positioning lever	43	Canopy operation wheel
2	Frequency selector (FuG 16 ZY)	14	Fuel tank selector lever	29	Artificial horizon	44	Oxygen flow indicator
3	Elevator trim switch	15	Undercarriage manual extension handle	30	Armament switch and round counter control unit (SZK 4)	45	Oxygen pressure gauge
4	Throttle friction knob	16	Cockpit ventilation knob	31	Rate-of-climb indicator	46	Oxygen flow valve
5	Undercarriage and flap actuation buttons	17	Rudder pedal with integral braking	32	Fuel contents gauge	47	Canopy jettison lever
6	Elevator trim 6 position indicator	18	Bomb fuzing selector unit	33	Gun sight unit	48	Clock
7	Undercarriage position indicators (L & R) Flap position (centre)	19	Disposable load indicator lights	34	Repeater compass	49	Flare box cover
8	Emergency circuit-breaker	20	21-cm rocket control unit	35	AFN 2 Homing indicator (FuG 16 ZY)	50	Operation data card
9	Flap degree indicator	21	Altimeter	36	Propeller pitch indicator	51	Starter switch
10	Throttle	22	Pitot tube heater light	37	Supercharger pressure gauge	52	Fuel pump circuit breakers
11	Instrument panel dimmer control	23	Air speed indicator	38	Ultra-violet cockpit light	53	Flare box cover plate release button
12	Engine starter brushes withdrawal button	24	Fuel and oil pressure gauge	39	Fuel low-level indicator light and rear tank switchover light	54	Compass deviation card
		25	MG 131 'Armed' lights	40	Tachometer	55	Armament circuit breakers
		26	Oil temperature gauge	41	Fuel gauge selector switch	56	Seat
		27	Windscreen washer lever	42	Flare pistol holder	57	Map slot
						58	Control column
						59	Machine-gun firing button
						60	Bomb release button

25
30
33
35
31
34
37
38
23
21
40
27
28
32
36
16
24
26
39
41
42
43
15
14
60
17
20
47
13
12
46
11
18
49
9
8
6
57
3
56
AUS

Fw 190A-8. Introduced at the close of 1943, the A-8 was the most widely produced subtype. It had the same airframe as the A-7 but a more powerful engine

An Fw 190A-5/U13 fitted with two of the faired Focke-Wulf 300-litre (66-Imp gal) fuel-tank racks

190D-9) was at last reaching III/JG 54 and the Luftwaffe had a fighter that could again match anything possessed by the Allies.

Though only slightly faster than earlier Fw 190s at medium altitudes, and certainly no more manoeuvrable, the Dora 9 was faster in the climb or dive and significantly better at altitudes above 8000 m (26 250 ft). Most were comparatively lightly armed, with two MG 151 and two MG 131, plus an SC500 bomb or tank, and only about 700 had been completed when the Allied advance progressively overran the vast complex of Fw 190 production factories. Right to the end, production of the radial-engined aircraft was on a much greater scale, the output of the F and G rising to unprecedented levels in 1944 and outstripping the Dora 9 by a factor of roughly ten to one. Total production of all versions is impossible to give with precision, especially as Albert Speer's ministry added in the totals of aircraft incorporating fuselages or wings from machines previously counted but damaged by bombing of the factories before completion. A good guess for aircraft delivered to the Luftwaffe is 19 600, while Focke-Wulf's figure for overall production of all versions, including the great diversity of prototypes, is 20 001. This does not include the Ta 152, described in a later part of this work, but it does include the many intermediate aircraft that led to it in 1942-43. Though the Ta 152 looked superficially like a Dora 9, it was actually intended to be an almost completely new design, with quite different structure and a DB 603 engine. Later much of the original 190 structure was restored, to speed production, and the 152 was built with both the DB 603 (152C) and Jumo 213 (152H) engines.

Though manufacture of the Fw 190 was naturally halted by capture of the German factories, which by 1944 extended throughout Germany, Czechoslovakia, Austria and, especially, Poland, there remained a network of plants in France that saw in the formidable Focke-Wulf a useful stop-gap fighter for their own Armée de l'Air. Most of the French factories involved were nationalized into SNCAC or SNCASO, the assembly line being at the SNCAC underground plant at Cravant, near Auxerre. When liberated, the Fw 190A-5 was on the line, and after a slight hiccup this continued in low-rate production with the French designation NC 900. Later in 1944 the A-8 was substituted and some 64 NC 900 fighter/bombers were delivered by 1946. They equipped Armée de l'Air GC III/5 Normandie-Niemen, but were not popular (probably on emotional grounds, though the engines were said to be unreliable). Other users of the Fw 190 included the Spanish Blue Division on the Eastern Front, the Turkish air force and Argentina.

Span: 10.5 m (34 ft 5½ in) *Length:* (A-0 to A-4) 8.8 m (28 ft 10½ in); (A-5 to A-9, F and G) 8.95 m (29 ft 4½ in); (D-9) 10.24 m (33 ft 7 in) *Gross weight:* (A-3) 3978 kg (8770 lb); (A-8, F-3 typical) 4900 kg (10 800 lb); (G-1 with SC1800) 6300 kg (13 900 lb); (D-9) 4840 kg (10 670 lb) *Maximum speed:* (radial-engined, clean, override boost, typical) 673 km/h (418 mph); (D-9) 685 km/h (426 mph)

An Fw 190G fitted with two 300-litre (66-Imp gal) drop tanks and carrying a 500-kg bomb

IWM

The Swedish cruiser *Fylgia* prior to her reconstruction in 1939-40 as a cadet training ship. Her service career spanned 50 years

Fw 200, Focke-Wulf German long-range antishipping aircraft See **Condor**

Fylgia

Swedish cruiser, built 1903-07. This vessel was unusual for her time in having not only a 102-mm (4-in) armour belt but four twin gun-mountings, all on a displacement of 4060 tons. In other words she was a light armoured cruiser, well protected and powerfully armed for her size. She was launched on December 20, 1905, at the Bergsund yard, Finnboda.

The twin turrets were disposed fore and aft and in sponsons amidships at the same level. Four 57-mm (2.24-in) guns in sponsons at the bow and stern, were removed in 1926-27.

During 1939-40 she was reconstructed as a cadet training ship, and her appearance was altered completely. The ram bow was replaced by a clipper bow, the funnels were reduced from three to two and a tall bridge was provided. The 57-mm guns were replaced by four 57-mm AA and four 40-mm (1.57-in) AA, and the underwater 45-cm (17.7-in) torpedo tubes were replaced by others of 53-cm (21-in) above water. The *Fylgia* was scrapped in 1955-56.

Displacement: (As built) 4060 tons (normal), 5000 tons (full load); (As modernized) 4310 tons (standard), 4700 tons (full load) *Length:* 115 m (377 ft 8 in) wl *Beam:* 14.78 m (48 ft 6 in) *Draught:* 6.29 m (20 ft 8 in) *Machinery:* 2-shaft 4-cylinder triple-expansion, 15 000 ihp= 21.5 knots *Protection:* 102 mm (4 in) belt; 51 mm (2 in) deck; 127-51 mm (5-2 in) turrets; 102 mm (4 in) conning tower *Armament:* (As built) 8 152-mm (6-in)/50-cal Bofors Model '03 (4×2); 14 57-mm (2.24-in) (14×1), reduced to 10, 1926-27; 2 37-mm (1.46-in); 2 45-cm (17.7-in) torpedo tubes (beam, submerged); (As training ship) 8 152-mm (6-in)/50-cal; 4 57-mm (2.24-in) AA (4×1); 2 machine-guns; 2 53-cm (21-in) torpedo tubes (beam, above water) *Crew:* 341

FZG 76

German flying bomb. Popularly known as the V-1, or Buzz-bomb, this was the first successful guided weapon. It was originally known as the Fieseler Fi 103 and was a midwing monoplane propelled by a Schmidt duct motor or pulse jet mounted above the rear of the fuselage.

Development of this motor began in 1933, finanical support being given to the inventor by the German army. In essence, it was a combustion chamber into which air was rammed by the forward movement of the craft. This air was compressed in the chamber, fuel oil was injected, and the explosive mixture then ignited. The resulting explosion forced the forward end flap-valves closed, so that the gas had to exhaust through the rear end, thus providing thrust. The expulsion of the gas caused a depression in the system which thus sucked in more air to begin the cycle over again. Up to 500 explosions a minute generated considerable thrust and allowed the missile to travel at more than 483 km/h (300 mph).

The missile carried a warhead holding 850 kg (1874 lb) of high explosive and provided with a multiple fuzing system. On the front end of the missile was a propeller connected to an adjustable revolution counter. The number of propeller revolutions for a given distance could be set in, and when this number of revolutions had taken place the missile's elevators were deflected and the missile dived to the ground.

Launching was done by a steam catapult mechanism in a fixed launching ramp, which threw the missile into the air at sufficient speed to sustain operation of the duct motor.

Development of the missile itself began on June 19, 1942, at Peenemünde, under the direction of Luftstabsingenieur (air staff engineer) Bree. The first successful launch took place on December 24, 1942, and the first operational launch on the night of June 12, 1944. Mass production began in March 1944 with a planned output of 8000 missiles per month by October of that year. The combined output of all production sources had been estimated at 25 000 missiles during 1944, of which 12 000 were ready for use when operations began. During 1945 another 9800 were made.

In all, 9251 were fired against England, of which 4261 were destroyed, and 6551 against Antwerp, of which 2455 were destroyed. When the advance of the Allied armies in France placed the prepared launching sites out of action, launch sites in the Netherlands were taken into use and a technique of launching the missiles from aircraft was developed. Due to the requirements of the engine, the V-1 was constrained to a specific height, and flew in a straight line at a constant speed. In spite of this being the ideal conditions for an antiaircraft gun's target, they were extremely difficult to counter, since they moved in a belt of sky which was too high for light guns and too low for heavy guns. Only the arrival of the American SCR276 radar and supplies of the first proximity fuzes allowed the heavier guns to compete.

Launch weight: 2200 kg (4850 lb) *Wingspan:* 5.33 m (17 ft 5¾ in) *Fuselage length:* 6.65 m (21 ft 9¾ in) *Overall length:* 7.73 m (25 ft 4½ in) *Warhead:* 850 kg (1874 lb) *Fuzing:* One electrical impact fuze El Az 106*, one mechanical 'allways' fuze KZ80A, one clockwork delay fuze ZZ 17B *Speed* (in level flight): 480-675 km/h (298-419 mph) *Cruise height:* 1000-1200 m (3280-3937 ft) *Maximum effective range:* 200 km (124 miles) *Flight time:* 20-25 minutes *Accuracy:* Circle of probable error 12 km (7.4 miles) radius

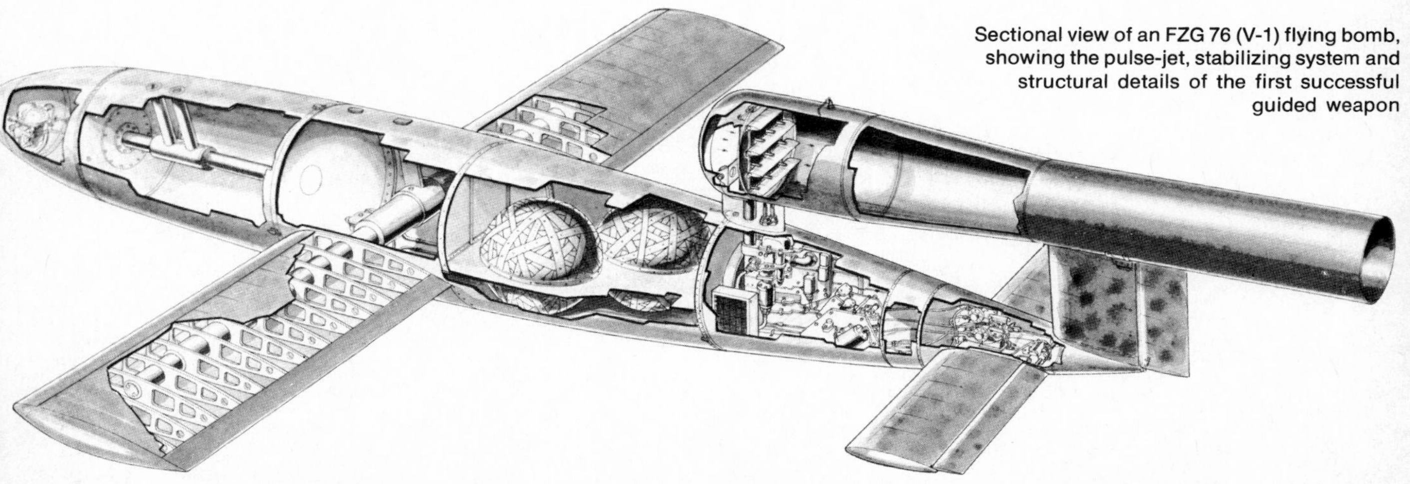

Sectional view of an FZG 76 (V-1) flying bomb, showing the pulse-jet, stabilizing system and structural details of the first successful guided weapon

'G' Class British destroyers (1905-08)
See ***Greyhound***

'G' Class British destroyers (1933)
See ***Beagle***

G Type German First World War bombers
See **A.E.G., Friedrichshaven, Gotha**

G.1

British submarine class, entered service between 1915 and 1917. The 'G' Class were double-hulled ocean-going submarines designed for patrols in the North Sea. *G.1* to *G.7* were ordered under the 1914 Estimates, and *G.8* to *G.15* in November 1915, under the Emergency War Programme. *G.1* to *G.5* were constructed by Chatham dockyard, *G.8* to *G.13* by Vickers at Barrow, *G.6* and *G.7* by Armstrongs, and *G.14* by Scotts. Another vessel, *G.15*, ordered from White, was cancelled in 1915. They were slightly larger than the 'E' Class and have been described as Britain's first true ocean-going submarines. During the war, their bows were raised slightly to increase buoyancy forward and improve their seakeeping.

G.1 to *G.6* served with the 11th Submarine Flotilla, based at Blyth, and the *G.7* to *G.14* with the 10th Flotilla, based on the Tees. Four were lost: *G.9* was sunk in error by the British destroyer *Petard* on September 16, 1917, *G.7* and *G.8* were lost from unknown

Above: **The British submarine *G.13* in Scapa Flow. In 1917 she sank *UC 43* off the Shetlands**

Below: *G.14* in Scapa Flow. During the First World War she was among the eight submarines that made up the 10th Flotilla based on the Tyne

causes on November 1 and November 14, 1918, respectively, while *G.11* was wrecked off Harwich shortly after the war, on November 22, 1918. On the credit side, *G.13* sank the German submarine *UC43* off the Shetlands on March 10, 1917, and *G.2* sank *U78* in the North Sea on October 28, 1918. The survivors were sold for scrap during 1920-23 except *G.4*, not sold until 1928.

Displacement: 700 tons (surfaced), 974 tons (submerged) *Length:* 57 m (187 ft) *Beam:* 6.86 m (22 ft 6 in) *Draught:* 3.96 m (13 ft) *Machinery:* 2-shaft diesel/electric drive, 1600/840 hp=14/10 knots (surfaced/submerged) *Armament:* 1 3-in (76-mm) AA gun; 1 21-in (53-cm) torpedo tube (stern); 4 18-in (46-cm) torpedo tubes (2 bow, 2 broadside) *Crew:* 31

Bur. Mar. Hist. v.d. Marinestaf

The Dutch torpedo boat *G.6*, one of 12 boats built between 1904-09 at the Fijenoord yard

G.1-12

Dutch torpedo boats built 1904-09. These were developments of the *Ophir* Class of 1900. The 12 boats were 48.76-m (160-ft) flush-decked vessels armed with two 50-mm (1.97-in) Krupp quick-firers and three 45-cm (17.7-in) torpedo tubes on single training mountings on deck. Two tubes were mounted right aft and one forward of the funnels.

All the boats were built by the Fijenoord yard at Rotterdam. *G.11* struck a mine off Vlieland in March 1918 and sank. *G.2* had been mined the month before and salvaged in sections, towed into harbour and rebuilt.

By 1930 only *G.12* and *G.2* survived, and they had been relegated to harbour duties, *G.12* going for scrap before the Second World War. *G.2* was captured by the Germans in May 1940 and was renumbered *TFA.10*. She was scuttled in 1945 with *TFA.9* (ex-*G.16*) and later scrapped.

See also *G.13-24, Ophir.*

Displacement: 144 tons (normal), 185 tons (full load) *Length:* 47 m (154 ft 3 in) pp *Beam:* 5.03 m (16 ft 6 in) *Draught:* 2.44 m (8 ft) max *Machinery:* 1-shaft reciprocating steam, 2600 ihp=25 knots *Armament:* 2 50-mm (1.97-in)/50-cal (2×1); 3 45-cm (17.7-in) torpedo tubes (3×1) *Crew:* 24

G.1-3

US submarine class, built 1910-14. In 1910 Simon Lake's company received its first contract from the US Navy to design a submarine, to be called *Seal* and to be built at Newport News. Orders for two more from the Lake company followed in 1911 and 1912, but as the *Seal* had been renumbered *G.1* on November 17, 1911, her sisters were *G.2* and *G.3*, and never received the intended names *Tuna* and *Turbot.*

The Lake design differed in many details from the Holland type which had been built previously, particularly in having twin torpedo tubes in the long deck casing (not in *G.3*). They also reverted to gasoline engines, with two mounted tandem on each shaft. The strong hull, which was a main feature of the Lake designs, was demonstrated in 1914, when *G.1* made a record dive to 78 m (256 ft). *G.1* was launched on February 8, 1911, by Lake's daughter, Margaret.

In December 1917 *G.1* was given hull number *SS.20*, in what was still an unofficial change to hull designators, and her sisters became *SS.27* and *SS.31*.

Unfortunately when the system became official after the war it was discovered that there was an overlap, because the loss of *F.1* had not been taken into account. As a result both *F.1* and *G.1* were labelled 'SS.20' and the *G.1* had to be saddled with the incongruous number *SS.19½* to reverse the error. She did not last long enough for anybody to be embarrassed as she was stricken in August 1921 and sold. *G.2* was lost on July 30, 1919, in Long Island Sound, with the loss of three men. She was officially stricken in September 1919 but the wreck was not raised until 1962. *G.3* was stricken in 1922 and sold.

Displacement: (*G.1*) 288/337 tons (surfaced/submerged); (*G.2*) 400/516 tons (surfaced/submerged); (*G.3*) 393/460 tons (surfaced/submerged) *Length:* (*G.1*) 41.07 m (134 ft 9 in) oa; (*G.2-3*) 49.07 m (161 ft) oa *Beam:* (*G.1*) 4.26 m (14 ft); (*G.2-3*) 3.96 m (13 ft) *Draught:* (*G.1*) 3.58 m (11 ft 9 in); (*G.2-3*) 3.84 m (12 ft 6 in) *Machinery:* (*G.1*) 2-shaft gasoline engines, 600 bhp/520 shp=13/10 knots (surfaced/submerged); (*G.2*) 2-shaft gasoline engines, 1200 bhp/520 shp=14/10 knots (surfaced/submerged); (*G.3* 2-shaft diesels, 1200 bhp/600 shp=14/9.5 knots (surfaced/submerged) *Armament:* (*G.1-2*) 4 18-in (46-cm) torpedo tubes (2 bow, 2 deck); (*G.3*) 6 18-in (46-cm) torpedo tubes (4 bow, 2 deck) *Crew:* 15-25

G.I, Fokker

Dutch fighter/close-support aircraft. Developed as a private venture bomber intercepter in the mid-1930s, the Fokker G.I was a twin-engined, twin-tailboom monoplane of mixed construction, the crew of two or three being housed in a central nacelle. It was built in two versions, the G.Ia, of which 36 were ordered by the Dutch air force, with 830-hp Bristol Mercury VIII engines, and the 750-hp Pratt & Whitney Twin Wasp Junior-powered G.Ib export model.

The G.Ia was armed with a formidable battery of eight 7.92-mm (0.312-in) machine-guns in the nose of the nacelle, plus another flexibly mounted at the rear, and could carry 300 kg (660 lb) of bombs. Twenty-three had been delivered by the time of the German invasion in May 1940, and although they fought well, when the fighting was over only one remained. This was flown to England by two escaping Fokker pilots. Meanwhile 26 two-seat G.Ibs had been ordered by Finland, 18 by Sweden and nine by Estonia; an order from the Spanish Republicans was prohibited by the Dutch government. By the time of the German invasion 12 of the Finnish G.Ibs and the nine confiscated Spanish machines were complete but the intended armament of two 23-mm (0.9-in) Madsen cannon and three 7.92-mm (0.312-in) machine-guns had not been fitted. However, three G.Ibs were armed with four machine-guns each and joined in the fighting: all were lost. The remainder, along with another 14 completed during the occupation, were used by the Luftwaffe as fighter-trainers.

(G.Ia) *Span:* 17.15 m (56 ft 3¼ in) *Length:* 11.5 m (37 ft 8¾ in) *Gross weight:* 4800 kg (10 580 lb) *Maximum speed:* 475 km/h (295 mph)

G2H1, Hiro

Japanese heavy bomber aircraft. Designed by the Hiro navy air arsenal in 1932, this land-based heavy bomber was not a particularly successful venture, and only eight were built. The prototype made its first flight in March 1933, and a number of faults were revealed during the flight test programme. Most serious were a weakness of the basic airframe structure, and a tendency to wing flutter. Difficulties were also encountered with the original powerplant, which consisted of a pair of 600-hp Hiro Type 94 water-cooled engines.

The production version carried a crew of seven, was armed with four 7.7-mm (0.303-in) Type 92 machine-guns, and carried an internal bombload of six 250-kg (551-lb) or four 400-kg (881-lb) bombs. Only six were built by Hiro, because of the generally unsatisfactory nature of the aircraft. Two others were completed by Mitsubishi, with 900-hp 18-cylinder engines. In 1934, Mitsubishi evolved the Ka-9 long-range reconnaissance monoplane based on the G2H1 design. The chief claim to fame of the two types was their influence upon the development of the highly successful Mitsubishi G3M bomber. The few G2H1s built took part in raids against mainland China during the Sino-Japanese war. Before long, however, most of them were destroyed in a fire at their base on Cheju Island in the Korea Strait.

Span: 31.68 m (103 ft 11¼ in) *Length:* 20.15 m (66 ft 1¼ in) *Gross weight:* 11 000 kg (24 251 lb) *Maximum speed:* 245 km/h (152 mph)

The Mitsubishi G3M2 main production version of this Japanese medium bomber which saw widespread service throughout the Second World War

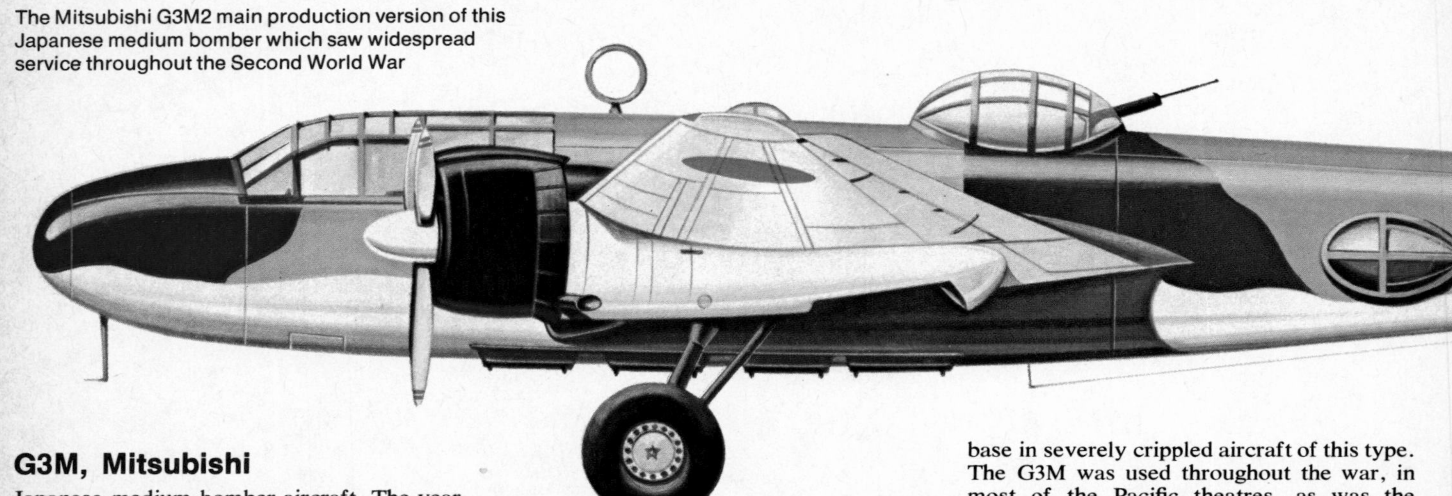

G3M, Mitsubishi

Japanese medium bomber aircraft. The year 1934 was something of a watershed for Japanese naval aviation, for the combat aircraft produced to meet the Imperial navy's specifications issued during that year were the first to put the service on a virtually equal technological footing with those of the western world. Two designs from this period stand out: the A5M carrier-based monoplane fighter and the G3M twin-engined medium bomber—both, coincidentally, Mitsubishi designs.

During the early 1930s, Mitsubishi had gathered considerable design and manufacturing experience from the construction of various German Junkers aircraft, and the influence of the Ju 86 bomber, in particular, was evident in Mitsubishi's prototype design, known as the Ka-15. Into this design also went experience gained from the Hiro G2H1 bomber and its derivative, the Ka-9 long-range reconnaissance monoplane flown by Mitsubishi in April 1934.

In its original prototype form the Ka-15, designed by Kiro Honjo, made its first flight in July 1935. Two 750-hp Hiro Type 91 12-cylinder V-type engines were mounted on the mid-set wings, which were essentially the same as those of the Ka-9. Twenty more prototype/preproduction Ka-15s were completed, of which three had Hiro engines; the remaining 17 were powered by 830-hp or 910-hp Mitsubishi Kinsei 2 or 3 14-cylinder two-row radial engines, giving enhanced performance. These aircraft had the designation G3M1, and unofficially they were subdivided into G3M1a (the four with Hiro engines and 'solid' noses), G3M1b (two with Kinseis and 'solid' noses), and G3M1c (the other 15 Kinsei-powered aircraft, which had a transparent bombing station in the nose). Twelve were used for service trials, but before these had been completed a production batch of 34 Kinsei 3-powered G3M1s, with modified cockpit windows, was authorized by the IJN. These had a crew of five, and could carry an 800-kg (1763-lb) torpedo beneath the fuselage; defensive armament consisted of two retractable dorsal turrets each containing one 7.7-mm (0.303-in) Type 92 machine-gun, with another of these guns in a retractable ventral turret.

The G3M1 was followed into production by the G3M2, which was a much improved model and destined to become the chief production version. It was, in fact, built in two basic variants, the Model 21 and Model 22. The 21 had uprated Kinsei 41 or 42 engines of 1075 hp, increased fuel tankage and modified dorsal turrets; the 22 had 1075-hp Kinsei 45s (also fitted to some late-production Model 21s), and a completely revised armament system that eliminated the retractable ventral and rear dorsal turrets, replacing the latter by a large turtleback enclosure housing a 20-mm (0.79-in) Type 99 cannon, and the former by a pair of blisters, one each side of the rear fuselage, each with single Type 92 gun. Between 1937-39, Mitsubishi built 343 Model 21s, following these in 1939-41 with 238 Model 22s.

When Mitsubishi production was then phased out in favour of the later G4M bomber, production of the G3M was carried on by the Koizumi factory of the Nakajima company, which built 412 G3M-type bombers, of which a proportion were of a fourth model, the G3M3. These had Kinsei 51 radials of 1300 hp each, and a further increase in fuel tankage, extending the maximum range to 6230 km (3870 miles) compared with the 4380 km (2720 miles) of the G3M2 Model 22.

At the time of Pearl Harbor, the backbone of Japan's long-range strike force consisted of just over 200 G3Ms (mostly G3M2s and G3M3s) and about 120 of the later G4M1s. The G3M ('Nell' under the Pacific system of codenames introduced by the Allies during the Second World War) had made its service debut in August 1937, with raids on Chinese mainland targets from bases on Kyushu (Omura) and Formosa (Taipei). During the Sino-Japanese war, the JNAF, like the Luftwaffe in Spain, was lulled by the excellent performance of its bombers into the false belief that they could operate safely without a fighter escort. They were to be quickly disabused. (This led to the peculiar situation in 1940 of one group of G3M bombers finding itself acting as escort, on a flight to China, of the first two squadrons of Mitsubishi A6M2 Zero fighters to be sent to that quarter!)

In the Second World War, the G3Ms took part in the early attacks against the Philippine Islands, and in the sinking of the British warships *Prince of Wales* and *Repulse.* They proved to be extremely battleworthy aircraft, and there were many cases of pilots regaining base in severely crippled aircraft of this type. The G3M was used throughout the war, in most of the Pacific theatres, as was the G3M1-L, a prewar transport conversion with Kinsei 45 engines which took part in the invasion of Celebes. Wartime transport conversions were the L3Y1 Model 11 and L3Y2 Model 12 (both codenamed 'Tina'), converted from G3M1s and G3M2s respectively by the First Naval Air Arsenal at Kasumigaura. These carried up to ten passengers, and had a single 7.7-mm (0.303-in) machine-gun for defence.

(G3M2 Model 22) *Span:* 25 m (82 ft 0¼ in) *Length:* 16.45 m (53 ft 11¾ in) *Gross weight:* 8000 kg (17 637 lb) *Maximum speed:* 373 km/h (232 mph)

G.4

US submarine, built 1911-14. In 1911 a submarine called *Thrasher* was ordered to designs submitted by the Italian Laurenti company. She was launched on August 15, 1912, by the Cramp shipyard at Philadelphia as *G.4,* but bore no relation to the contemporary Lake boats *G.1-3.*

She was commissioned in January 1914 but was very unsatisfactory as she lacked stability. After an undistinguished career she was stricken and sold in 1920 (the hull number SS.26 was allocated to her).

Displacement: 360/457 tons (surfaced/submerged) *Length:* 47.32 m (157 ft 6 in) oa *Beam:* 5.33 m (17 ft 6 in) *Draught:* 3.35 m (11 ft) *Machinery:* 2-shaft gasoline engines, 1000 bhp/440 shp=14/9.5 knots (surfaced/submerged) *Armament:* 4 18-in (46-cm) torpedo tubes (bow) *Crew:* 24

G4M, Mitsubishi

Japanese medium bomber aircraft, first prototype flew 1939. The Mitsubishi G4M, or 'Betty' in the Allied Pacific codenames system, is remembered chiefly for two distinctive, but entirely separate reasons. It was more highly combustible when hit by bullets than almost any other Japanese aircraft of the time. It was also the only operational carrier of the Ohka 'kamikaze' suicide bomb.

Its inherent weakness, which earned it the totally unwelcome sobriquet of 'the one-shot lighter'—and others less printable—was not altogether surprising when it is considered that the September 1937 JNAF requirement to which it was designed demanded a twin-

engined aircraft with a range of nearly 4830 km (3000 miles) and, over 3706 km (2300 miles), an 800-kg (1764-lb) weapon load. This 'range at all costs' philosophy could only be met by cramming every available bit of wing space with 4900 litres (1078 Imp gal) of fuel, and only then by omitting any kind of armour protection for either the crew or the fuel tanks. Everything else had to go into the fuselage and, by the standards of the day, was necessarily large and bulky.

As with the G3M, Kiro Honjo again led the design team, and the first flight by the first of two prototypes was made on October 23, 1939. Almost immediately afterwards—as if Mitsubishi did not have enough to contend with in the original specification—its development was channelled in an entirely different direction. The company was instructed by the navy to adapt it instead for bomber escort duties. This meant sacrificing some 25% of the fuel load to offset the added weight of extra guns and ammunition, and increasing the crew to a total of ten men, compared with seven in the bomber version. No fewer than 30 examples of the G6M1, as this version was known, had been completed and put through service acceptance trials in 1940 before the JNAF was forced to admit that performance was just not good enough for the escort job. The aircraft themselves were later adapted to serve as G6M1-K trainers and, later still, as G6M1-L2 paratroop transports.

Continuing G4M development, however, Mitsubishi managed to get another 14 of these bombers completed by the end of March 1941, and in April this version was accepted for service as the G4M1 Model 11. They were soon in successful operation against targets in China, and by the time of the Pearl Harbor attack at the end of that year, 120 or so were in service. The Model 11 was armed with four single 7.7-mm (0.303-in) Type 92 machine-guns in nose, waist and dorsal positions, and a 20-mm (0.79-in) Type 99 cannon in the tail, and could carry the specified 800-kg (1764-lb) weapon load. Powerplant was a pair of 1530-hp Mitsubishi Kasei 11 14-cylinder two-row radial engines. The Model 11 scored a number of early successes, but when losses began to mount, Mitsubishi produced the improved G4M1 Model 12, with Kasei 15 engines.

After the Solomon Islands campaign in August 1942, when losses were particularly heavy because of the bomber's extreme inflammability, there quickly followed the prototype G4M2. This had more powerful engines—1800-hp Kasei 21s with water-methanol injection—and several aerodynamic improvements. Armament was increased by adding two more 7.7-mm (0.303-in) guns in the nose and replacing the dorsal 7.7-mm by a turret-mounted 20-mm (0.79-in) cannon; internal bombload went up to 1000 kg (2204 lb). Fuel capacity was increased, to 6490 litres (1427 Imp gal), but still the tanks remained virtually unprotected. Despite this, the G4M2 was built in such numbers as to become the second most important production model, a total of 1154 being completed compared with 1200 G4M1s. These included the G4M2 Model 22A (Type 99 cannon in the waist positions) and 22B (all four Type 99 cannon of a later type); the G4M2a Model 24 (with 1850-hp Kasei 25 engines and bulged bomb bay doors); the G4M2b Model 25 testbed (1795-hp Kasei 27s); two G4M2c Model 26s (testbeds for turbocharged Kasei 25s); the G4M2d Model 27 testbed (1825-hp Kasei 25b engines); and the G4M2e Model 24J—a version with one 7.7-mm (0.303-in) and four 20-mm (0.79-in) guns. In the face of continuing heavy losses, in 1944 Mitsubishi built 60 examples of the G4M3, with armour protection for the crew and a much-redesigned wing containing a reduced fuel load of 4490 litres (988 Imp gal), stored in fully-protected tanks. Final versions were two G4M3 Model 36 prototypes, which made test flights with exhaust-driven engine turbochargers.

Of the total production of 2446 G4M-series aircraft—greater than that of any other Japanese bomber—many G4M1s were converted into trainers, maritime reconnaissance aircraft or 20-passenger troop transports towards the end of the Second World War. The G4M can also claim to have served from beginning to end of the Pacific war, for a pair of white-painted G4M1s were used to transport the Japanese delegation to Ie-Shima on August 19, 1945, to sign the instrument of surrender.

As remarked earlier, the 'Betty' did perform one function which gave it a unique place in aviation history: it was the carrier aircraft for the air-launched Yokosuka MXY-7 Ohka piloted flying bomb, developed in the latter half of 1944. The Ohka should have entered service at the end of that year, but the first consignment of 50 was lost in November, when the carrier *Shinano* was sunk on its way to the Philippines. The first combat encounter was thus deferred until March 21, 1945, when a force of 16 Ohka-carrying G4M2e Model 24J bombers (the version chosen for this role), with an escort of 30 Zero fighters, was despatched against a US task force some 480 km (298 miles) off Kyushu. On the way, however, the force was met by more than 50 US Hellcat fighters, and lost every Ohka-carrying bomber and half of the escorting Zeros. In order to attach the Ohka beneath the belly of the G4M2e, the latter's bomb bay doors were removed. Launch was usually made from an altitude of around 8200 m (26 900 ft), at an airspeed of about 319 km/h (198 mph), the Ohka then gliding towards its target, cutting in the rocket motor only for the last few miles of flight and the terminal dive.

(G4M2a Model 24) *Span:* 24.89 m (81 ft 8 in) Length: 19.63 m (64 ft 5 in) *Gross weight:* 15 000 kg (33 069 lb) *Maximum speed:* 436 km/h (271 mph)

G7a and G7e

German torpedoes of the Second World War. As early as 1922 the Germans started to evade the restrictions imposed by the Treaty of Versailles on testing new weapons, and in 1923 work started in Sweden on trials of new electrically-propelled types. After four years of design and two years of test-running the design was frozen until full production could start in Germany.

The standard 53-cm (21-in) torpedo used by the German navy (Kriegsmarine) was the G7a thermal type (which used heated compressed air), and the battery-driven variant was known as the G7e. Up to the end of January 1945 a total of about 10 000 torpedoes were

A U-Boat armourer prepares a G7e battery-driven torpedo prior to loading it into its tube

Bundesarchivs

Bur. Mar. Hist. v.d. Marinestaf

G.13, one of a class of 11 torpedo boats built in Rotterdam for the Dutch navy between 1912-13

Weight of material	1939	1943
Copper (kg)	370	169
Tin (kg)	61	22
Nickel (kg)	46	2
Man-hours	3730	1707
Cost (Reichsmarks)	24 000	13 500

fired by the Kriegsmarine—2300 were G7a, 7000 were G7e, 640 were acoustic homers and the remainder were pattern-runners.

The G7a had a compressed air/decalin piston engine, and the high standard of workmanship demanded made it a difficult weapon to mass produce. Therefore the design was simplified and cheapened to save materials.

The main reason for going to electric propulsion was in fact to simplify production, and the development of the G7e dated back to 1918. An electric torpedo had then been capable of 28 knots and a range of 25 600 m (28 000 yards), and development of this weapon was what continued successfully in Sweden in 1923-27.

The British were unaware of the existence of the G7e until an unexploded one was recovered from the side of the liner SS *Volendam* after the outbreak of war. The first complete torpedo was recovered when *U 570* surrendered in 1941.

The G7e had a range of 7315 m (8000 yards) and a speed of about 29 knots. It had to be kept at 30°C for maximum range, and if fired at a colder temperature range dropped to 6035 m (6600 yards) (the batteries were heated when entering the patrol area). Each battery had 26 cells with 18 plates—and the two weighed 680 kg (1500 lbs) in all. The motor was an 8-pole series-wound DC type rated at 91 volts, 950 amps at 1755 rpm, and it weighed about 113 kg (250 lb). It was to be used in all other electric weapons.

Both G7a and G7e torpedoes had the same TNT/HND/AI warhead weighing 300 kg (660 lbs). There were three forms of the G7e: the T2, in service at the start of the war, with a range of 4940 m (5400 yards) and a speed of 30 knots, the T3 (T2 with a magnetic fuze) and the T3a, which had the higher performance quoted above. A pattern-running version had an improved battery giving 125 amp-hours instead of the 93 amp-hours given by the standard 13T210 battery. This ran for 7500 m (8200 yards) at 30 knots.

A lower-powered battery fitted to a T3 became the *Marder* midget submarine. The T3b, running 4023 m (4400 yards) at 18.5 knots, was also fired from midget submarines. The T3d was used in the slow-running Dackel.

The T3, the version of the G7e fitted with a magnetic influence fuze, caused the German navy a great deal of trouble in the early months of the war. This was particularly noticeable in the Norwegian campaign when the magnetic fuze was affected by the abnormal magnetic deviation in the high latitudes, but in fact the fuze itself had design faults which had not been eliminated during testing. It is believed that *U 47* fired T3s against the battleship *Royal Oak*, in October 1939, and that three exploded beneath her keel, which would account for the detonation of her ammunition.

G.13-24

Dutch torpedo boats built 1912-15. These were enlarged versions of the *G.1-12*, with a raised forecastle for better seaworthiness and heavier guns. Like the earlier class they were built at the Fijenoord yard, Rotterdam.

In February 1919 *G.14* suffered a boiler explosion and was scrapped, and all but *G.13*, *G.15* and *G.16* were stricken in 1930. The three survivors were reduced to harbour duties, and were still in service at the start of the Second World War.

The guns were 75-mm (2.95-in) Bofors, and were officially designated No 4 Model, with a 5.9 kg (13-lb) shell and a muzzle velocity of 620 m/sec (2034 ft/sec). The torpedo tubes disposed side by side in the well forward of the bridge, and one on the centreline aft.

On May 14, 1940, *G.16* was scuttled at Den Helder, but the Germans raised her and repaired her as the torpedo recovery vessel *TFA.9* (with *TFA.10*, ex-*G.12*). Both vessels had the forecastle extended abaft the bridge, and the two funnels were trunked into a single casing. She was scuttled at Kiel in May 1945.

See also *G.1-12*.

Displacement: 180 tons (normal), 230 tons (full load) *Length:* 49.56 m (162 ft 6 in) pp *Beam:* 5.18 m (17 ft) *Draught:* 1.75 m (5 ft 9 in) *Machinery:* 2-shaft reciprocating steam, 2600 ihp= 25 knots *Armament:* 2 75-mm (2.95-in)/30-cal (2× 1); 3 45-cm (17.7-in) torpedo tubes (3× 1) *Crew:* 27

G.46, Fiat

Italian trainer aircraft. The first G.46-1 flew in 1948 powered by a 205-hp Alfa-Romeo 115*bis* driving a two-blade constant-speed propeller. Structure was all-metal; tandem seats were enclosed by hoods hinging to the right, and the landing gear retracted inwards. Production versions were the G.46-2 with a 205-hp de Havilland Gipsy Six or 250-hp Gipsy Queen 30, and the -3, -4 and -5 with 225-hp Alfa 115*ter*. Over 300 were built for the Aeronautica Militare Italiana, the suffix A being added to denote single-seaters, and B the normal two-seater. Ski landing gear was

The ex-Dutch torpedo boat *G.16* in German service as torpedo recovery vessel *TFA.9*

available. About 50 were exported, 30 to Argentina and the rest to Austria and Syria.

Span: 10.4 m (34 ft 1½ in) *Length:* 8.48 m (27 ft 10 in) *Gross weight:* (G.46-2) 1430 kg (3150 lb) *Maximum speed:* (G.46-2) 325 km/h (200 mph)

G.50, Fiat Italian fighter aircraft See **Freccia**

G.55, Fiat Italian fighter aircraft See **Centauro**

G.59, Fiat

Italian trainer aircraft. From the wartime G.55 fighter the Fiat company developed the postwar G.55A single-seat fighter/trainer and G.55B dual trainer, both with 1310-hp Fiat RA.1050 (licence-built Daimler-Benz 605) engine. Among the customers were Argentina, Egypt and Syria. In 1948 the engine was switched to the Rolls-Royce Merlin T.24 or Mk 500, rated at 1630 hp, the former being fitted to the G.59-1 and -2 and the Mk 500 the -3 and -4. The -4 had a lower rear fuselage to match a blister hood. In each case the suffix A denoted a single-seater and B a dual two-seat version. Single-seat versions could have two 20-mm (0.79-in) Hispano cannon and camera gun, and racks for two 100-kg (220-lb) bombs. Production G.59s were delivered to Italy and Syria. A proposed family of true fighter derivatives with 2000-hp Packard V-1650-11 (Merlin) engines was not proceeded with.

Span: 11.85 m (38 ft 10½ in) *Length:* 9.49 m (31 ft 1½ in) *Gross weight:* (G.59-4b) 3388 kg (7470 lb) *Maximum speed:* 600 km/h (373 mph)

G.82, Fiat

Italian jet trainer aircraft. The first true jet aircraft built in Italy (discounting the piston-engined Caproni-Campini N.1) was the prototype Fiat G.80, flown on a 1360-kg (3000-lb) thrust D.H. Goblin turbojet on December 10, 1951. After exhaustive flight development a batch of ten G.80-3B fighter/trainers were built in 1954 and delivered to the Aeronautica Militare Italiana. By this time the same basic tandem-seat or single-seat design had been developed into the G.82, with modified inlets feeding a fuselage plenum-bay housing a Rolls-Royce Nene RN.6-21 rated at 2450-kg (5400-lb) thrust. The basic Italian production version was the tandem-seat G.82-1B

Hunting Engineering

An Italian Fiat G91 jet fighter-bomber/reconnaissance aircraft armed with BL 755 cluster bombs

with two 12.7-mm (0.5-in) Breda-SAFAT machine-guns in the nose, and wing racks for two 113-kg (250-lb) bombs or eight 127-mm (5-in) rockets.

Span: (over tip tanks) 11.6 m (38 ft) *Length:* 12.95 m (42 ft 6 in) *Gross weight:* 6114 kg (13 480 lb) *Maximum speed:* 930 km/h (580 mph)

G91, Fiat/Aeritalia

Italian fighter-bomber/reconnaissance aircraft, first prototype flew 1956. The Fiat G91 was one of eight designs submitted in 1954 in a competition for a lightweight tactical fighter for NATO, of which the winner was intended to become standard equipment for the air forces of the member countries. It was the only Italian submission, the remainder being French, but it fulfilled the requirement for a tactical fighter with strike capabilities, a maximum level speed of Mach 0.92, and the ability to take off and land on small or hastily-prepared airstrips. An order was placed in June 1955 for three prototypes and 27 pre-production aircraft.

Designed by Giuseppe Gabrielli, the first prototype flew on August 9, 1956, powered by a 1837-kg (4050-lb) st Bristol Orpheus B Or.1 turbojet. Control problems arose later, during a high-speed level run, and the structural failure of the tail caused the pilot to eject. After exhaustive tests on the tail unit, the second prototype was fitted with a larger tailplane and a small ventral keel; the cockpit was also raised by some 63-mm (2.5-in). Powered by a 2200-kg (4850-lb) st Bristol Orpheus B Or.3 turbojet, this aircraft flew for the first time in July 1957. It was equipped with one of the basic sets of armament: four 0.50-in (12.7-mm) Colt-Browning machine-guns, two mounted on each side below the cockpit and each having 300 rounds of ammunition. Alternative installations were two 20-mm (0.79-in) or two 30-mm (1.18-in) cannon (one each side), with 200 or 120

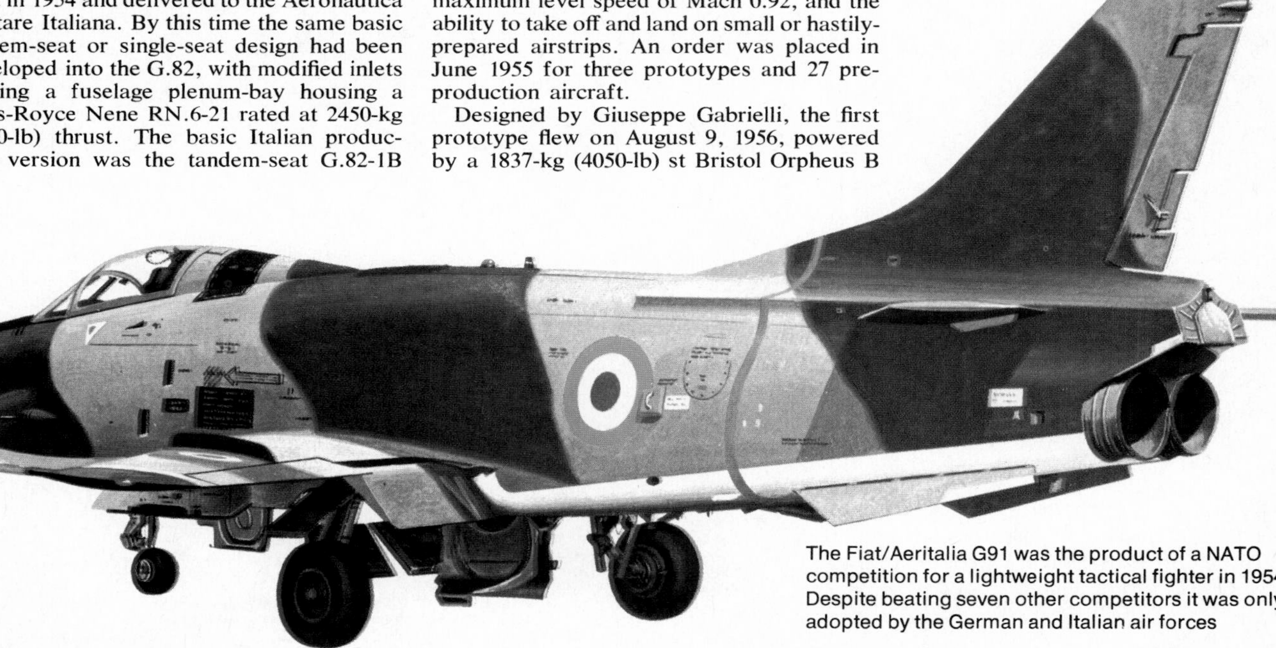

The Fiat/Aeritalia G91 was the product of a NATO competition for a lightweight tactical fighter in 1954. Despite beating seven other competitors it was only adopted by the German and Italian air forces

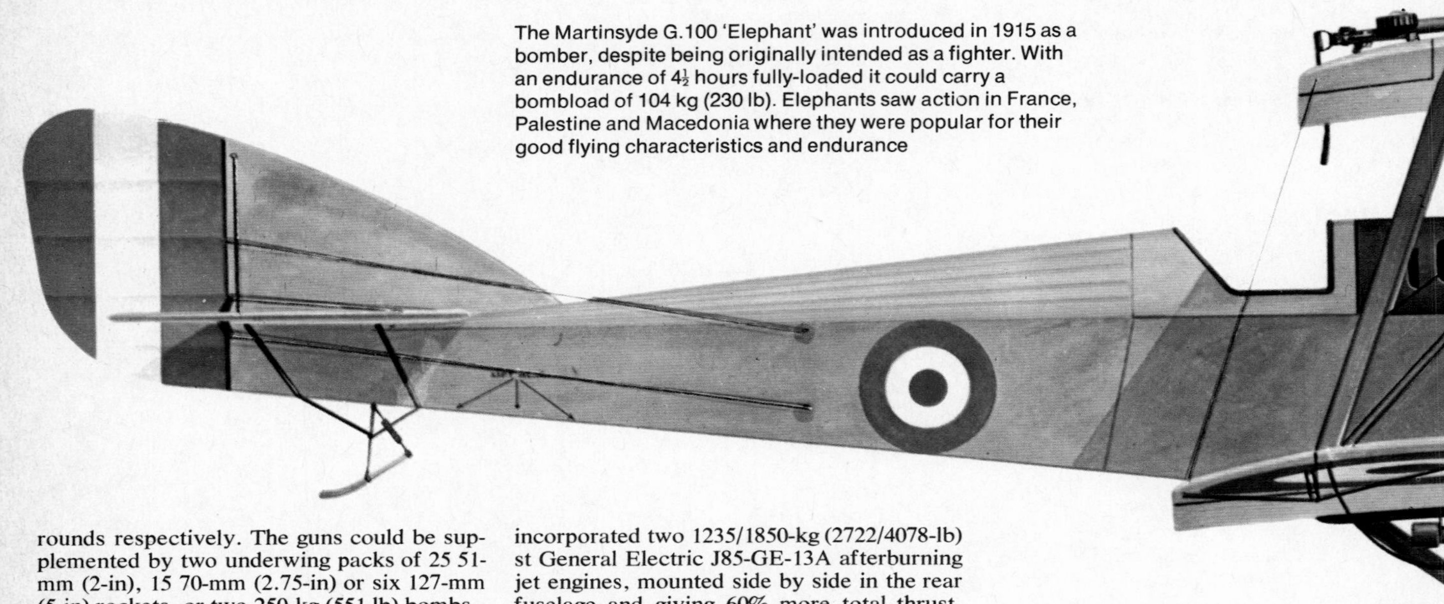
The Martinsyde G.100 'Elephant' was introduced in 1915 as a bomber, despite being originally intended as a fighter. With an endurance of 4½ hours fully-loaded it could carry a bombload of 104 kg (230 lb). Elephants saw action in France, Palestine and Macedonia where they were popular for their good flying characteristics and endurance

rounds respectively. The guns could be supplemented by two underwing packs of 25 51-mm (2-in), 15 70-mm (2.75-in) or six 127-mm (5-in) rockets, or two 250-kg (551 lb) bombs.

Construction was conventional and simple. There was an all-metal semimonocoque fuselage built in three sections, with an armoured cockpit fitted with a Martin-Baker Mk 4 ejection seat. The nosewheel retracted rearward under the cockpit, the main undercarriage inward into a central fuselage bay. A braking parachute was fitted at the base of the rudder. The first of the preproduction G91s was flown in February 20, 1958, and in August of that year the 103° Gruppo Caccia Tattici Leggeri (Light Tactical Fighter Group) of the Italian air force was formed for operational evaluation. After limited squadron service, 16 of the preproduction aircraft were modified in 1964 for use by the Italian aerobatic team, receiving the new designation G91PAN (Pattuglia Acrobatica Nazionale).

Two basic service versions of the original G91 were developed: the G91R single-seat reconnaissance-fighter and the G91T tandem two-seat combat trainer/tactical fighter. Both had blunt nose housings for three aerial cameras, instead of the pointed nose of the early aircraft. Twenty-four G91R/1s and the same number of R/1As (with improved navigational aids) were delivered to the Aeronautica Militare Italiano, together with 50 G91R/1B fighter-bombers. These models all carried the armament of four 0.50-in (12.7-mm) machine-guns, as did the 101 G91T/1 trainers also delivered. It was, however, the Federal German Luftwaffe which employed the largest number of G91s, receiving 344 G91R/3s, nearly 300 of which were built in that country by Dornier, Heinkel and Messerschmitt. Fifty Italian-built G91R/4s and 66 Fiat/Dornier-built G91T/3s, all with twin 30-mm (1.18-in) DEFA cannon, also served with the Luftwaffe. The German G91Rs (transferred later to the Portuguese air force) had two additional underwing pylons inboard, each capable of carrying 227 kg (500 lb) of stores.

In the event, no other NATO country was to adopt the G91, but in the spring of 1965 details were announced of the G91Y, a single-seat twin-jet tactical fighter-bomber developed as a follow-on type for the AMI. Based on the two-seat G91T airframe, it incorporated two 1235/1850-kg (2722/4078-lb) st General Electric J85-GE-13A afterburning jet engines, mounted side by side in the rear fuselage and giving 60% more total thrust. Two prototypes (converted G91Ts) were flown on December 27, 1966, and September 1967, respectively. In July 1968 the first of 20 preproduction G91Ys appeared, and orders for a further 45 followed. Delivery of these was completed by mid-1976, and they are now in service with the 1° and 13° Gruppi in Italy. They have provision for JATO (jet assisted takeoff) units which can halve the distance required for takeoff, and three nose-mounted cameras are fitted as standard. Armament comprises two 30-mm (1.18-in) DEFA cannon in the nose, and four underwing hardpoints for up to 1814 kg (4000 lb) of bombs, rockets or napalm canisters.

(G91T/1) *Span:* 8.60 m (28 ft 2½ in) *Length:* 11.70 m (38 ft 4½ in) *Gross weight:* 5500 kg (12 125 lb) *Maximum speed:* 1030 km/h (640 mph)

(G91Y) *Span:* 9.01 m (29 ft 6½ in) *Length:* 11.67 m (38 ft 3½ in) *Gross weight:* 8700 kg (19 180 lb) *Maximum speed:* 1110 km/h (690 mph)

G.100/102, Martinsyde 'Elephant'

British First World War single-seat fighter. The first Martinsyde G.100 appeared in late 1915. Production examples were powered by a 120-hp Beardmore, though later conversions (G.102) used the 160-hp Beardmore engine. Armament comprised a single 0.303-in (7.7-mm) Lewis machine-gun above the upper-wing, and occasionally a second Lewis, firing rearwards, by the cockpit. A total of 271 examples were eventually built, but only one unit, 27 Squadron Royal Flying Corps was wholly equipped with the type. They flew G.100/102s from March 1916 until December 1917 on operations in France, and the squadron's unique equipment is perpetuated today in 27 Squadron's official badge motif of an elephant. Many other individual 'Elephants' saw active service in Palestine and Macedonia with 14, 30, 63, 67 and 72 Squadrons of the RFC. Larger than most contemporary single-seaters, the 'Elephant' was renowned for good flying characteristics, while its endurance of approximately 4½ hours, fully-loaded, was considered excellent for what were then regarded as reconnaissance and bombing sorties. The maximum bombload was 104 kg (230 lb). Only a very few survived beyond 1918.

Span: 11.58 m (38 ft) *Length:* 7.92 m (26 ft) *Maximum speed:* (G.102) 166 km/h (103 mph) at ground level

G222, Aeritalia

Italian tactical transport aircraft, first prototype flew 1970. Few aircraft based on existing technology have had such a protracted and spasmodic a genesis as this relatively small machine, which was at last built in small numbers for several customers. The original contract was awarded by the Italian air force in 1963 to what was then Societa per Aviazioni Fiat. The project stemmed from Fiat's submission in the NATO NBMR-4 design competition for a tactical V/STOL (vertical/short takeoff and landing) transport with jet lift engines. One of more than 12 entries, it was the only project to be pursued to the hardware stage, though the V/STOL feature was abandoned. Originally the powerplants were all Rolls-Royce, the main engines being two Dart turboprops. Four lift jets were to be installed in the rear of each turboprop nacelle. Gradually the design changed and eventually the lift jets were removed, but new models appeared for ASW (antisubmarine warfare) and other uses, including military and civil cargo transport, which had outer wings of greater span. In 1966 the decision was taken to change to two General Electric T64 main engines and subsequently the 3400 shp T64-P4D single-shaft engine was adopted, with Hamilton propeller, and put into licence-production by the Fiat engine company.

Initially two prototype G222s were built, the first flying at Turin on July 18, 1970. A production programme was agreed in which Fiat (now Aeritalia) make fuselages at Pomiglio d'Arco, Naples. Wing centre-sections are made by Piaggio and outer panels by Aermacchi; tails by SIAI-Marchetti; landing gear by

CIRSEA; and various other airframe sections by SACA. The Italian air force ordered 44 G222 transports, and Aeritalia strenuously marketed the aircraft in many countries, achieving limited success with orders for three from Argentina and one from Dubai.

The G222 is very like a small twin-engined C-130, with tandem landing wheels on each side suitable for unprepared airstrips, a full-section rear ramp door, pressurized interior and C-130 type flight deck. Wings and tail are de-iced by pneumatic rubber boots. With a crew of three, the standard aircraft carries up to 44 troops, 32 paratroops, 36 stretcher casualties or up to 8500 kg (18 740 lb) of cargo. Aeritalia successfully completed trials with the G222 SAMA, a water-bombing firefighting version.

Span: 28.7 m (94 ft 2 in) *Length:* 22.7 m (74 ft 5½ in) *Gross weight:* 26 500 kg (58 422 lb) *Maximum speed:* 540 km/h (336 mph)

Gabbiano

Italian corvette class, first laid down 1942. The activities of British submarines operating out of Gibraltar, Malta and Alexandria during the early days of the war led to heavy losses among Italy's merchant fleet. The large Italian destroyers were unsuitable for convoy duties covering the small two- to six-ship slow convoys in the Adriatic, Aegean and across to North Africa. Because of this and because insufficient numbers of torpedo boats—which were inadequately armed for A/S (antisubmarine warfare) operations—were available, the Italian navy drew up a design for an A/S corvette. A large class of 60 vessels was ordered, the first being laid down in January 1942. Of the 60 ordered only 48 were completed.

Gabbiano (C.11); *Procellaria* (C.12); *Comorano* (C.13); and *Pellicano* (C.14)—built by Cerusa, Voltri

Cicogna (C.15); *Folaga* (C.16); *Ibis* (C.17); *Gru* (C.18); *Tuffetto* (C.51); *Marangone* (C.52); *Strolaga* (C.53); and *Ardrea* (C.54)—built by Ansaldo, Genoa

Antilope (C.19); *Gazzella* (C.20); *Camoscio* (C.21); *Capriolo* (C.22); *Alce* (C.23); *Renna* (C.24); *Daino* (C.55); *Cervo* (C.56); and *Stambecco* (C.57)—built by Odero-Terni-Orlando, Livorno

Ape (C.25); *Vespa* (C.26); *Lucciola* (C.27); *Grillo* (C.28); *Cicala* (C.29); *Calabrone* (C.30); *Cavaletta* (C.31); *Libellula* (C.32); *Crisalide* (C.58); *Farfalla* (C.59); *Maggiolino* (C.60); and *Cocciniglia* (C.61)—built by Navalmeccanica, Castellammare di Stabia

Scimitarra (C.33); *Baionetta* (ex-*Parigiana*, C.34); *Colubrina* (C.35); *Springarda* (C.36); *Carabina* (C.37); *Bombarda* (C.38); *Scure* (C.62); *Clava* (C.63); and *Zagaglia* (C.64)—built by Breda, Porto Marghera

Artemide (C.39); *Persefone* (C.40); *Euterpe* (C.41); *Minerva* (C.42); *Urania* (C.65); *Berenice* (C.66); *Egeria* (C.67); *Melpomene* (C.68); *Tersicore* (C.69); and *Euridici* (C.70)—built by Cantieri Riuniti dell'Adriatico, Monfalcone

Driade (C.43); *Danaide* (C.44); *Pomana* (C.45); *Flora* (C.46); *Sfinge* (C.47); *Chimera* (C.48); *Sibilla* (C.49); and *Fenice* (C.50)—built by Cantieri Riuniti dell'Adriatico, Trieste

Construction of the vessels was given high priority and by the time of Italy's surrender in September 1943 a total of 29 had been completed. The remaining 31 ships had all been laid down and were in various stages of completion, many of them launched. Of these ten were completed by the Germans and either lost in action or scuttled on Ger-

The Italian *Gabbiano* Class corvette *Antilope* built for convoy escort work in 1942

Foto Drüppel

***Euterpe*, a *Gabbiano* Class corvette captured by the Germans in 1943 and designated UJ 2228**

Aldo Fraccaroli

Aldo Fraccaroli

Minerva (C.42). Built at Monfalcone, she was launched in 1942, and completed in 1943

many's surrender. The remainder of the uncompleted vessels were either scuttled or damaged beyond repair in air raids. Of the 29 completed ships, three were lost as a result of enemy action while six were lost in action or scuttled at the end of the war.

In all 22 served in the postwar Marina Militare, rated as frigates with the pendant numbers F.547-549, 561-579. The armament was changed to 20-mm (0.79-in) and 40-mm (1.57-in) guns and antisubmarine weapons, while eight attached to the Command Training School had single 45-cm (17.7-in) torpedo tubes at the break of the forecastle. The *Pomona* (F.573), *Folaga* and *Fenice* (F.576-577) were stricken in 1965; the *Driade* (F.568) in 1966; the *Danaide* (F.563) in 1968; *Minerva* (F.562) in 1969; *Gru* (F.566), *Flora* (F.572) and *Pellicano* (F.574) in 1970; and the *Crisalide* and *Farfalla* (F.547-548), *Ibis* (F.651), *Scimitarra* and *Sibilla* (F.564-565), *Urania* and *Gabbiano* (F.571-572) in 1972. In 1978 there were still four of these hard-worked ships on the strength, the *Ape* (now a support ship for frogmen), and the *Bombarda, Chimera* and *Sfinge*, which were used as targets.

These corvettes were the first ships in the Italian navy to be completed with a navigating bridge. Because of a shortage of guns the first units to be completed were to have had 76-mm (3-in) guns, but sufficient 100-mm (3.9-in) weapons were found to arm all units when completed. Their appearance was distinctive, with a short funnel close to the bridge.

Displacement: 670-673 tons (standard), 737-743 tons (full load) *Length:* 64.3 m (211 ft), 64.4 m (211 ft 3¼ in) oa *Beam:* 8.71 m (28 ft 6 in) *Draught:* 2.53 m (8 ft 3½ in) *Machinery:* 2-shaft Fiat diesel, 3500 bhp (as designed)= 18-19.47 knots; 2 150-hp electric motors for silent running *Armament:* 1 100-mm (3.9-in)/47-cal; 7 20-mm (0.79-in)/65-70-cal; 2 40-mm (1.57-in)/56-cal AA; 2 45-cm (17.7-in) torpedo tubes; 10 depth charge throwers and 2 sets of chutes *Crew:* 110 (approx)

Gabbiano

Italian experimental torpedo boat built 1906-07. The Italians tested the idea of oil-fired boilers by building an experimental torpedo boat, but to reduce the cost the decision was made to use two sets of triple-expansion machinery from the old Schichau-built torpedo boats *110.S* and *111.S*.

Gabbiano was launched at the Royal dockyard, La Spezia, in April 1907 and was completed five months later. She resembled her contemporaries, with a flush deck and a turtleback forecastle, and three single 36-cm (14-in) torpedo tubes on deck. The age of the machinery (it was nearly 20 years old when installed) gave considerable trouble and the design was not repeated. In 1914 she was at Venice and was used for training, but on the entry of Italy into the First World War she was sent to Taranto with the 5th Division, and remained there until the Armistice: she was discarded in May 1921 and scrapped.

Displacement: 161.8 tonnes (normal), 174 tonnes (full load) *Length:* 49.62 m (162 ft 9½ in) oa *Beam:* 5.92 m (19 ft 5 in) *Draught:* 1.7 m (5 ft 7 in) *Machinery:* 2-shaft reciprocating steam 2200 ihp= 22 knots *Armament:* 2 47-mm (1.85-in)/40-cal (2×1); 3 36-cm (14-in) torpedo tubes (3×1); 14 mines (in place of torpedo tubes) *Crew:* 32

Gabbiano, CRDA Cant Z.501

Italian reconnaissance/light bomber flying-boat, first flew 1934. In 1931 the Cantiere Navale Triestino company acquired the services of Filippo Zappata, and also changed its name to Cantieri Riuniti dell'Adriatico, under which a number of civil and military seaplanes and land-based aircraft were subsequently produced. The first Zappata-designed prototype aircraft from the CRDA was a single-engined flying-boat, designed as a maritime reconnaissance-bomber. Designated Z.501 and named Gabbiano (seagull), it flew for the first time at Monfalcone, Trieste, in 1934. With the civil registration I-AGIL, it set up an international distance record for seaplanes in October 1934, flying non-stop for 4120 km (2560 miles) from Monfalcone to Massawa in Eritrea. A short time later a French aircraft took the record, but the Gabbiano reclaimed it in July 1935 with a 4957-km (3080-mile) flight from Monfalcone to Berbera in Somaliland.

However, it was in its designed role that the Z.501 entered service with the Squadriglie da Ricognizione Marittima (marine reconnaissance squadron) of the Regia Aeronautica (Italian air force) in 1936, after an order for production aircraft had been placed; an eventual total of 445 were built. In full military condition, the Gabbiano's maximum range was considerably more modest, at 2400 km (1490 miles). The flying-boat was of wooden construction, with fabric-covered wings and tail, and was powered by a 900-hp Isotta-Fraschini Asso XI R2 C15 12-cylinder V-type engine mounted above the centre-section of the parasol wing. It carried a normal crew complement of four or five men. Initial armament was three 7.7-mm (0.303-in) Breda-SAFAT machine-guns, one in an open position above the nose and the other two in semi-enclosed positions in the middle of the fuselage and in the rear of the over-wing engine nacelle. Racks attached to the inner-wing bracing struts could carry a variety of small bombs up to a maximum load of 640 kg (1410 lb), typical combinations including two 250-kg (551-lb), four 160-kg (353-lb) or four 100-kg (220-lb) bombs. Romania purchased a few Z.501s in 1937-38, and some saw service on the rebel Nationalist side in the Spanish civil war of 1936-39.

When Italy entered the Second World War

in June 1940, the Regia Aeronautica had 202 Z.501s in front-line service with maritime reconnaissance squadrons, air/sea rescue and other units. During the following year the nose gun was removed, to allow for an enclosed observer's cockpit in that position. At the Italian armistice in September 1943 the Gabbiano was still in use; about 20 continued serving with the co-belligerent Italian forces, and others with the pro-German Aviazione della RSI (the airforce of Mussolini's short-lived Italian Social Republic set up after the armistice), until the end of the war, and a few survived with the Italians until 1950.

Span: 22.50 m (73 ft 9¾ in) *Length:* 14.30 m (46 ft 11 in) *Gross weight:* 7050 kg (15 542 lb) *Maximum speed:* 275 km/h (170 mph)

RAF Beaufighters roar over a Z.501 Gabbiano anchored at Preveza

Gabriel, Israel Aircraft Industries

Israeli antiship missile. At the time of writing, Gabriel was the West's only antiship missile to have been used in combat, having sunk nine ships in four engagements during the 1973 October war with the Arab states. The weapon was originally planned to arm the Israeli navy's ex-British 'Z' Class destroyers of Second World War vintage, which were outgunned by the Soviet-built *Skory* destroyers operated by Egypt. In 1962, however, the Egyptian navy received its first *Komar* Class fast patrol boats, each carrying two SS-N-2 Styx antiship missiles. These were followed from 1966 by the larger *Osa* Class, with double the armament. In October 1967 the emergence of the small naval com-

Designed by the brilliant Filippo Zappata who had joined the new CRDA organization from the French firm of Blériot, the Z.501 was still in service in 1950, 16 years after its first flight. In the 1930s it became a familiar sight on the Italian coasts and despite being officially named Gabbiano (seagull) was also nicknamed Mammaiuto (Mamma, help!) from the reaction of Italian children seeing it for the first time. The aircraft in this illustration is painted in the striking 'anti-camouflage' pattern developed experimentally by the Italians

PPL

An Israeli Gabriel antishipping missile streaks towards the target vessel, the destroyer *Yaffo*

PPL

Gabriel explodes on the stern of the *Yaffo*. The missile has a 150-kg (330-lb) warhead

PPL

The destroyer burns. Gabriels sank nine ships in combat during the 1973 Yom Kippur war

batant was emphasized by the sinking of the Israeli 'Z' Class destroyer *Eilat*, which was struck by three Styx.

Israel's reply was to install Gabriel on the *Sa'ar* Class patrol boats built in France and spirited away by Israeli crews to prevent their delivery being embargoed. All 12 were in service by the outbreak of the October war, and they were augmented by the first two *Reshef* Class boats constructed in Israel. At least 15 of the 415-tonne *Reshefs* have been delivered or are on order; they are employed mainly in the Red Sea, leaving the Mediterranean to be patrolled by the 230-tonne *Sa'ars*. All carry at least six launchers for Gabriel and some are fitted with as many as eight.

Targets detected by the vessel's surveillance radar are handed over to the radar tracker, and an optical sight also aligns automatically with the enemy ship. Gabriel was originally designed for a range of 20 km (12 miles) in the anti-*Skory* role and is therefore at a disadvantage when engaging patrol boats carrying the Styx, which has more than twice this range. To overcome this problem, the Israeli navy has evolved a coordinated battle plan, which calls for its ships to detect and identify the enemy as early as possible, use electronic countermeasures while closing as rapidly as possible to within Gabriel range, then press home the attack with several missiles and, if necessary, gunfire at close range.

A Gabriel can be fired 60 seconds after the decision to engage a target is taken. A solid-propellant boost motor burns for four seconds to accelerate the round out of its glass-fibre container/launcher, which may be fixed or be one of three launchers on a rotating pedestal. The missile reaches a maximum height of 80-100 m (262-328 ft) and a speed of 220 m/sec (720 ft/sec) by the time the booster is expended, then descends gradually to 50-60 m (164-196 ft) for the initial stage of cruising flight. Midcourse guidance is provided by a twin-gyro platform and radio altimeter. During the early stages of its mission, the missile is normally tracked manually from the bridge by means of the optical sight. Steering corrections are then transmitted to bring the round on to the target bearing, as determined from the tracking radar. A television camera can be boresighted to the radar tracker for use during all-optical engagements, and the sight can track both missile and target if necessitated by heavy jamming.

In Gabriel Mk 1, terminal guidance switches to semi-active radar homing once the missile has approached within 10-12 km (6-7.4 miles) of its target, by which time it is cruising at a height of some 20 m (65 ft). At a distance of 1200 m (1312 yards) from its target, the round descends further to sea-skimming height. Gabriel has hit a 1 sq m (10 sq ft) target mounted at 45° to the line of flight, and overall hit probability is 80%, The 150-kg (330-lb) warhead is detonated on impact.

Beam-riding guidance can also be used in the presence of jamming, and the longer-range Mk 2 version additionally incorporates active radar guidance. The Mk 2's range is doubled by fitting a larger solid-propellant sustainer motor, and the flight-control system is more sensitive. Israel Aircraft Industries is working on Gabriel II, a supersonic over-the-

Israel Aircraft Industries

Gabriel at the moment of launch. It has been sold in Africa, South America and the Far East

horizon antiship missile for the early to mid-1980s, and is also possibly developing a 65-km (40-mile) Mk 3 variant of the basic weapon. Export customers for the earlier versions include Singapore, Thailand, Argentina, Malaysia, Taiwan and South Africa.

Length: 3.35 m (11 ft) *Span:* 1.38 m (4.5 ft) *Diameter:* 32 cm (12.5 in) *Weight:* 400 kg (881 lb)

Gael

British destroyer class. The design of these ships was prepared under the 1944 Programme and orders for eight equally distributed between four shipbuilders. The war ended before much progress had been made in their construction and the entire class was cancelled on December 12, 1945.

In outline they were smaller editions of the *Daring* Class, with the same speed and torpedo armament but with the main gun armament reduced from 6 to 4 4.5-in (114-mm) guns. The general hull and superstructure design was similar to that of *Daring* with the forefunnel enclosed in a lattice foremast and a second funnel further aft between the two banks of torpedo tubes. The twin 4.5-in (114-mm) gun mountings were the same as those in *Daring*, one being fitted on the forecastle and one on the after superstructure. Twin radar controlled 40-mm (1.57-in) AA guns were mounted abreast the after funnel and 20-mm (0.79-in) AA guns, which would certainly have been changed to 40-mm (1.57-in) prior to completion, in the bridge wings. Control was provided by a main director control tower on the bridge for long-range surface and AA fire and a medium-range AA director mounted abaft the funnel, both systems being equipped with radar and remote power control. The design also provided for alternative armaments to give the ships maximum versatility in the operational role. This entailed removing one or both torpedo tubes to allow for the addition of extra AA guns or A/S weapons or high-speed minesweeping gear.

It was perhaps unfortunate for the Royal Navy that these ships were not completed, for they may well have been of greater utility in the peacetime fleet than the *Darings*.

The class comprised: *Gael, Gallant, Gauntlet, Gift, Glowworm, Grafton, Greyhound, Guernsey.*

Displacement: 2200 tons (standard), 3000 tons (full load) *Length:* 111.25 m (365 ft) *Beam:* 12.04 m (39 ft 6 in) *Draught:* 3.04 m (10 ft) *Machinery:* 2-shaft geared steam turbines, 40 000 shp=34 knots *Armament:* 4 4.5-in (114-mm) (2×2); 4 40-mm (1.57-in) AA (2×2); 4 20-mm (0.79-in) AA (2×2); 10 21-in (53-cm) torpedo tubes (2×5) *Crew:* 280

Gainful

Soviet surface-to-air missile. The SA-6 Gainful was revealed to the West as early as 1967 and probably entered full-scale service in 1971. However, its capabilities had not been appreciated by the US by the time the Arab-Israeli conflict broke out in October 1973. Israeli air crews used to dealing with the comparatively crude SA-2 Guideline and SA-3 Goa were taken by surprise when their losses to Gainfuls mounted alarmingly. Their limited electronic countermeasures equipment had little effect against Gainful's associated Straight Flush fire-control radar. Indeed, when a captured battery was evaluated in the US after the war, defence officials admitted that the Soviet Union could 'give us instructions on simplicity and effectiveness'.

The SA-6 missile is fired from tracked transporter/launchers based on the chassis of the PT-76 light tank; each carries rails for three rounds. The associated Straight Flush radar vehicle also uses the same chassis, allowing a complete battery to move alongside the armoured vehicles which it is defending. Each Soviet army group incorporates five Gainful batteries made up of three triple launchers, a Straight Flush and a loading vehicle. Three of the batteries would be deployed only 5 km (3 miles) behind the front line, with the other two covering the gaps from positions some 10 km (6 miles) to the rear of the forward units. Long Track surveillance radars, also used with the SA-4 Ganef, provide early warning of an attack.

The exact method of guidance used with Gainful is not known, in spite of the weapon's widespread use in the October war, and the trials subsequently carried out in the US. The Straight Flush codename is a reference to the five frequencies used in the system: targets are acquired with beams

Gainful surface-to-air missiles deployed on their mobile launcher during an exercise in Russia

Novosti

Lockheed

Dwarfing a Lockheed Shooting Star chase plane, a Lockheed C-5A Galaxy lumbers across the sky during USAF evaluation trials in the late 1960s

operating at two frequencies, one used against high and far targets and the other for low, near aircraft. Tracking is then thought to be assumed by a pencil beam, with mid-course guidance commands being transmitted to the missile—which is itself tracked with the aid of an on-board beacon. Semi-active terminal guidance is used, while some sources also refer to infrared homing. Infrared proximity fuzes have been mentioned, and the successful use of Hot Brick decoys by the Israeli air force points to some heat-sensitive element of the system.

The missile itself is powered by a ram-rocket, a discovery which produced some hysterical reaction in the US. A solid-propellant boost charge accelerates the round to a speed of Mach 1.5, propulsion then being taken over by a solid-fuel ramjet which uses the empty boost-section casing as a combustion chamber. The exhaust from a solid-fuel gas-generator enters the chamber via a convergent-divergent nozzle and is mixed with air fed via four axial intakes. The mass flow is thus greatly increased, and further combustion of the hot-gas stream occurs when ram air is mixed with it. The ram-rocket rapidly accelerates Gainful to its cruise speed of Mach 2.8.

Gainfuls have been supplied to several countries outside the Warsaw Pact. Those supplied to Egypt replaced Ganefs, but in the Soviet army the weapon is now superseding batteries of 57-mm (2.24-in) antiaircraft cannon.

Length: 6.2 m (20 ft) *Diameter:* 33 cm (13 in) *Weight:* 550 kg (1212 lb) *Maximum range:* 35 km (22 miles) *Maximum altitude:* 12 000 m (39 370 ft) *Warhead:* 80 kg (176 lb)

Galaxy, Lockheed C-5A

US heavy transport aircraft. In 1963 the USAF's Military Air Transport Service (now Military Airlift Command) issued a requirement for a very large logistics transport aircraft. Finally, this and other requirements evolved into specification CX-HLS (Cargo, Experimental—Heavy Logistics System), which demanded an aircraft capable of carrying a payload of 56 700 kg (125 000 lb) over a range of 12 875 km (8000 miles) and twice that

A Galaxy touches down—it can carry a payload of 56 700 kg (12 500 lb) over 12 875 km (8000 miles) or twice the weight over shorter distances

Lockheed

Lockheed

The Galaxy was first used operationally during the Vietnam war, but has since been employed lifting supplies and aid to disaster areas

weight over shorter distances. It also had to be able to take off from the same runways as the smaller C-141 StarLifter and have the capacity to land on roughly-prepared strips in combat areas. In May 1964 the Boeing, Douglas and Lockheed companies were asked to develop their submitted designs further. The gross weight requirement had by then been increased to 317 500 kg (700 000 lb), and General Electric and Pratt & Whitney were invited to design a suitable powerplant. Towards the end of the following year the choice was made in favour of a Lockheed/General Electric partnership, and the aircraft was officially designated C-5A Galaxy.

Eight test and evaluation machines were built, beginning in August 1966, and the Galaxy flew for the first time on June 30, 1968. It is a high-wing cantilever monoplane, with a semimonocoque two-deck fuselage of aluminium and titanium alloy construction and a cantilever all-metal 'T' tail. The nosewheel unit retracts rearward hydraulically, as do the four main undercarriage bogies, each consisting of two sets of wheels in tandem on each side of the fuselage. Powered by four General Electric TF39-GE-1 turbofan engines, each rated at 18 600 kg (41 005 lb) thrust at sea level, the Galaxy carries a maximum usable fuel load of 185 480 litres (40 800 Imp gal) and can be refuelled in flight from a KC-135 tanker via an inlet in a fairing on top of the forward fuselage, just aft of the flight deck. For takeoff, a fully-loaded Galaxy needs 2135 m (7004 ft) of runway, but can land in a modest 680 m (2230 ft).

A crew of five is normally carried, including a loadmaster, and there is a forward rest area on the upper deck for 15 persons (relief crew, etc). Although intended primarily as a freighter, the basic version can carry 75 troops at the rear of the upper deck and 270 on the lower deck. More typical operational loads, however, might comprise two M-60 tanks; 16 ¾-ton lorries; one M-60 tank and two Bell Iroquois helicopters; five M-113 personnel carriers; one M-59 2½-ton truck and an M-151 ¼-ton truck; ten Pershing missiles, plus towing and launching vehicles; or 36 standard freight pallets. Other loads lifted have included a 35 380-kg (78 000-lb) Minuteman ICBM and its 3175-kg (7000-lb) launching cradle; two 44 905-kg (99 000-lb) M-48 tanks; or three Boeing Vertol Chinook heavy-lift helicopters. Loading can be done from front or rear, or from both ends simultaneously. There is an upward-hinged nose door and loading ramp at the front; the rear straight-in loading ramp, when closed, forms part of the undersurface of the rear fuselage.

Flight testing of the Galaxy continued until the summer of 1971. Deliveries of production aircraft to Military Airlift Command began on December 17, 1971, and were completed in May 1973. The C-5A became operational in 1970, and from July of that year was flying regular trips to Southeast Asia and Europe; it was utilized extensively during the Vietnam war for rapid transport of heavy equipment. In 1978, a total of 77 of these giant transports still remained in the MAC inventory, of the 81 aircraft built. These were in service with the 60th, 436th, 437th, and 443rd Military Airlift Wings, based at Travis Air Force Base, California; Dover, Delaware; Charleston, South Carolina; and Altus, Oklahoma.

Throughout the 1970s, the Galaxy remained the world's largest military transport aircraft, being almost as large and heavy as the later-model Boeing 747 Jumbo jets. Lockheed has calculated that, if required by the USAF, it is capable of being optimized for payloads even greater than the present 100 227-kg (220 964-lb) maximum, without increasing the maximum takeoff weight. In recent years, these aircraft have been put to invaluable use on non-military mercy missions to disaster-stricken areas such as the floods in Chile in 1974 and those in Pakistan. Much-needed equipment and supplies were taken to earthquake-ravaged Nicaragua by Galaxy aircraft, and in early 1977 and 1978 they were used to ferry snow-clearing equipment to several areas within the United States. After protracted structural trouble, wings are being rebuilt.

Span: 67.88 m (222 ft 8½ in) *Length:* 75.54 m (247 ft 10 in) *Gross weight:* 346 770 kg (764 496 lb) *Maximum speed:* 919 km/h (571 mph)

Galil

Israeli assault rifle. The Galil was developed against a requirement that came out of the Arab-Israeli Six Day War of 1967, when it was thought that the conventional FN rifles and machine-guns were too heavy and too powerful for the tasks that the modern infantryman is called upon to perform. After fairly prolonged trials with many different designs then current, the Israeli Galil, designed by Israel Galili and Yarcov Lior, was found to be the best. The trials laid particular emphasis on operation in desert conditions and severe dust, dirt and heat, where presumably the European weapons had shown themselves to be wanting. The announcement of the adoption of the Galil by the Israeli defence forces was made in 1972. Since then the rifle has come into service only comparatively slowly, although they were used in the battle of the Golan Heights in 1973.

The Galil is designed as a modern assault rifle capable of replacing the conventional submachine-gun, rifle and light machine-gun. It can also fire grenades from the muzzle and one version has a folding butt so that it can be carried by vehicle crews. The calibre of 5.56 mm (0.218 in) was chosen deliberately to keep the weight low, yet still fire a bullet with sufficient lethality for the battlefield.

In general design the Galil is a mixture of several ideas, but it owes much to the Finnish M62, which is itself a version of the Soviet AK-47. In fact the prototype Galils used Finnish bodies. The weapon works by gas action using a top-mounted cylinder and piston operating a simple two-lug turning bolt, and the cocking handle and change lever are all very similar to the AK. There are two barrel lengths, the shorter one being intended for the submachine-gun, and all of these versions have a folding tubular stock. The rifle versions may have a wooden, plastic or folding stock. The rifle has a light bipod fitted to the gas block and a particular feature of this bipod is that it can be used as a wire-cutter in an emergency.

The magazines are in three sizes, 12, 35 and 50. The most usual size is the 35, the 50 being a little large though it is most useful in the LMG (light machine-gun) role. The weapon is easily stripped into six parts and no special tools are needed. The sights are simple with only two range settings, 300 m (984 ft) and 500 m (1640 ft). All weapons are fitted with luminous night sights which fold out of the way by day.

The construction is of steel, with the maximum use made of stampings and pressings. Parts exposed to direct gas wash are chromium-plated and the whole design is extremely workmanlike and efficient. It is a little heavy for a 5.56-mm (0.218-in) weapon, but the robustness and reliability make this worthwhile, at least in the estimation of the Israeli army.

Calibre: 5.56 mm (0.218 in) *Length:* 97 cm (38.2 in); (folded) 74 cm (29.1 in) *Barrel length:* 46 cm (18.1 in) *Weight:* 3.9 kg (8.5 lb) *Cyclic rate of fire:* 650 rds/min *Muzzle velocity:* 920 m/sec (3020 ft/sec) *Magazine:* 12-, 35- or 50-round box

The Israeli Galil 5.56-mm assault rifle with butt folded which reduces its length from 97 cm (38.2 in) to only 74 cm (29.1 in)

La Galissonnière

French light cruiser class, completed between 1935 and 1937. The first two ships of this class (*La Galissonnière* and *Jean de Vienne*), designated B type cruisers by the French navy, were ordered in 1931. They were designed to the maximum possible parameters within the 1932 Geneva Treaty limitations, figures which were ratified at the London Conference in 1936. The following year, 1932, four more cruisers were ordered to the same design.

The armour protection was based on the same scheme as that of *Algérie* and was designed to withstand hits from 152-mm (6-in) shells. They were exceptionally fast cruisers and very well armed, the main armament having a maximum range of 25 790 m (28 200 yards) and a strong secondary armament sited amidships aft of the long forecastle break. The heavy extending catapult (capable of launching a Loire 130 flying boat) was mounted on the after 152-mm (6-in) gun turret. The machinery installation proved extremely successful, the trials results far exceeding the designed figures. They were designed to develop 84 000 shp to give a speed of 31 knots, and the builders hoped to achieve 97 000 shp at a speed of 32.5 knots on trials under good conditions. The trials figures achieved, however, far surpassed this with 100 000 shp developed and speeds of between 35 and 36 knots achieved. Fuel consumption also proved very economical, the designed radius of 6440 km (4000 miles) at 18 knots being exceeded in practice by 2410 km (1500 miles). These cruisers are generally considered to have been the most successful class of light cruisers ever designed.

La Galissonnière, Jean de Vienne, Gloire and *Georges Leygues* were given two extra 37-mm (1.46-in), a twin 25-mm (1-in) and two twin 13.2-mm (0.519-in) mounts in 1941. On November 27, 1942, *La Galissonnière, Jean de Vienne* and *Marseillaise* were scuttled in Toulon harbour as the Germans marched into the port. The three cruisers were allocated to the Italians who managed to refloat *Jean de Vienne* and *La Galissonnière* renaming them FR.11 and FR.12 respectively. Work proceeded on repairing the ships and making them ready for sea, but Italy surrendered before work on them had been completed. They were taken over by the Germans, *Jean de Vienne* being sunk in an air raid on November 24, 1943, *Marseillaise* on March 7, 1944, and *La Galissonnière* on April 18, 1944.

Georges Leygues, Gloire and *Montcalm* had left Toulon in September 1940 and reached French North African ports. They remained there until the Allies landed in North Africa when the ships joined Allied forces. They were refitted in America during 1943 when the light AA was entirely replaced with six quadruple 40-mm (1.57-in) mounts and 20 single 20-mm (0.79-in) mounts. American radar was also added, and the aircraft and catapult and hangar removed. On April 13, 1943, the *Georges Leygues* intercepted the blockade runner *Portland* off West Africa, the German ship scuttling herself. The three ships subsequently took part as bombardment vessels in the Allied landings in Normandy and in the South of France.

In 1945 the ships returned to America for a further refit during which the radar outfit was renewed and a new mast to support extra radar aerials added aft of the foremast. Although the vessels had done a great deal of steaming and displacement had risen to 10 850 tons they were still capable of achieving speeds up to 32 knots. *Gloire* was paid off and scrapped in January 1958, *Georges Leygues* in November 1959 and *Montcalm* paid off in 1958 to serve as an accommodation ship in Toulon.

La Galissonnière was laid down in October 1931, launched in November 1933 and completed in December 1935.

Jean de Vienne was laid down in December 1931, launched in May 1935 and completed in April 1937.

Gloire was laid down in 1933, launched in September 1935 and completed in December 1937.

Marseillaise was laid down in 1933, launched in July 1935 and completed in October 1937.

Montcalm was laid down in 1933, launched in October 1935 and completed in December 1937.

Georges Leygues was laid down in 1933, launched in March 1936 and completed in December 1937.

Displacement: 7600 tons (standard), 9100 tons (full load) *Length:* 179.5 m (589 ft) oa *Beam:* 17.5 m (57 ft 5 in) *Draught:* 5.3 m (17 ft 4 in) *Machinery:* 2-shaft geared turbines, 84 000 shp=31 knots *Protection:* 105 mm (4 in) main belt; 38 mm (1.5 in) deck; 50-100 mm (2-4in) turrets; 50-95 mm (2-3¾ in) conning tower *Armament:* 9 152-mm (6-in)/50-cal (3×3); 8 90-mm (3.54-in)/50-cal (4×2); 8 37-mm (1.46-in) (4×2); 12 13.2-mm (0.519-in) guns; 4 55-cm (21.7-in) torpedo tubes *Aircraft:* 4 *Crew:* 540

The French *La Galissonnière* Class cruiser *Georges Leygues* shown after her 1943 refit. She participated in the D-Day and Anvil bombardments in 1944, was refitted again in 1945, and with improved AA armament and radar served with the French fleet until she was paid off and scrapped in November 1959. This class was among the most successful light cruisers ever designed.

Musée de la Marine

Georges Leygues, laid down in 1933, was still capable of speeds up to 32 knots after the war

Musée de la Marine

Montcalm (above) escaped from Toulon and with *Gloire* and *Georges Leygues* joined the Allies

Galosh

Soviet antiballistic missile. Under the terms of the 1972 antiballistic missile (ABM) treaty, the US and Soviet Union are each allowed two ABM forces—one to defend the national command centre and the other to protect an ICBM (intercontinental ballistic missile) launch complex. Neither force can operate more than 100 ABMs, and the number of radars is also limited. The US deployed its Safeguard system, including Sprint and Spartan missiles, to defend the Minuteman ICBM base at Grand Forks in North Dakota. However, this has since been deactivated, so the 64 ABM-1 Galosh missiles at four sites around Moscow were by the summer of 1978 the world's only operational ABMs.

Early warning is provided by the Hen series of radars spread across the path of incoming ICBMs. Hen Egg is an E-band radar with a peak power of 2-3 MW; Hen Roost generates 2° beams at the higher power of 5 MW; Hen Nest operates at a frequency of 800 MHz with an output of 3-5 MW and Hen House has a peak power exceeding 10 MW. The last-named has a series of complicated beam scans: two each in azimuth and elevation, and one in a circular pattern. The radar faces measure 300 m×20 m (984 ft ×65 ft) and are inclined at 45°. Maximum range is some 600 km (372 miles) and Hen House can track targets while scanning for others, using a variety of pulse widths and repetition frequencies.

Each group of 16 Galosh missiles is associated with a pair of Try Add engagement-radar sites. Initial target acquisition and tracking are carried out by phased-array VHF Dog House radars around Moscow, which hand over to Chekhov target-tracking radars. Each Try Add site also incorporates two smaller guidance and interception radars.

The Soviet Union is continually experimenting with new ABM radars and missiles. Many of the Hen series radars, for example, may have been superseded by more modern equipment. Recent work in the ABM field includes the SH-4 Improved Galosh missile, which can restart its motor in flight several times after loitering periods while it waits for targets to be assigned to it. The radar used with the SA-5 Gammon surface-to-air missile has been tested in modified form in the ABM mode, and a new phased-array C-band radar designated X-3 has been reported. Trials are thought to be aimed at two systems: a Galosh replacement, using new radars, an improved long-range missile and a shorter-range weapon operating inside the atmosphere in a similar manner to the US Sprint; and a mobile system which uses very fast missiles to intercept the US air-launched SRAM (Short-Range Attack Missile) and battlefield-support weapons such as Lance.

Length: approx 20 m (65 ft) *Range:* approx 300 km (186 miles) *Warhead:* nuclear

Galveston

US guided missile cruiser class. Of the 27 *Cleveland* Class light cruisers that were completed to the original design, six were converted into single-ended guided missile cruisers between 1956-60. It had originally been intended to convert seven more, but the initial conversions were so difficult and so expensive for the limited results achieved that the remaining ships were left in their original condition, and new guided missile frigates built instead. All the unconverted *Cleveland*s were discarded between 1959-70. The three *Cleveland* conversions that were fitted with the Terrier medium-range SAM (surface-to-air missile) were reclassified as the *Providence* Class, whilst the three fitted with the larger Talos long-range SAM were reclassified as the *Galveston* Class.

PPL

USS *Oklahoma City*, a *Galveston* Class light guided missile cruiser recommissioned in 1960

Name	laid down	launched	completed
Galveston	20/2/1944	22/4/1945	24/5/1946
Little Rock	6/3/1943	27/8/1944	17/6/1945
Oklahoma City	8/3/1942	20/2/1944	22/12/1944

The *Galvestons* were originally armed with 12 6-in (152-mm)/47-cal guns arranged in two triple turrets superimposed fore and aft, six twin 5-in (127-mm)/38-cal mounts (one superimposed fore and aft and one on either side of the fore and aft superstructure), and 28 40-mm (1.57-in) AA. They had a catapult and hangar aft and carried four seaplanes. *Galveston* had her after 6-in (152-mm) and 5-in (127-mm) mounts removed and a new enlarged superstructure was fitted where the after superimposed 5-in (127-mm) mount had been. This was surmounted by a platform carrying the SPS-30 long-range 3-D radar; the after superstructure also carried two SPG-49 missile control radars. The twin Talos Mk 7 Mod O SAM launcher was mounted on the quarterdeck, with a magazine capacity of 46 missiles. There was a helicopter pad at the extreme stern, but no hangar or maintenance facilities were fitted. A lattice foremast was fitted to carry the SPS-43 long-range search radar, and a very tall lattice mainmast was added immediately abaft the second funnel, with an SPS-39 3-D air-surveillance radar mounted at the masthead out of the way of the hot funnel gases. Her forebridge was also remodelled and enclosed. *Little Rock* and *Oklahoma City* were similarly rebuilt, except that their forward superstructures were totally altered to provide much greater space for offices and communications facilities so that they could act as flagships. The forward superstructure was therefore greatly enlarged and extended, necessitating the removal of the original forward 5-in (127-mm) mounts, and the replacement of B 6-in (152-mm) turret by a twin 5-in (127-mm)/38-cal mount.

All three were built by William Cramp at Philadelphia. *Galveston* (CL-93) began her conversion at Philadelphia naval yard in August 1956 and completed it in September 1958, though she was recommissioned on May 28, 1958. She was reclassified first as CLG-93 and then on May 23, 1957 as CLG-3. When she recommissioned as a guided missile cruiser she was the first operational ship to mount the Talos SAM. She was finally decommissioned on December 21, 1973. *Little Rock* was converted by the New York Shipbuilding Corporation at their Camden yard, New Jersey, between January 1957 and June 1960. She was reclassified as CLG-4 and recommissioned on June 3, 1960. She acted as flagship either of the Sixth Fleet (in the Mediterranean) or the Seventh Fleet (in the Western Pacific) in rotation with *Oklahoma City* and with *Providence* and *Springfield* of the *Providence* Class. She was stricken on November 22, 1976, to undergo refitting as a museum at Boston navy yard. *Oklahoma City* was converted at the Bethlehem Steel shipyard at San Francisco between May 1957 and September 1960. She was reclassified as CLG-5 and recommissioned on September 7, 1960. Her last commission was as flagship of the Seventh Fleet. The *Galvestons* can be distinguished from the *Providence* Class because the *Providences* have a much lower mainmast, and instead of having a platform on the after superstructure they have a third lattice mast.

Displacement: 10670 tons (standard), 14400 tons (full load) *Length:* 185.9 m (610 ft) oa *Beam:* 20.2 m (66 ft 4 in) *Draught:* 7.6 m (25 ft) *Machinery:* 4-shaft geared steam turbines 100000 shp=31.6 knots *Protection:* 127-38 mm (5-1½ in) belt; 76-51 mm (3-2 in) deck; 127-76 mm (5-3 in) turrets *Armament:* 1 twin Talos SAM launcher; 6 6-in (152-mm); 6 5-in (127-mm) *Crew:* 1350 approx

The Gloster Gamecock became popular with the public in the 1920s at RAF aerobatic displays

IWM

Gamecock, Gloster

British single-seat day fighter, prototype delivered 1925. A development of the popular Gloster Grebe fighter which equipped several RAF units from 1923-28, the Gamecock was, initially, a reengined variant of the Grebe, using the new Bristol Jupiter IV radial engine. Ordered originally as the Grebe II in August 1924, the prototype Gamecock I (as it became titled) was delivered to Martlesham Heath for service tests in February 1925. Trial reports were enthusiastic, resulting in an initial order for 30 production machines in September 1925.

First to take delivery of the production Gamecocks was 23 Squadron RAF, at Henlow, in May 1926; followed by 3, 17, 32 and 43 Squadrons. Although designed for day fighting, the Gamecocks issued to 3 and 17 Squadrons were specially modified for night interception duties. During the next five years, Gamecocks, embellished with the colourful unit markings of the era, were prominent in the many public displays organized by the RAF, and demonstrated the type's outstanding manoeuvrability in many superb aerobatic exhibitions.

Delightful to fly, the Gamecock nevertheless recorded a relatively high accident rate in service use; 22 having crashed within 19 months of its introduction to the RAF, and killing eight pilots. A variety of modifications were embodied progressively to eliminate the Gamecocks' tendencies to spin abruptly and give wing flutter at high speed. Despite such characteristics, service Gamecocks quickly demonstrated their fast performance by taking the first three places in the 1927 Sassoon Cup Race for RAF fighter squadrons.

Though development of the basic Gamecock was undertaken, resulting in the Gamecock II and III, the latter saw no service use. In 1928 the Finnish government, having been much impressed by various displays of the Gamecock's versatility, placed an order for the type. By 1929 licensed production of the design (renamed Kukko) began at Helsinki. One unit, Fighter Squadron 24, continued to fly this variant from 1929 until 1935; while one Finnish Gamecock (GA-46) remained in service until late 1944. The Finnish versions were powered by Gnome-Rhône-built Jupiter VI engines.

Last of the all-wood construction fighters in RAF use, the Gamecock achieved fame in perpetuity when the reformed 43 Squadron adopted a fighting cock as its chosen official badge motif; the unit being known ever since as 'The Fighting Cocks'.

The Gamecock's service ceiling was 6736 m (22 100 ft) and endurance was 2½ hours at 4572 m (15 000 ft). Armament consisted of two fixed, synchronized 0.303-in (7.7-mm) Vickers Mk I machine-guns. Ammunition carried was 1200 rounds.

Span: (upper) 9.07 m (29 ft 9½ in); (lower) 7.89 m (25 ft 11 in) *Length:* 5.99 m (19 ft 8 in) *Maximum speed:* 233 km/h (145 mph)

Gammon

Soviet surface-to-air missile. Formerly known as Griffon, the SA-5 Gammon is a long-range surface-to-air missile which may have a limited secondary antiballistic missile role. The weapon is thought to have become operational in 1967, and ten years later the number deployed had risen to some 1800. The associated tracking and fire-control radar is codenamed Square Pair, and command guidance is thought to be employed; the warhead, which is probably available in interchangeable high-explosive and nuclear forms, may have its own motor for terminal manoeuvring in conjunction with active radar homing.

Length: 16.5 m (54 ft) *Span:* 3.65 m (11.9 ft) *Diameter:* 90 cm (35 in) *Maximum range:* 250 km (155 miles) *Maximum altitude:* 30 000 m (98 425 ft)

Ganef

Soviet surface-to-air missile. The SA-4 Ganef was introduced in 1964 to provide field armies with long-range defence against air attack. Two missiles are carried on an armoured chassis which doubles as a transporter and launcher; the weapon may additionally have a secondary surface-to-surface role. A Soviet army group deploys nine Ganef batteries, each of which comprises three transporter/launchers, a loading vehicle and the mobile Pat Hand acquisition and fire-control radar. Ganef batteries are normally deployed in the gaps between formations of SA-6 Gainful missiles, three following only some 10 km (6 miles) behind the advancing forward troops and the remaining six batteries forming a belt about 25 km (15.5 miles) to the rear of the front line. All elements of a Ganef battery can be redeployed in An-22 Cock transport aircraft.

Advance warning of an attack is given by Long Track radars operating in E-band and completing a surveillance scan every four seconds. Targets are then acquired by the G/H-band Pat Hand. Ganef is accelerated off its launcher by four wrap-round solid-propellant boosters, cruise propulsion then being assumed by an air-breathing engine fed from an annular intake. The sustainer powerplant is often quoted as being a ramjet, but a turbojet is possible. The missile is guided via a command link, and the high-explosive warhead carries proximity and contact fuzes.

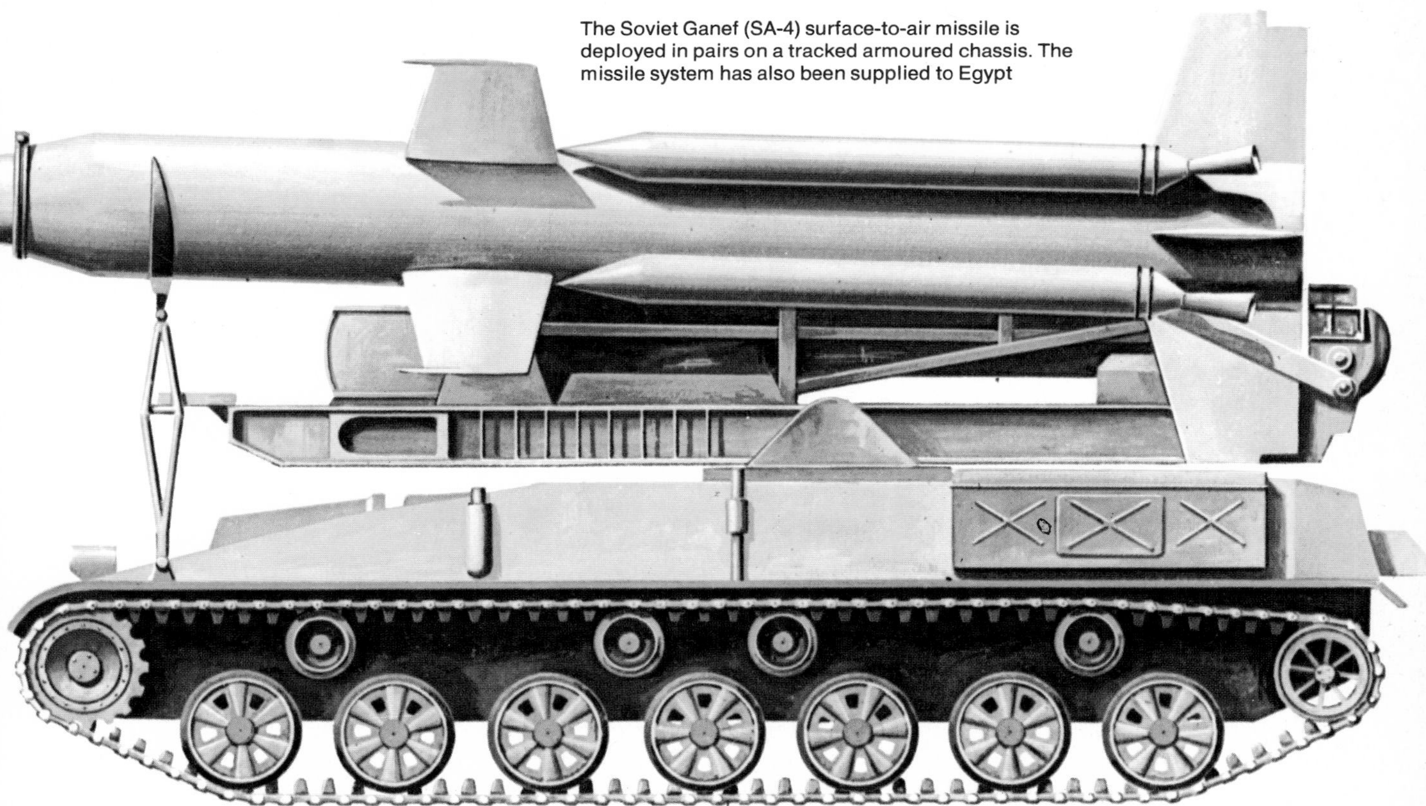

The Soviet Ganef (SA-4) surface-to-air missile is deployed in pairs on a tracked armoured chassis. The missile system has also been supplied to Egypt

The Russian *Gangut* Class battleship *Petropavlovsk* in Soviet service. Having been torpedoed in 1919, she was salved and refitted in the late 1920s with the new name *Marat*

In 1978 Ganef was still being deployed with the Soviet, Czech and East German armies in place of the earlier Guideline system, and a shortened version with uprated performance had been reported.

Length: 9.2 (30 ft) *Span:* 2.3 m (7.5 ft) *Diameter:* 80 cm (31 in) *Maximum range:* 70 km (43 miles) *Maximum altitude:* 15 000 m (49 212 ft)

Gangut

Russian battleship class. The four *Ganguts* were the first Russian Dreadnoughts, and were intended to replace the Baltic fleet battleships that had been sunk by the Japanese at Tsushima on May 27, 1905. Most of the world's major shipyards were approached in an attempt to create the finest possible battleship, and over 50 designs were actually submitted by Russian and foreign firms. When it seemed certain that the contract was going to be awarded to the German firm of Blohm & Voss, the Russian government stepped in and insisted that the ships should be built in Russian yards.

The opportunity was taken to produce a fresh design, and the resulting *Ganguts* were very strongly influenced both by the ideas of the Italian General Cuniberti and the lessons that the Russians had learnt from the battle of Tsushima. Cuniberti laid stress on speed and gunpower rather than armour, and the *Ganguts*' arrangement of triple 305-mm (12-in) turrets equispaced along the centreline was very similar to that of the first Italian Dreadnought, *Dante Alighieri.* The emphasis on speed, which was also learnt from Tsushima, meant that the hull was made as light as possible, with the maximum use being made of high tensile (HT) steel. The resulting hull was indeed light, but it was also very weak, with the unfortunate result that full broadsides could not safely be fired.

Like the preceding pre-Dreadnought *Imperator Pavel I* Class, the *Ganguts* had relatively thin armour spread over most of the hull. This was to prevent a repetition of the debacle at Tsushima, where the Russian battleships had been overwhelmed by a rain of light shells after the initial long-range action. To protect them against heavier shells, the *Ganguts* had another belt set 3.35 m (11 ft) inboard, which was intended to catch the splinters from the shells that were supposed to be burst by the outer belt. This was ingenious but quite heavy (thus to a certain extent nullifying the lightness of the hull), and in any case worked better at short or medium ranges than at long range. This was odd because the Russians' own 305-mm (12-in)/52-cal was not only longer ranged than foreign contemporaries, but it was also more accurate than most heavy guns at these long ranges, so the Russians were in the best possible position to appreciate the necessity for protection against this kind of attack.

Other bad features of the design were the position of the secondary armament, and the absence of torpedo bulkheads. Both were mainly due to the desire for a light hull. The torpedo bulkheads were not fitted purely to save weight, and the 120-mm (4.7-in) guns were mounted low on the main deck to ensure that the beam did not have to be increased to maintain stability. They were also grouped alongside the main barbettes, introducing weak points in the system of protection at the points where strength was most needed.

The *Ganguts* had a very unusual silhouette, with a flush deck, four equidistant turrets, two prominent funnels (the second much larger than the first), and a vestigial superstructure. They were very uncomfortable ships to serve in because the extensive side armour meant that there was very little ventilation to most of the below-deck compartments.

Gangut and *Poltava* were built at the Baltic Works, and *Petropavlovsk* and *Sevastopol* at the Galernii Works at St Petersburg. The length of time they took to build was due partly to the use of high tensile steel, which could not then be made in quantity in Russia, and partly to the inexperience of the yards, but it had the unfortunate result of making the ships obsolescent before they even entered service.

During the First World War the *Ganguts* were fettered by orders that forbade risks being taken with them, and as a result they scarcely ventured outside the Gulf of Finland. All played prominent roles in the Revolutions, when their crews formed the backbone of the Kronstadt Sailors' Soviet. However, by 1920 they were all in very poor condition, and *Petropavlovsk* had been torpedoed by a British coastal motor boat in 1919. She was salved, and renamed *Marat,* and in the late 1920s she was refitted. She was converted to oilburning, her forebridge was enlarged, and her forefunnel raised and the top part raked back. *Sevastopol* (renamed *Parizhskaya Kommuna*) and *Gangut* (renamed *Oktyabrskaya Revolutsia*) were similarly rebuilt, but *Poltava* (renamed *Mikhail Frunze*) was badly damaged by fire in the early 1920s, and the hulk was cannibalized for spares. The three survivors were used for shore bombardment during the Finnish campaign, and later took part in the defence of Leningrad. *Marat* was hit by bombs from German Stukas on September 23, 1941. Magazine A exploded and the bow was blown off, but after repairs the remaining three turrets continued to be used. In 1942, she reverted to her original name, as did *Sevastopol* and *Gangut. Petropavlovsk* was broken up in the early 1950s, but the other two lasted until 1956-57, when they were finally taken out of service and scrapped.

Name	laid down	launched	completed
Gangut	7/1909	9/1911	1/1915
Petropavlovsk	7/1909	10/1911	1/1915
Sevastopol	7/1909	6/1911	11/1914
Poltava	7/1909	7/1911	12/1914

Displacement: 25 000 (standard), 26 170 (full load) *Length:* 184.86 m (606 ft 6 in) oa *Beam:* 26.90 m (88 ft 3 in) *Draught:* 9.30 m (30 ft 6 in) *Machinery:* 4-shaft geared steam turbines 42 000 shp=23 knots *Protection:* 125-255 mm (4.9-10 in) belt; 25-38 mm (1-1.5 in) deck; 105-203 mm (4.1-8 in) turrets *Armament:* 12 305-mm (12-in); 16 120-mm (4.7-in); 8 7.62-mm (0.30-in) mg; 4 46-cm (18-in) torpedo tubes *Crew:* 1286

Gannet, Fairey (Westland)

British ASW (antisubmarine warfare) and AEW (airborne early warning) aircraft, first flew 1949. During the Second World War the Royal Navy had no purpose-designed ASW aircraft. After several years pondering on the problems of packaging the required sensors and weapons into an aircraft compatible with an aircraft carrier, specification GR.17/45 was issued in late 1945.

Unlike the US Navy, which adopted the hunter/killer philosophy, using aircraft in pairs, one carrying sensors and the other weapons, GR.17 specified an aircraft capable of operating effectively from carriers whilst carrying sensors and weapons and doing the whole job of finding and killing submarines by itself. It was a far-sighted specification, but unfortunately a combination of vacillation by the customer and poor performance by the contractor delayed entry to service of any GR.17 aircraft until ten years after the requirement was formulated.

At first GR.17 called for a two-seat aircraft, and prototypes were built of the Blackburn YA.5 and Fairey 17 (named for the specification). The Fairey, a notably clean design, flew at Aldermaston on September 19, 1949, and was the first aircraft ever to fly on the power of a coupled turboprop. The engine, an Armstrong Siddeley Double Mamba, comprised two Mamba power sections—each a neat axial turbine engine—bolted to a common gearbox with concentric output shafts driving front and rear coaxial propellers. The idea was that, whilst offering ample power for takeoff or combat emergency, either half of the engine could be shut down in cruising flight, the relevant propeller (the front or rear half of the double unit) being feathered. This would extend engine life and stretch the range attainable on the aircraft's fuel. Fairey had pioneered the concept in 1938-41 with the P.24 Prince double piston engine, test-flown in a Battle lighter bomber. A further advantage of turbine propulsion, fully utilized by the Royal Navy, was that it used ship's oil fuel instead of high-octane gasoline.

Bundesministerium der Verteidigung

A Fairey Gannet in service with the West German Marineflieger who ordered 15 AS.4s and one T.5

This put Fairey ahead of Blackburn, and although the latter soon flew the YB.1 with the same Double Mamba engine—and in some ways it was the superior aircraft—Fairey got the main production contract, the GR.17 being renamed Gannet.

After many delays due to technical problems, and redesign to accommodate a third crew member, the first production Gannet AS.1 flew in June 1953, entering service with Royal Navy 826 Sqn in 1955. The fuselage was bulky to accommodate the double engine and twin tailpipes, nose gear, large weapon bay for all shipboard air weapons, including two torpedoes, retractable radar in the rear fuselage, various other sensors and (later) electronic-warfare equipment, and cockpits for the pilot, observer/navigator and radio/radar operator. The wings folded at two points so that the outer panel remained horizontal, and the tail had two auxiliary fins. Fairey began production of the AS.1 at Hayes (serial WN339) but starting from WN370, assembly was also at Stockport.

After building 25 AS.1s, the T.2 dual-control trainer appeared on the line, and this version, which had a periscope for the instructor in the middle cockpit, continued to be slotted in at intervals. In 1956 a more powerful Double Mamba became available, the Mk 100 of 2950 ehp giving way to the Mk 101 of 3035 ehp, and so following production of 169 AS Gannets the Mk number changed from 1 to 4; the corresponding more powerful trainer was the T.5. The Royal Australian Navy received 20 AS.4s, for use from *Melbourne* and shore bases. The West German Marineflieger received 15 AS.4s and a T.5,

Royal Navy Gannets in formation off Malta. Developed as a specialized antisubmarine aircraft the Gannet was capable of carrying two torpédoes, a retractable radar in the rear fuselage, A/S sensors and later ECM equipment. The wings folded in two points for stowage

IWM

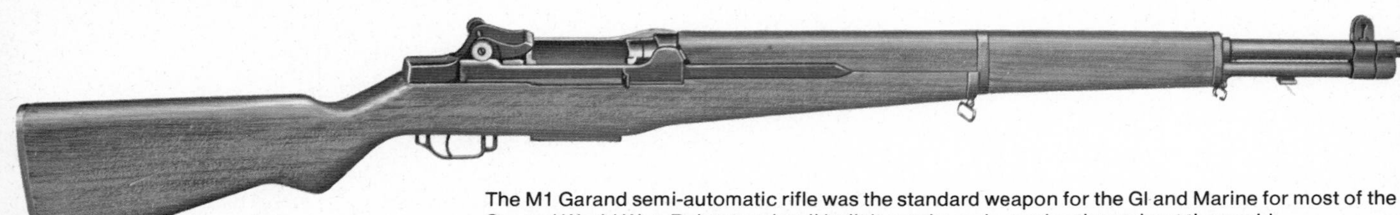

The M1 Garand semi-automatic rifle was the standard weapon for the GI and Marine for most of the Second World War. Robust and well built it continues in service throughout the world

while the Indonesian navy received 16 AS.4s and two T.5s. All these aircraft remained in active service until the 1960s. Rebuilt AS.4 Gannets with extra electronics were styled AS.6 and 7.

Experience with the AD-4W Skyraider showed the Royal Navy the value of AEW (airborne early warning) aircraft, and in August 1958, Fairey (soon to be taken over by Westland) flew a Gannet with a completely new fuselage and tail for this role. Powered by the 3875-ehp Double Mamba 102, the Gannet AEW.3 seated the pilot well forward and two radar observers inside the rear fuselage, with side doors, to manage the APS-20A radar salvaged from the faithful Skyraiders. Numerous other changes included a stalky landing gear. Westland built the 38th and last AEW.3 Gannet in 1961, and these equipped 849 Sqn right up to 1977. As the Royal Navy's fixed-wing carrier squadrons were deactivated, the radars from most of the AEW.3s were used to convert Shackletons into the AEW.2 version. Thus, some APS-20A series sets have served in three types of aircraft.

Span: 16.56 m (54 ft 4 in) *Length:* 13.1 m (43 ft) *Gross weight:* (AS.4) 10200 kg (22500 lb) *Maximum speed:* (AS.4, radome retracted) 484 km/h (300 mph)

Associated Press

An American paratrooper levels his Garand at a German officer captured in Normandy in 1944

Garand

US self-loading rifle. In 1919, the US together with many other countries, realized that the current small arms were all too powerful and too heavy for sensible infantry use. Throughout the 1920s the US Army conducted a series of trials and tests to find a suitable self-loading rifle. One of the requirements was that the calibre should not be less than 0.25 in (6.35 mm) which seemed to be an invitation to use a smaller cartridge than the 30-06 which was the standard round, and a wide variety of ideas was put forward. John Garand was prominent among these inventors, and he joined the staff of Springfield arsenal which may have given him a slight advantage. However, his design was accepted in 1929, and put forward as the final solution in 1932.

At that time it was in 0.276-in (7-mm) calibre, but General MacArthur insisted that it should fire the 30-06 since stocks were so large, and so the ten-round magazine was adapted to take the larger round. Thus the capacity was reduced to eight. First issues started in 1936, and by 1941 most of the US Army carried it. However, the rapid expansion in 1942 meant that there were not enough to go round until 1943, and Springfields continued to be used.

The Garand was the only self-loading rifle to be a complete issue to any army in the Second World War, although other armies used them as specialist weapons. The Garand was a tough, straightforward design with few frills and great resistance to rough handling and abuse. In concept it was relatively old-fashioned with a one-piece stock, an integral magazine and a fair weight. It was a gas-operated weapon, using a long-stroke piston tapped off from the extreme front end of the barrel. The piston extension worked a cam which opened and closed the short bolt and this same extension had the return spring around it. This enabled the receiver to be kept short, and it was also immensely strong and resistant to malfunctions.

Loading was by means of an eight-round clip, and only a full clip could be inserted. This was a weakness of the design since it meant that the magazine could not be topped up with odd rounds. Another feature was that the clip was ejected when all rounds were fired. Despite these minor criticisms the Garand was the best rifle of the Second World War, and its design was perpetuated in the M14 of 1957, which is still in service. For

United Nations soldiers clean their M1s during a break in the Korean war in February 1951

US Navy

James W Goss

USS *Voge* (FF1047), one of the ten *Garcia* Class frigates constructed for A/S and escort duties

that matter, so are many Garands. There were numerous variants of the basic model, including selected sniping rifles, and attempts were made to produce a jungle carbine and a large-magazine selective-fire assault rifle.

(M1) *Calibre:* 7.62 mm (0.30 in) *Length:* 110.5 cm (43.5 in) *Weight:* (empty) 4.30 kg (9 lb 8 oz) *Barrel:* 61 cm (24 in) *Magazine:* 8-round internal box *Muzzle velocity:* 853 m/sec (2800 ft/sec)

Garcia

US frigate class. This class of ten vessels was originally ordered in the 1961-63 programmes as destroyer escorts DE.1040-1051. The design is a development of the earlier *Bronstein* Class and, although the *Garcia* Class are larger and have a better ASW (antisubmarine warfare) capability than many destroyers, they have, since June 1975, been classified as frigates (FF). This is because the ships have only a single propeller shaft which limits their speed. The ships are fitted with an advanced pressure-fired steam-generating plant developing 70% more power than previous steam plants of similar weight and size. The two boilers are each fitted with an integrated supercharger and control system providing automatic regulation of fuel, air and water. The boilers use Naval Distillate (ND) fuel which simplifies boiler cleaning and maintenance and facilitates the ballasting of the fuel tanks with sea water. The simplified boiler maintenance and fully automatic control system means that the machinery requires far fewer engineers to control it.

The original design provided for the ships to mount the 5-in (127-mm)/54-cal gun. However, to keep costs down, it was decided to mount the older 5-in (127-mm)/38-cal weapon which has a slower rate of fire and a shorter range. Unfortunately, this reduces the effectiveness of this otherwise all-missile armed A/S (antisubmarine) ship. The 5-in (127-mm) guns provide the only self-defence armament of these vessels, and so they were designed to operate in conjunction with the very similar *Brooke* Class equipped with an AA missile armament. The design is flush-decked with a distinctive 'mack' (combined mast and stack, or funnel) amidships. The stem is acutely raked with a bow anchor. A second anchor is carried just forward of the 5-in (127-mm) gun on the port side and the ships are fitted with gyrostabilizers.

In the original design, plans were made for the ships to operate DASH (drone antisubmarine helicopter). Owing to the cutback in the DASH programme, only the *Bradley* operated a DASH for a short while. The *Bradley* was also equipped with a Sea Sparrow BPDMS (basic point defence missile system) between the after 5-in (127-mm) mount and the mack in 1968-69. This was subsequently removed for installation in the carrier *Forrestal*. Originally the ships were fitted with two Mk 25 torpedo tubes for wire-guided torpedoes in the transom stern. This was removed from early units and later units were never equipped with the tubes. During the early 1970s the hangar on all but the *Albert David* and *Sample* was modified to operate the LAMPS SH-2D helicopter.

Displacement: 2620 tons (standard), 3043 tons (full load) *Length:* 126.33 m (414 ft 6 in) oa *Beam:* 13.5 m (44 ft 3 in) *Draught:* 7.31 m (24 ft) *Machinery:* 1-shaft geared steam turbine 35 000 shp=27 knots *Armament:* 2 5-in (127-mm)/38-cal (2×1); 2 triple Mk 32 torpedo tubes; 1 ASROC 8-tube launcher; 1 LAMPS SH-2D helicopter *Crew:* 239-247

No and name	commissioned
FF1040 *Garcia*	12/1964
FF1041 *Bradley*	5/1965
FF1043 *Edward McDonnell*	2/1965
FF1044 *Brumby*	8/1965
FF1045 *Davidson*	12/1965
FF1047 *Voge*	11/1966
FF1048 *Sample*	3/1968
FF1049 *Koelsch*	6/1967
FF1050 *Albert David*	10/1968
FF1051 *O'Callahan*	7/1968

Gardner

British naval gun. William Gardner of Toledo, Ohio, enlisted as a soldier in the US Army and retired, after the Civil War, with the rank of Captain. Having seen numerous attempts to make machine-guns, he then devoted his time to devising one of his own and perfected a gun in 1874. Failing to interest any financial backer, he sold the patent rights to the Pratt & Whitney company who then produced the gun under licence.

The Gardner consisted of two side-by-side barrels in a common cylindrical casing. Behind each barrel was a reciprocating bolt, driven by a connecting rod attached to a cross-shaft. The throws of this shaft were 180° apart, so that when the shaft was turned by an outside handle, the two bolts were thrust forward and back alternately, one bolt

The Gardner machine-gun, developed by an American and used by the Royal Navy in the 1880s

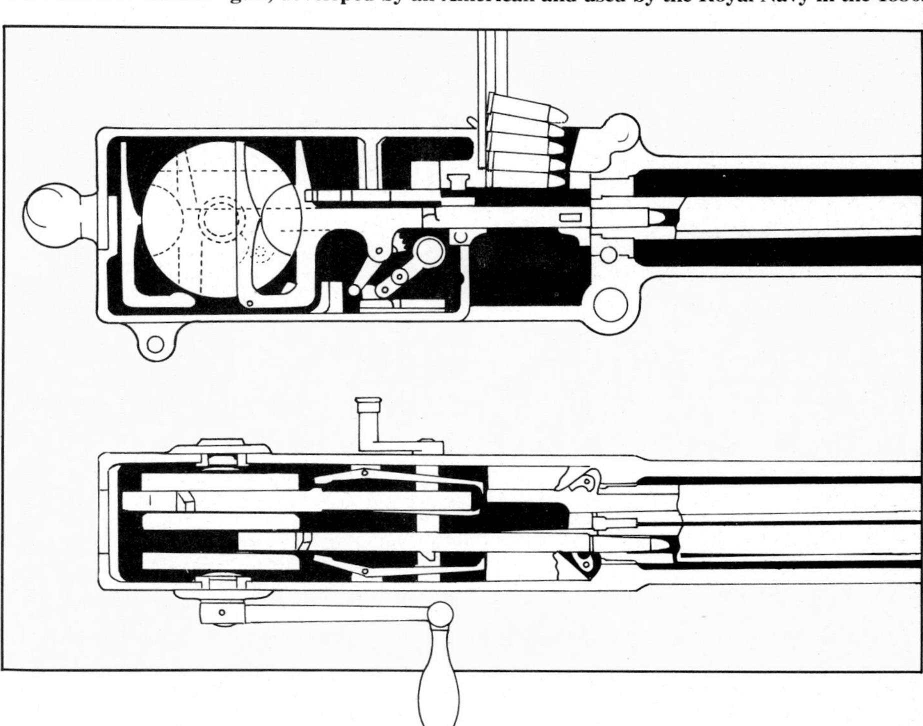

being open while the other was closed. A central feed column held cartridges by their rims and delivered them to an oscillating feed arm, also driven by the hand crank. As the crank was turned, the arm collected a cartridge from the feed column and carried it across to the right breech, after which the breech bolt closed and fired it. Further turning of the crank caused the feed arm to swing to the left side, picking up a cartridge as it passed the feed column, loading it, the bolt closing and firing. This alternate action continued so long as the handle was turned.

Tests of the Gardner gun were carried out by the US Navy in 1879, during which the test gun fired 10000 shots in 27 minutes 36 seconds, a rate of 360 rds/min. Nevertheless, neither the US Army nor the US Navy would take the gun, largely because they were committed to the Gatling at that time. Gardner then developed a five-barrelled gun, working on the same principles, and took it to England where he demonstrated it to the Admiralty, during which demonstration it fired at 814 rds/min. The Royal Navy, anxious to find a gun for use against torpedo boats and against personnel exposed on the decks of enemy ships, adopted a five-barrel model in 0.45-in (11.43-mm) calibre in 1882, followed by a two-barrel model in 1884. They were mounted aboard ship on cone mountings and were also provided with wheeled field mountings for use by naval landing parties. It is of interest to note that the introduction of the Gardner marked the first official use of the phrase 'machine-gun' in British military nomenclature.

Apart from British use, though, the Gardner gun did not achieve much success, since it was soon to be superseded by the automatic Maxim gun. It was the last, and best, of the mechanical period of machine-gun development. Feed was by the continuous insertion of cartridges into a feed column. Rate of fire was governed by the speed of rotation of the hand crank.

(5-barrel Mk 1) *Calibre:* 11.43 mm (0.45 in) *Length:* 1.36 m (4 ft 5½ in) *Barrel length:* 0.84 m (2 ft 9 in) *Weight:* 131.5 kg (290 lb)

(2-barrel Mk 1) *Calibre:* 11.43 mm (0.45 in) *Length:* 1.19 m (3 ft 11 in) *Barrel length:* 0.76 m (2 ft 6 in) *Weight:* 98.9 kg (218 lb)

The German Gast air-cooled aircraft machine-gun with quick-change ammunition drums

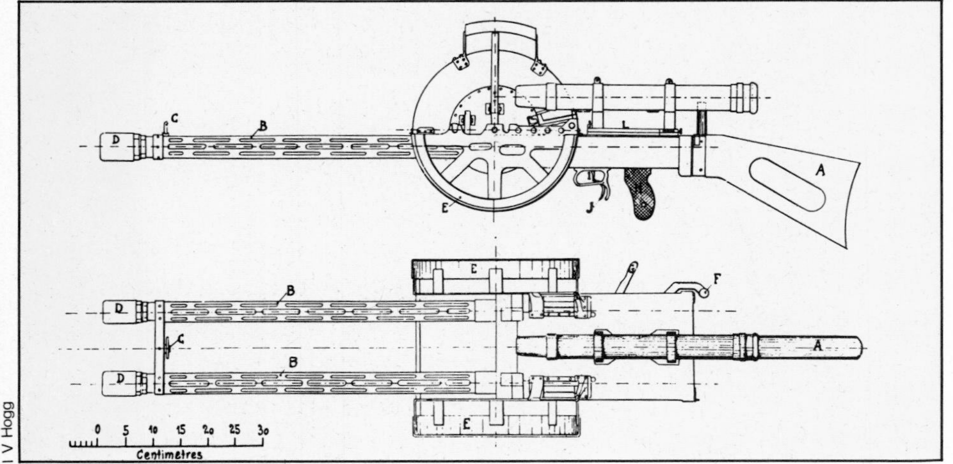

Gargoyle

US air-to-surface missile. The Luftwaffe's reasonable degree of success with stand-off antiship weapons such as the Fritz-X guided bomb and Hs 293 missile showed that even heavily armoured and manoeuvring warships could be crippled or sunk by one or two accurately delivered knockout blows. The addition of some form of guidance greatly reduced the tonnage of explosives needed to achieve these results, and launching from stand-off ranges gave some immunity from the target's antiaircraft defences. The US was not slow to see the implications, and a series of guided weapons was initiated based on existing high-explosive bombs.

One of these was Gargoyle, a radio-controlled rocket-powered air-to-surface missile carrying a 450-kg (990-lb) warhead. The weapon was designed to be launched from carrier-based aircraft against manoeuvring targets in good visibility, and had a range of nearly 8000 m (26250 ft) when delivered in a 30° dive from the optimum altitude of 4500 m (14760 ft). Gargoyle had to be released at a speed of at least 320 km/h (200 mph) to avoid stalling its low-mounted wings, and a standard 8AS1000 JATO (Jet-Assisted Takeoff) unit installed in the rear fuselage produced 450 kg (990 lb) of thrust for eight seconds to accelerate the weapon to its maximum speed of 960 km/h (596.5 mph).

The operator in the launch aircraft steered the Gargoyle by means of a joystick, commands being transmitted to the weapon over a radio link. Control in pitch was effected by simultaneous deflection of the combined rudders and elevators on the V-tail, and individual operation of these controls produced yaw/roll coupling which turned the weapon. Gargoyle could pull 4 g laterally and had a turning circle of 777 m (2550 ft). Flares at the rear of the missile helped the operator to keep it in view, and the radio link had a maximum range of some 45 km (28 miles), so control at significant stand-off ranges was possible.

Gargoyle, which was designated LBD-1 and later KSD-1 carried a standard AN-M59 semi-armour-piercing or AN-M65 general-purpose bomb in the forward fuselage; both weighed 450 kg (990 lb) and were detonated on impact. McDonnell began production of the weapon in late 1944, but the Second World War ended before the missile could be deployed operationally and it ended its career as a test vehicle.

Length: 3 m (9 ft 10 in) *Span:* 2.6 m (8 ft 6¼ in) *Weight:* 748 kg (1650 lb)

Gaskin

Soviet surface-to-air missile. The SA-9 Gaskin is fired from canister launchers mounted on modified BRDM-2 reconnaissance vehicles. Most carry eight launchers, but a four-round installation has also been seen. The weapon is thought to have entered service in 1972, and some may have been operated by the Egyptian army during the October war the following year.

The SA-9 missile is thought to be an improved version of the SA-7 Grail, using the same infrared seeker but carrying a larger warhead and a more powerful rocket motor. A version with improved tracking ability and greater manoeuvrability than the initial variant has been reported, and this may correspond to the similarly uprated SA-7B or Grail Mk 2. The launcher on definitive Gaskin vehicles can be rotated, although that on the initial units was fixed. An optical sight is mounted in the glazed control cabin.

Gaskin vehicles are operated alongside Shilka radar-directed cannon at the forward edge of an advance. Target information from the Shilka's powerful Gun Dish tracking radar can be transmitted to Gaskin vehicles when the battery is stationary. An ECM (electronic-countermeasures) van normally accompanies the Shilka/Gaskin battery to give protection, since the Gun Dish radar can be detected from the air at ranges up to 75 km (47 miles).

Length: approx 1.7 m (5 ft 7 in) *Weight:* approx 30 kg (66 lb) *Range:* approx 4 km (2.5 miles) *Warhead:* 7 kg (15 lb)

Gast

German aircraft machine-gun. The weapon was invented by Karl Gast, a German engineer, in response to a demand for a fast-firing machine-gun for use in aircraft. Development was done by the Vorwerke Company of Barmen during 1916-18. The first models for service test were sent to a German air force unit at Doberitz in March 1918, but these early guns went back to the factory several times for modification, and it was not until September 1918 that production was authorized.

The Gast consisted of two recoil-operated guns mounted side by side and controlled by a common trigger. The gun breech blocks were cross-coupled so that the recoil of one gun provided the power to feed and fire the other, the two guns firing alternately. Feed was from two vertically-mounted drums, one at each side of the gun assembly where they could be rapidly changed. The theoretical drawback to this type of weapon is that a misfire on one gun will stop both from firing, but the Gast proved to be extremely reliable in all positions (an important point where aircraft guns are concerned) and the design was notable for the small number of moving parts and the minimum of screws and

The Gast machine-gun was an advanced design tested by the German air force in 1918 but available too late to be used in any quantity during the First World War. No further work took place after 1918

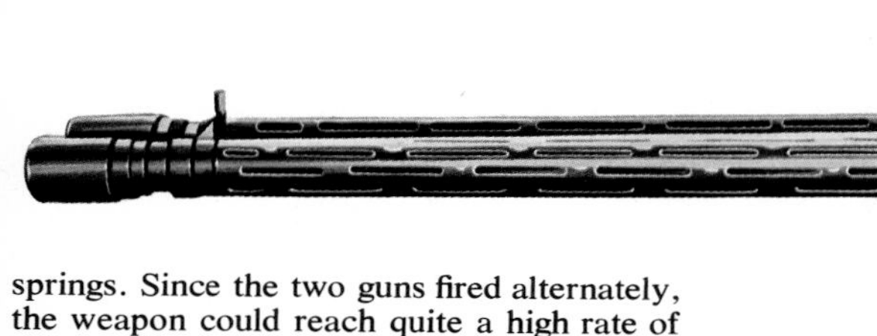

springs. Since the two guns fired alternately, the weapon could reach quite a high rate of fire without overheating.

After the Armistice of 1918 the Gast gun was examined with great interest by the Allies, but no further development of the design took place, although the gun was well in advance of any comparable weapon. Eventually some 1340 guns were destroyed by the Allied Control Commission, only a handful being retained as museum specimens.

Calibre: 7.92 mm (0.312 in) *Length:* 139 cm (54.72 in) *Barrel length:* 72 cm (28.35 in) *Weight:* 18.5 kg (40 lb 12 oz) *Magazine:* 2 192-round drums *Rate of fire:* 1300 rds/min *Muzzle velocity:* 885 m/sec (2900 ft/sec)

Gatling

US multi-barrelled machine-gun. Probably the most famous of all the mechanical machine-guns, the Gatling was the invention of Richard Jordan Gatling of North Carolina. The inventor qualified as a doctor but never practised medicine; his true forte was mechanical engineering, and he designed and patented a number of useful agricultural implements in the 1850s.

In 1861 he began work on a machine-gun which had six barrels revolving around a central axis and driven by a hand crank. It was fed with steel tubes preloaded with powder and ball and carrying a percussion cap on the end. During the rotation of the barrels these tubes were fed in, chambered, fired, and extracted at the various positions of the barrel, firing always taking place at the bottom-most position of travel. Gatling demonstrated this gun in 1862 and the US Secretary of War was sufficiently interested to order six to be made and sent to Washington for test. Unfortunately the guns, and all the drawings, were accidentally destroyed.

Gatling then redesigned the gun to fire a self-contained rimfire cartridge, and small numbers of this pattern were made. Although he sold a few to units of the Union army, he could raise no official interest because his politics were, wrongly as it happened, considered suspect. In 1864 he built an improved model and this was adopted by the US Army in 1866, manufacture being undertaken by the Colt company. With this official adoption to recommend the gun, he then began to sell it abroad. The British Army tested it in 1870, Gatling himself coming to Woolwich arsenal to fire the sample gun, and a ten-barrel model was adopted by the Army in 1874, followed by a similar model in 0.65-in (16.5-mm) calibre by the Royal Navy. Batches were also bought by the French and Russian governments. The Russian guns were made in the US under the supervision of General Gorloff of the Imperial army, and he had nameplates bearing his own name made for them. These

A .50-in (12.7-mm) calibre Gatling machine-gun on a field gun type carriage in 1865

I V Hogg

The improved drum-fed version of the Gatling built by Colt after the American Civil War. This gun was tested by the British Army in 1870 and adopted in 1874. It served until March 1905 when it was declared obsolete

US Navy

The *Gato* Class submarine USS *Cavalla* (SS.244) which was stricken in 1969 but preserved as a memorial like her sisters *Cobia, Drum* and *Cero*

were substituted for the original Gatling plates before the weapons were shipped. As a result the gun was always known in Russian service as the Gorloff and claimed as a Russian invention.

In 1883 the design was improved by the adoption of a new drum feed designed by James Accles, an Australian engineer then working for Gatling. Accles later came to England and developed an improved model in 0.303-in (7.7-mm) calibre which he sold as the 'Accles Positive Feed Gun' in the 1880s. In 1893 Gatling fitted an electric motor drive to a gun to obtain a rate of fire of 3000 rds/min. There was little practical value in the idea at that time, but it was later revived and formed the basis of the Vulcan gun.

Gatling died in 1903, but his gun survived for some years after. It was last used in combat by the Russian defenders at the siege of Port Arthur in 1904, but remained in US service until declared obsolete in 1911.

Data refer to the models used by the British Army and Navy.

(Army Mk 1) *Calibre:* 0.45 in (11.43 mm) *Length:* 150.9 cm (59.41 in) *Weight:* 201 kg (444 lb) *Barrel length:* 81.15 cm (31.95 in) *Magazine:* 240-round drum *Rate of fire:* to 800 rds/min* *Muzzle velocity:* 396 m/sec (1300 ft/sec) approximately

(Navy Mk 1) *Calibre:* 0.65 in (16.5 mm) *Length:* 168.9 cm (66.5 in) *Weight:* 370 kg (816 lb) *Barrel length:* 83.82 cm (33 in) *Magazine:* 50-round drum *Rate of fire:* to 600 rds/min* *Muzzle velocity:* 328 m/sec (1000 ft/sec) approximately

*As with all hand-operated machine-guns, the rate of fire depended entirely on the crank speed.

'Gatling'

German/US/Soviet multi-barrelled automatic aircraft gun. The general principle of achieving a high rate of fire in an automatic rifled gun, as patented by Richard Jordan Gatling, was explored by several inventors of guns for aircraft. So far as is known, none got much further than the drawing board until, in 1942, the German arms firm of Waffenfabrik Mauser AG was ordered to take over a promising high-velocity fast-firing cannon from Krieghoff. A Mauser engineer, Politzer, introduced the concept of a multi-barrel revolver chamber and thus opened the way to the MG 213 upon which all postwar single-barrel aircraft cannon were based. Meanwhile, many other radical guns included the Rheinmetall SG 117, 118 and 119, and the even stranger Gustloff HF 15. The SG 117 had seven 30-mm (1.18-in) barrels based on that of the established MK 108. Each barrel contained one round, and when the first was fired electrically the seven-barrel drum recoiled as a unit firing the other six so rapidly that projectiles were only about 6 m (20 ft) behind each other. Both vertical and horizontal installations were fired in the air. The 118 and 119 were multiple 117 developments intended to enable a pilot to fire a single devastating blast at the correct instant. The HF 15 (Höhe Feuerfolge, high rate of fire) had only one barrel but used burning propellant to fire a succession of projectiles at a rate estimated to be 36 000 rds/min.

All this work came to a halt in 1945, but the basic radical concepts were immediately studied in the United States and Soviet Union (Britain and France did not look beyond single-barrel revolver-feed). By far the most important aircraft gun of the modern world took shape at General Electric's ordnance laboratories (now Aircraft Equipment Division) at Burlington, Vermont, as Project Vulcan in 1948-51. By the latter year prototype guns were being fired. Most were of 20-mm (0.79-in) calibre, and had six barrels driven by an external power source, usually hydraulic but often electric. As the M61A1 this gun went into production in 1954, its first application being in the F-104A Starfighter. Subsequently it was developed in many versions, including the T171 flexible remotely-sighted installation in the tail of the B-58A and B-52H, various versions for packaging in SUU-16 or SUU-23 external pods, and the GAU-4 self-powered gun driven by gun gas bled from four of the barrels.

General Electric has since produced many additional 'Gatling' aircraft guns. By far the hardest hitting (the highest-horsepower gun ever to be airborne, so far as is known) is the GAU-8/A Avenger installed in the A-10A. The M134 (GAU-2/A) is the familiar Minigun, usually of 7.62-mm (0.30-in) calibre, used in at least 25 aeroplane and helicopter armament subsystems. The M197 is a lightweight three-barrel offspring of the M61 used in various small aircraft. A remarkable, newer gun is the XM188, again with three barrels, even lighter, despite having 30-mm (1.18-in) calibre. XM214 is a 5.56-mm (0.219-in) weapon, weighing only 15 kg (33 lb) complete with drive but firing up to 10 000 rds/min from five barrels. Philco-Ford abandoned its 25-mm (1-in) gun with caseless ammunition originally planned for the F-15 Eagle, but, as Ford Aerospace, is developing the new CHAG (Combat High-performance Aerial Gun) using traditional Gatling principles, in competition with LP (liquid propellant) and 'inverse Gatling' prototypes funded mainly by the USAF.

For many years the Soviet Union has been testing Gatling-type aircraft guns, but no reliable details are yet known in the West. The first aircraft to enter service with one of these guns was the MiG-27 'Flogger D', with a six-barrelled 23-mm (0.9-in) gun.

See also Avenger, General Electric, Vulcan.

Gato

US submarine class. This was the last submarine class to be designed for the US Navy before the Second World War, and embodied all the experience gained from the *Porpoise, Salmon* and *Tambor* Classes. So successful was the design that, apart from minor modifications required as a result of war experience, it was extended to the following *Ballao* and *Tench* Classes. More than 200 submarines were ordered.

No and name	launched	fate
SS.212 *Gato*	8/1941	Sold for scrapping 1960
SS.213 *Greenling*	9/1941	Sold for scrapping 1960
SS.214 *Grouper*	10/1941	Sold for scrapping 1970
SS.215 *Growler*	11/1941	Sunk by own torpedo 11/1944
SS.216 *Grunion*	12/1941	War loss 7/1942
SS.217 *Guardfish*	1/1942	Sunk as target 10/1961
SS.218 *Albacore*	2/1942	War loss 11/1944
SS.219 *Amberjack*	3/1942	War loss 2/1943
SS.220 *Barb*	4/1942	Italian *Enrico Tazzoli* 1955
SS.221 *Blackfish*	8/1942	Stricken 1959
SS.222 *Bluefish*	2/1943	Sold for scrapping 1959
SS.223 *Bonefish*	3/1943	War loss 6/1945
SS.224 *Cod*	3/1943	Stricken 1971
SS.225 *Cero*	4/1943	Stricken 1967 preserved as memorial
SS.226 *Corvina*	5/1943	War loss 11/1943
SS.227 *Darter*	6/1943	Ran aground wrecked 10/1944
SS.228 *Drum*	5/1941	Stricken 1968 preserved as memorial
SS.229 *Flying Fish*	7/1941	Sold for scrapping 1959
SS.230 *Finback*	8/1941	Sold for scrapping 1959
SS.231 *Haddock*	10/1941	Sold for scrapping 1960
SS.232 *Halibut*	12/1941	War loss 1/1944, scrapped 1947
SS.233 *Herring*	1/1942	War loss 6/1944
SS.234 *Kingfish*	3/1942	Sold for scrapping 1960
SS.235 *Shad*	4/1942	Sold for scrapping 1960
SS.236 *Silversides*	8/1941	Stricken 1969
SS.237 *Trigger*	10/1941	War loss 3/1945
SS.238 *Wahoo*	2/1942	War loss 10/1943
SS.239 *Whale*	3/1942	Sold for scrapping 1960
SS.240 *Angler*	7/1943	Stricken 1971
SS.241 *Bashaw*	7/1943	Used as target 1969
SS.242 *Bluegill*	8/1943	Scuttled for training 1970
SS.244 *Bream*	10/1943	Used as target 1969
SS.244 *Cavalla*	11/1943	Stricken 1969 preserved as memorial
SS.245 *Cobia*	11/1943	Stricken 1970 preserved as memorial
SS.246 *Croaker*	12/1943	Stricken 1971
SS.247 *Dace*	4/1943	Italian *Leonardo da Vinci* 1955
SS.248 *Dorado*	5/1943	Bombed in error 1943
SS.249 *Flasher*	6/1943	Sold for scrapping 1963
SS.250 *Flier*	7/1943	War loss 8/1944
SS.251 *Flounder*	8/1943	Sold for scrapping 1959
SS.252 *Gabilan*	9/1943	Sold for scrapping 1959
SS.253 *Gunnel*	5/1942	Sold for scrapping 1959
SS.254 *Gurnard*	6/1942	Sold for scrapping 1961
SS.255 *Haddo*	6/1942	Sold for scrapping 1961
SS.256 *Hake*	7/1942	Stricken 1967
SS.257 *Harder*	8/1942	War loss 8/1944
SS.258 *Hoe*	9/1942	Sold for scrapping 1960
SS.259 *Jack*	10/1942	Greek *Amfitriti* 1958
SS.260 *Lapon*	10/1942	Greek *Poseidon* 1957
SS.261 *Mingo*	11/1942	Japanese *Kuroshio* 1955
SS.262 *Muskallunge*	12/1942	Brazilian *Humaita* 1957
SS.263 *Paddle*	12/1942	Brazilian *Riachuelo* 1957
SS.264 *Pargo*	1/1943	Sold for scrapping 1961
SS.265 *Peto*	4/1942	Sold for scrapping 1961
SS.266 *Pogy*	6/1942	Sold for scrapping 1951
SS.267 *Pompon*	8/1942	Sold for scrapping 1960
SS.268 *Puffer*	11/1942	Sold for scrapping 1960
SS.269 *Rasher*	12/1942	Stricken 1971
SS.270 *Raton*	1/1943	Used as target 1969
SS.271 *Ray*	2/1943	Sold for scrapping 1960
SS.272 *Redfish*	4/1943	Sold for scrapping 1971
SS.273 *Robalo*	5/1943	War loss 7/1944
SS.274 *Rock*	6/1943	Used as target 1969
SS.275 *Runner*	5/1942	War loss 6/1943
SS.276 *Sawfish*	6/1942	Sold for scrapping 1960
SS.277 *Scamp*	7/1942	War loss 11/1944
SS.278 *Scorpion*	7/1942	War loss 2/1944
SS.279 *Snook*	8/1942	War loss 4/1945
SS.280 *Steelhead*	9/1942	Sold for scrapping 1961
SS.281 *Sunfish*	5/1942	Sold for scrapping 1960
SS.282 *Tunny*	6/1942	Used as target 1969
SS.283 *Tinosa*	10/1942	Foundered 1961
SS.284 *Tullibee*	11/1942	Sunk by own torpedo 3/1944

Gato

By adopting the same basic and well-proven design for subsequent classes, the Americans were able to embark on a massive submarine construction programme. Less than half a dozen American shipyards were involved in building these classes and by adopting the same design utilizing the fully-welded hull and prefabrication construction techniques, large numbers were completed in a very short time. The average time of construction was about 12-14 months and keels were often laid down in the same yards at the rate of one every month. *Gato*, the first submarine in the class, was laid down in October 1940 and commissioned in December 1941. *Croaker*, the last boat in the class, was laid down in April 1943 and commissioned a year later in April 1944.

Both were built by the Electric Boat company at Groton, Connecticut. Four shipyards built the *Gato* Class: Electric Boat company, Groton (SS.212-227, SS.240-264); Manitowoc Shipbuilding company (SS.265-274); Mare Island navy yard, California (SS.236-239, SS.281-284); and Portsmouth navy yard (SS.228-235, SS.275-280).

The *Gato* Class was 1.2 m (4 ft) longer than the preceding *Tambor* Class which it closely resembled. The extra length arose from dividing the engine room into two compartments. Propulsion was provided by a diesel electric reduction gearing system which war experience soon showed to be too noisy for carrying out operations with any degree of safety in enemy-infested waters. Subsequent classes had a direct drive system (see *Ballao*).

USS *Drum* (SS.228). Launched in May 1941 she was stricken in 1968 but preserved as a memorial. *Gato*s were the standard US submarine during the Second World War. Notable members of the class were the *Flasher* which sank 100 231 tons (21 ships) and the *Rasher*, *Barb*, *Tang* and *Silversides* which sank over 90 000 tons

The original design provided for the 3-in (76-mm) gun to be mounted abaft the conning tower, which some of the early units carried. Later vessels, however, carried a 5-in (127-mm) gun forward of the conning tower and 20-mm (0.79-in) on extensions fore and aft of the conning tower. To accommodate these extensions the conning tower was built to a slightly smaller design. There were a number of variations in the armament mountings, a few units being fitted with a 4-in (102-mm) gun in place of the 3-in (76-mm) or 5-in (127-mm) and some carried a 40-mm (1.57-in) in place of the 20-mm (0.79-in) on the forward extension of the conning tower. Positions were also reversed on some units, the heavy gun being sited abaft the conning tower.

The *Gato* Class served with distinction throughout the war. *Flasher* (SS.249) achieved the highest score in the Pacific sinking 21 Japanese merchant ships totalling 1 123 000 grt (gross registered tonnage). Altogether the *Gato* Class were credited with

Below: USS *Peto* in 1944. *Gato* Class submarines like the *Peto* waged an eminently successful campaign against the Japanese

US Navy

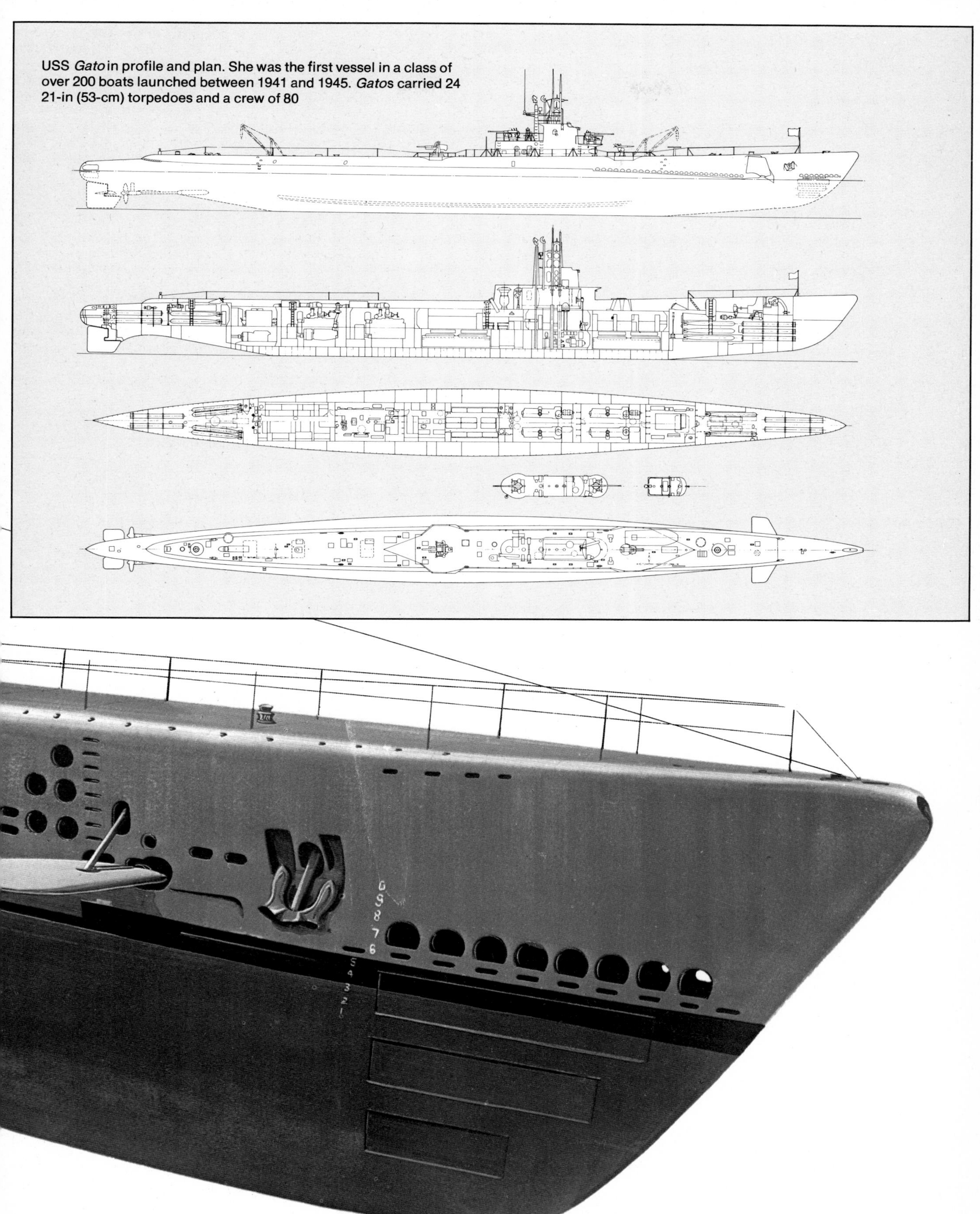
USS *Gato* in profile and plan. She was the first vessel in a class of over 200 boats launched between 1941 and 1945. *Gato*s carried 24 21-in (53-cm) torpedoes and a crew of 80

US Navy

The *Gato* Class submarine USS *Flying Fish* shortly after her launch on July 9, 1941

sinking large numbers of Japanese merchant ships as well as a large number of warships. Among the most notable achievements were the sinking of the carrier *Taiho* by *Albacore* (SS.218) in June 1944—*Albacore* also sank the light cruiser *Tenryu* and two destroyers—and the escort carrier *Unyo* by *Barb* (SS.220) in September 1944. *Darter* (SS.227) and *Dace* (SS.247) achieved the greatest distinction, being responsible for locating and reporting the position of the main Japanese force heading to attack the American landings in the Philippines on October 23, 1944. This sighting led directly to the last great battle, Leyte Gulf. During their shadowing of the Japanese fleet, *Darter* sank the heavy cruiser *Atago* and damaged the heavy cruiser *Takao* while *Dace* sank the heavy cruiser *Maya*.

After the war, a number of the class were converted to hunter/killer submarines, the gun armament being removed and the conning tower rebuilt to a streamlined design. Boats so converted were: *Angler, Bashaw, Bluegill, Bream, Cavalla, Croaker, Grouper.* Other units were converted to radar picket vessels with a variety of aerials on short masts fore and aft of the conning tower. They were: *Pompon, Rasher, Raton, Ray, Redfin* and *Rock.*

Tunny was fitted to launch the Regulus guided missile, being equipped with a watertight hangar aft of the conning tower and a launching cradle. The conning tower was rebuilt to a streamlined design and all guns were removed.

Displacement: 1526/2424 tons (surfaced/submerged) (SS.228-235 and SS.275-280 2410 tons submerged) *Length:* 95.02 m (311 ft 9 in) oa *Beam:* 8.30 m (27 ft 3 in) *Draught:* 4.65 m (15 ft 3 in) *Machinery:* 2-shaft diesel/electric, 5400 bhp= 20.25 knots/2740 hp= 8.75 knots (surfaced/submerged) *Armament:* 1 3-in (76-mm)/50-cal; 2 0.30-in (7.62-mm) mg; 10 21-in (53-cm) torpedo tubes (6 forward, 4 aft, 24 torpedoes carried) *Diving depth:* 91.4 m (300 ft) *Crew:* 80-85

Gator

US air-launched mine. Gator is the generic name given to a series of weapons intended to deliver antitank and antipersonnel mines from helicopters and fixed-wing aircraft. The project is run by the US Air Force's Armament Development and Test Centre on behalf of the army and navy in addition to the air force. The three services will use different methods to deliver clouds of mines which are aerodynamically shaped so that they spin during descent, thus aiding dispersion.

Gator is scheduled to enter service at the end of the 1970s. The mine is designed to penetrate the underside of a tank on detonation, and it incorporates a self-destruct mechanism so that friendly forces can safely enter the seeded area after a preset interval. No data available.

GAU-8, General Electric US aircraft gun
See **Avenger**

Gauntlet, Gloster

British fighter aircraft, first prototype flew 1928. Designed by HP Folland, and developed from a long line of fighter biplanes, the Gauntlet was the last open-cockpit aircraft of that type to serve with the RAF. Designed initially to meet the requirements of Specification F.9/26, the Gloster S.S.18 prototype flew in 1928 in competition with the Bristol Bulldog and Hawker Hawfinch to satisfy the revised Specification F.20/27. Although taking third place, Gloster continued privately with trials and in 1929 replaced the Mercury IIA engine with a Bristol Jupiter VIIF, redesignating the aircraft S.S.18A. In 1930 the powerplant was changed to an Armstrong-Siddeley Panther III (later a IIIA), but these so increased the weight that Gloster reverted to the Jupiter.

In 1931 the prototype, J9125, reappeared as the S.S.19 with a Jupiter VIIFP engine and armed with two synchronized Vickers guns on the fuselage sides, firing through the propeller arc, and two Lewis guns under the upper and two under the lower wings. However, the four wing guns were eventually removed and replaced by night-flying equipment. Service trials continued and when, in 1933, the 640-hp Bristol Mercury VIS2 nine-cylinder air-cooled radial became available, a production order for 24 Gauntlet Is with this powerplant was issued. Deliveries began on May 25, 1935, to No 19 Squadron of the RAF at Duxford. By this time the Gloster company had been taken over by Hawker Aircraft, and when an order for a further 104 aircraft was placed in April 1935, they were designated Gauntlet II, differing in the method of construction and in having Mk V instead of Mk III Vickers guns. A third order for 100 Gauntlet IIs was issued in September 1935, bringing overall production, including the prototype, to 229 aircraft.

Gauntlets reached their peak deployment with 14 squadrons equipped, and served altogether with some two dozen RAF squadrons. The Mk Is were phased out during

A Gloster G.32B Gauntlet II, powered by a 600-hp Bristol Mercury VIS2 engine. Gauntlets saw wide service between the wars with the RAF

1938/39, but others continued to serve at home and in the Middle East, finally as trainers, until 1940; a few continued in service until as late as 1943.

(Gauntlet II) *Span:* 10 m (32 ft 9½ in) *Length:* 8.05 m (26 ft 5 in) *Gross weight:* 1800 kg (3970 lb) *Maximum speed:* 370 km/h (230 mph)

Gazelle

German light cruiser class, built 1897-1904. They were designated *kleine kreuzer* (small cruisers) and were the first cruisers to be built as scouts for the new fleet which Tirpitz was creating through the Navy Laws. As such they were the forerunners of the light cruisers which served so well in the First World War.

Gazelle, Nymphe and *Amazone* were built by Krupp's Germania yard at Kiel, *Niobe, Ariadne, Medusa, Frauenlob* and *Arcona* by AG Weser, Bremen, *Thetis* by the Imperial dockyard, Danzig and *Undine* by Howaldt, Kiel. The first to join the fleet was *Niobe*, in June 1900, and *Undine* did not join until January 1904.

The ten ships did not vary greatly in appearance, having two slender funnels, a slight turtleback to the forecastle and an exaggerated ram bow. The ten 105-mm (4-in) L/40 guns were distributed in pairs, two abreast on the forecastle, three on each side in the waist amidships, and two abreast on the poop. The *Gazelle* had three 45-cm (17.7-in) torpedo tubes, two fixed broadside tubes on deck and one submerged below the spur of the ram, but the third tube was omitted from the remainder of the class.

Gazelle served on foreign stations from 1902 to 1904, *Thetis* from 1902 to 1906, the *Niobe* from 1906 to 1909 and *Arcona* from 1907 to 1910. The others all served in the North Sea and Baltic with the High Seas Fleet, with the exception of *Nymphe*, which served as a training ship, and *Undine*, which joined the fleet in 1904 as a gunnery training ship. All were allocated to coastal defence in August 1914, and *Ariadne* was soon sunk on August 28 in the action in Heligoland Bight with the loss of 64 of her crew, when British battlecruisers raided the patrol line. On November 7, 1915, *Undine* was torpedoed in the Baltic by the British submarine *E.19*, with the loss of 14 men. *Frauenlob* was sunk at the battle of Jutland (or Skagerrak) by gunfire from the British cruiser *Southampton* during the night action, with the loss of all 323 men.

The growing demands of the U-Boat campaign led to these old cruisers being relegated to subsidiary duties. In 1916 *Gazelle* became a mine storage hulk, first at Cuxhaven and later at Wilhelmshaven; *Nymphe* became an accommodation and drill ship at Kiel; and *Medusa* became a tender to the battleship *König Wilhelm*. In 1917 *Niobe* became a headquarters and accommodation ship at Wilhelmshaven, *Thetis* became a gunnery training ship, and *Amazone*, after a year as a target ship for U-Boats, became an accommodation ship at Kiel. *Arcona* had been converted to a minelaying trials ship, and had her stern cut away to facilitate minelaying, and from 1914 was used as a fleet minelayer, with a capacity for 200 mines.

Gazelle was stricken in 1920 and scrapped but the remaining six were retained by the Reichsmarine, when it was reconstituted under the Weimar republic. *Niobe* was stricken in 1925 but was rebuilt as a training ship and sold to Yugoslavia and renamed *Dalmacija*. In 1941 she was captured by the Italians and renamed *Cattaro*, and on December 22, 1943, she was sunk by the British *MTB.276* in the Adriatic. *Thetis* was stricken in 1929 and *Nymphe* in 1930, and both ships were scrapped. *Amazone* was stricken in 1931 but was retained at Kiel as an accommodation ship, and after 1945 served as accommodation for refugees at Bremen, and was not scrapped until 1954. *Medusa* became an accommodation ship at Wilhelmshaven in 1929, and in 1942 she was reactivated as a floating antiaircraft battery in the harbour. She was sunk in May 1945 and her remains were scrapped in 1949-50. *Arcona* was similarly relegated in 1930, and also served as a flak-battery at Wilhelmshaven from 1942. She was sunk at the end of the war and later scrapped.

Dalmacija (ex-*Niobe*) was armed with six Skoda 85-mm (3.35-in)/55-cal antiaircraft guns, but in Italian hands was armed with additional 20-mm (0.79-in) AA guns. *Arcona* and *Medusa* were given five 105-mm (4-in) L/65 flak guns, two 37-mm (1.46-in) and a quadruple 20-mm (0.79-in) *vierling*. *Dalmacija* was completely transformed, with a clipper bow, tripod foremast and raked tops to her funnels, while *Medusa* and *Arcona* retained their original hulls and funnels, but had new superstructures; one twin 105-mm (4-in) mounting was positioned on the forecastle, and one twin and one single aft.

Displacement: 2360 tons (normal), 2650 tons (full load) *Length:* 105 m (344 ft 6 in) oa *Beam:* 12.2 m (40 ft) *Draught:* 4.84 m (15 ft 10 in) *Protection:* 50-20 mm (2-0.79 in) deck, 80-20 mm (3.14-0.79 in) conning tower *Machinery:* 2-shaft reciprocating steam, 6000-8000 ihp=20-21 knots *Armament:* 10 105-mm (4-in)/40-cal (10×1); 14 machine-guns; 2/3 45-cm (17.7-in) torpedo tubes *Crew:* 257

Gazelle, Aérospatiale/ Westland

Franco-British helicopter. Though the original SA 340 Gazelle was designed entirely in France, the production helicopters have been produced under a collaborative agreement

Gazelle, Aérospatiale/Westland

Gazelles of 705 Squadron based at RNAS Culdrose, with a Wessex in the background. The Gazelle, developed by the British firm of Westland and the French Aérospatiale company, is a multi-role military and civil machine with a top speed of 310 km/h (193 mph). Armed with Tow antitank missiles it is a formidable tank hunter, being small and highly manoeuvrable

George Dovey, MOD

Gazelle, Aérospatiale/Westland

with Westland of the UK, extending also to the engines. A completely new design, owing only superficial cabin shape to the Alouette III, the Gazelle is a multi-role military and civil machine with two seats in front and a three-seat bench behind. A baggage/cargo bay further aft is accessible from the cabin or via a door to starboard. Either front seat can be equipped for a pilot. The fuselage is notably streamlined, and the tail includes a swept fin incorporating a Fenestron multi-blade antitorque rotor. The semi-articulated main rotor is of advanced design with plastics/glass-fibre and honeycomb construction. The usual engine is the Turboméca Astazou IIIA, rated at 590 shp, made jointly with Rolls-Royce; some later Gazelles, such as the 342K for Kuwait, have the 870-shp Astazou XIVH.

The first prototype flew on April 7, 1967, and production aircraft followed from August 6, 1971. Standard equipment includes skid landing gear, 700-kg (1540-lb) cargo sling, 136-kg (300-lb) rescue hoist and (usually) attachments for two stretchers, photographic and surveying cameras, and various armament options. Chief military models include: SA 341B, used by the British Army as the Gazelle AH.1; 341C, Royal Navy utility trainer, Gazelle HT.2; 341D, Royal Air Force trainer, Gazelle HT.3; 341E, Royal Air Force communications and VIP, Gazelle HCC.4; 341F, French army; 341H, basic military export variant; and 342K, basic uprated military export variant with Mk XIVH engine. By mid-1978 more than 750 Gazelles of all types had been delivered, and production was continuing.

Simple armament schemes include side pylons for four pods of 36-mm (1.42-in) rockets, two GPMG pods or other rifle-calibre machine-guns, electronic payloads, smoke markers or reconnaissance flares. Guided antitank missiles require a special built-in stabilized-sight system. The first guided-missile installation comprised four SS.11 wire-guided missiles, or two heavier AS.12s, with the APX-Bézu 334 gyro-stabilized optical sight. Subsequently four, and then six Hot or Tow missile tubes have been cleared for use, the British Army having adopted the Tow aimed by the XM26 sight system. A GPMG, GE Minigun or other machine-gun can be mounted in the port side door aperture, and various chin turrets or the Emerson MiniTAT remotely-aimed turret system can be incorporated together with the pantograph-type sight system.

ECP Armées

A French army Gazelle equipped with launchers for Hot wire-guided antitank missiles

Rotor diameter: 10.5 m (34 ft 5½ in) *Length:* (fuselage) 9.53 m (31 ft 3 in) *Gross weight:* (typical) 1800 kg (3970 lb) *Maximum speed:* 310 km/h (193 mph)

A Royal Marines Gazelle of Salerno Flight, 41 Commando Group pictured with a 'County' Class guided-missile destroyer HMS *Kent* off Valetta

Royal Marines

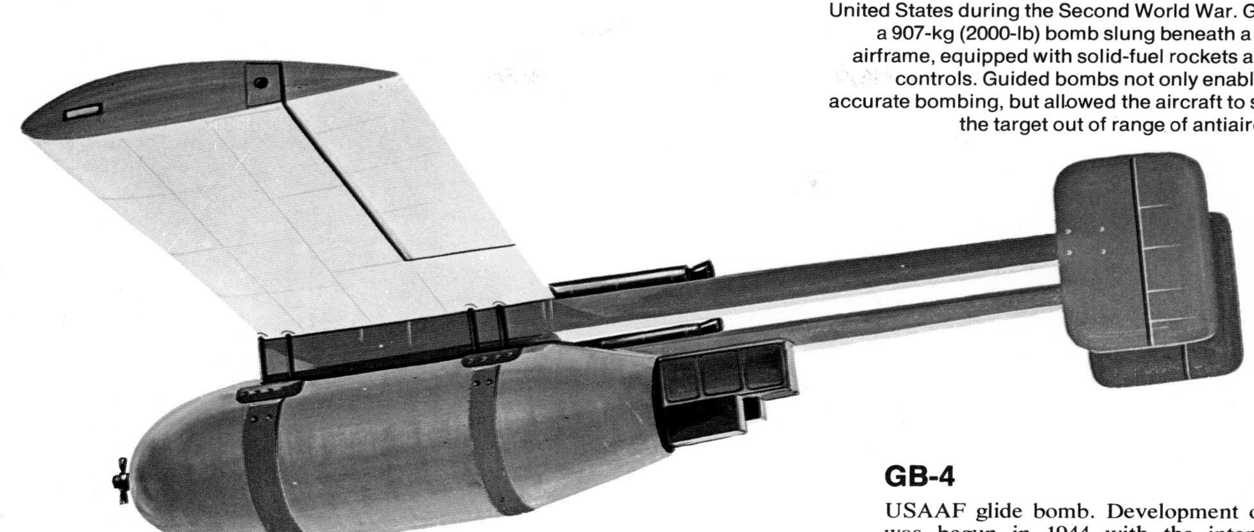

GB-8, one of the guided bombs developed in the United States during the Second World War. GB-8 was a 907-kg (2000-lb) bomb slung beneath a wooden airframe, equipped with solid-fuel rockets and radio controls. Guided bombs not only enabled more accurate bombing, but allowed the aircraft to stand off the target out of range of antiaircraft fire

Below: **Gazelles of No 705 Squadron, Royal Naval Air Station, Culdrose, flying in perfect line formation over the Cornish countryside near Helston during training in February 1976**

MOD

GB-4

USAAF glide bomb. Development of GB-4 was begun in 1944 with the intention of providing an accurate stand-off weapon able to be air-launched from safe distances against heavily defended point targets. A plywood airframe with wings and a tail unit incorporating an elevator and twin rudders was attached to a standard 907-kg (2000-lb) general-purpose bomb. Below the bomb was a television camera pointing downwards at three degrees and giving a field of view 14° wide and 18° high. The weapon was designed to be carried externally on a B-17 Flying Fortress or B-25 Mitchell bomber, and released about 27 km (17 miles) from the target at a speed of 280 km/h (175 mph) and an altitude of under 4575 m (15 000 ft). After release the television camera transmitted a picture to the operator in the launch aircraft, who was able to transmit radio signals to alter the direction of the missile, which was stabilized by a directional gyro. The average flight time from launch to impact, with a glide ratio of 6:1, was four minutes, and the average circular error only 61 m (200 ft). The bomb could only be used against targets easily distinguishable on a television screen, and only in good visibility.

Weight: 1150 kg (2535 lb) *Span:* 3.66 m (12 ft) *Length:* 3.71 m (12 ft 2 in) *Body diameter:* 0.61 m (2 ft)

GB-8

USAAF glide bomb. Designed for use against large installations, the GB-8 was a radio-controlled glide bomb, tracked visually from the launch aircraft with the aid of flares. The warhead was a standard 907-kg (2000-lb) general purpose bomb slung below a wooden airframe comprising plywood-covered wings and a wooden boom carrying rudders and elevator, which was covered with metal to avoid damage from the red and white flares mounted on the boom. The bomb was launched outside normal antiaircraft fire range at an altitude of 3050-4575 m (10 000-15 000 ft) and was gyro-stabilized and guided by radio signals to a receiver mounted below the tail boom.

Weight: 1158 kg (2555 lb) *Wing span:* 3.66 m (12 ft) *Length:* 3.53 m (11 ft 7 in)

Giorgio Arra

The Turkish destroyer *Adatepe* in 1973. She was formerly USS *Forrest Royal* and was transferred to Turkey in 1971 after FRAM 1 conversion

GCT-155

French self-propelled gun. GCT means *Grande Cadence de Tir*, or high rate of fire. The gun is a 40-calibre weapon with muzzle brake and an hydraulically-operated vertical sliding block breech. It is mounted in a turret on a modified AMX-30 tank chassis, giving a 360° arc of fire and elevation from −5° to +66°. The turret contains an automatic loading system comprising two mechanisms, one for loading shells and the other for loading the combustible cartridges. Before firing, the breech is opened and the type and number of rounds to be fired selected on a control panel. On pressing the firing button, the first round is selected, loaded and fired, taking about 20 seconds; thereafter the programmed rounds are fired at about eight-second intervals.

The crew consists of four men; the gun commander, gun layer, loader, and driver. Forty-two rounds are carried in racks in the turret, from which they are automatically selected and loaded; the turret rear can be opened and the ammunition racks reloaded in about half an hour. High explosive, smoke and illuminating shells are provided; existing patterns of shell—for example the US M107 and French Type 56—can be used, but a complete new range of projectiles has been produced for this gun. In addition to the conventional shell, a rocket-assisted shell capable of extending the range to 30 000 m (32 800 yds), is under development. It is scheduled for issue in 1978-79.

(Gun) *Calibre:* 155 mm (6.1 in) *Barrel length:* 6.20 m (20 ft 4 in) *Rate of fire:* 7 rds/min *Shell weight:* 43.75 kg (96 lb 7 oz) *Charges:* 7 *Muzzle velocity:* 810 m/sec (2660 ft/sec) *Maximum range:* 23 600 m (25 810 yards)

(Chassis) *Type:* AMX-30C *Engine:* Hispano-Suiza 720 bhp *Speed:* 60 km/h (37 mph) *Range:* 450 km (280 miles) *Weight:* 41 655 kg (41 tons)

Gearing

US destroyer class, launched between 1944 and 1951. Experience with the *Allen M Sumner* Class had shown that for the Pacific they were unable to develop their full potential owing to a limited radius of action. However the basic design had shown itself to be a success and it was decided to repeat the class with an extra 4.26-m (14-ft) section added amidships between the two funnels to provide extra bunkerage. A beneficial side effect of the increased length was that the stability of the *Gearing*s was much improved.

A total of 157 *Gearing* Class destroyers were ordered from seven builders, but owing to the end of the war and the run down of the fleet only 92 of these were completed. Yards involved in the construction of the *Gearing*s were: Bethlehem (San Pedro, Staten Island, San Francisco and Quincy yards), Charleston navy yard (all the orders placed with this yard were subsequently cancelled), Bath Iron Works, Boston navy yard (like Charleston all orders were cancelled), Federal Shipbuilding yard of Kearny, the Consolidated Steel corporation at Orange, Maine, and the Todd Pacific yard at Seattle.

The main armament remained as in the *Allen M Sumner* Class, but light AA varied considerably between units, and was concentrated amidships around the after funnel and just abaft it. Shortly after completion, some units had the second quintuple torpedo tube bank replaced by extra AA and improved A/S weapons (being reclassed as destroyer escorts) while others had the forward torpedo tube bank replaced by a long-range radar aerial and were reclassed as radar pickets. Destroyers: DD710 *Gearing*, DD711 *Eugene A Greene*, DD712 *Gyatt*, DD713 *Kenneth D Bailey*, DD714 *William R Rush*, DD715 *William M Wood*, DD716 *Wiltsie*, DD717 *Theodore E Chandler*, DD718 *Hammer*, DD719

Below: **USS *Glennon*, a *Gearing* Class destroyer having undergone FRAM conversion**

PPL

Epperson, DD742 *Frank Knox*, DD743 *Southerland*, DD763 *William C Lawe*, DD764 *Lloyd Thomas*, DD765 *Keppler*, DD782 *Rowan*, DD783 *Gurke*, DD784 *McKean*, DD785 *Henderson*, DD786 *Richard B Anderson*, DD787 *James E Kyes*, DD788 *Hollister*, DD789 *Eversole*, DD790 *Shelton*, DD791 *Seaman*, DD805 *Chevalier*, DD806 *Higbee*, DD807 *Benner*, DD808 *Dennis J Buckley*, DD817 *Corry*, DD818 *New*, DD819 *Holder*, DD820 *Rich*, DD821 *Johnston*, DD822 *Robert H McCard*, DD823 *Samuel B Roberts*, DD824 *Basilone*, DD825 *Carpenter*, DD826 *Agerholm*, DD827 *Robert A Owens*, DD828 *Timmerman*, DD829 *Myles C Fox*, DD830 *Everett F Larson*, DD831 *Goodrich*, DD832 *Hanson*, DD833 *Herbert J Thomas*, DD834 *Turner*, DD835 *Charles P Cecil*, DD836 *George K MacKenzie*, DD837 *Sarsfield*, DD838 *Ernest G Small*, DD839 *Power*, DD840 *Glennoh*, DD841 *Noa*, DD842 *Fiske*, DD843 *Warrington*, DD844 *Perry*, DD845 *Baussell*, DD846 *Ozbourn*, DD847 *Robert L Wilson*, DD848 *Witek*, DD849 *Richard E Kraus*, DD850 *Joseph P Kennedy Jr*, DD851 *Rupertus*, DD852 *Leonard F Mason*, DD853 *Charles H Roan*, DD858 *Fred T Berry*, DD859 *Norris*, DD860 *McCaffery*, DD861 *Harwood*, DD862 *Vogelgesang*, DD863 *Steinaker*, DD864 *Harold J Ellison*, DD865 *Charles R Ware*, DD866 *Cone*, DD867 *Stribling*, DD868 *Brownson*, DD869 *Arnold J*

Isbell, DD870 *Fechteler*, DD871 *Damato*, DD872 *Forrest Royal*, DD873 *Hawkins*, DD874 *Duncan*, DD875 *Henry W Tucker*, DD876 *Rogers*, DD877 *Perkins*, DD878 *Vesole*, DD879 *Leary*, DD880 *Dyess*, DD881 *Bordelon*, DD882 *Furse*, DD883 *Newman K Perry*, DD884 *Floyd B Parkes*, DD885 *John R Craig*, DD886 *Orleck*, DD887 *Brinkley Bass*, DD888 *Stickel*, DD889 *O'Hare*, DD890 *Meredith*.

The following units (some of which had been named, laid down and even launched in one or two cases) were eventually cancelled: DD720-721, 766-767 (all launched), DD768-769 (both laid down), DD791 (completed, but never commissioned), DD809-816, 854-856, 891-930, DD927-30 were eventually built as DL2-5 of the *Mitscher* Class. Of those completed the following were reclassed as radar pickets (DDR) in 1949-53: 711, 713-715, 742-743, 784, 805-808, 817, 829-835, 838, 842, 863, 870, 873-883, 888-889. The following were reclassed A/S escorts (DDE): 719, 764-765, 818-820, 824-825, 827, 847-848, 858-861, 871.

During the 1960s the class underwent the FRAM modernization which with the increased length and improved stability of the *Gearings* proved a far better proposition than the FRAM project of the *Allen M Sumner*.

Timmerman (DD828) was used as an experimental ship to test high pressure lightweight machinery; she was sold for scrap in 1959. *Witek* (DD848) was also used as an experimental ship, being fitted with two water-jet propulsion systems in place of the propellers. She was scrapped in 1969. *Gyatt* (DD712) was armed with a twin Terrier surface-to-air missile system aft in 1955-56. This was the first time a destroyer had been armed with guided missiles and she was used to test the suitability of the Terrier missiles as an installation on small ships. She retained A and B gun mounts and two twin 3-in (76-mm) amidships. She was equipped with two small rotating missile magazines in a deck house aft on the main deck holding 14 missiles. The Terrier was found to be unsuitable for small ship operation and a new smaller missile, the Tartar, was developed for use on destroyers. The Terrier installation on *Gyatt* was removed in 1962.

Like the *Allen M Sumner* Class, the *Gearings* remained in service until the early 1970s by which time they were no longer capable of meeting the high technical and performance standards required by modern warships. The class was rapidly run down and sold or stricken for scrap.

Gearing Class destroyers stricken: 834 (9/1969); 870, 858 (9/1970); 823 (11/1970); 843 (10/1972); 710, 808, 844, 850, 884 (7/1973); 860, 874 (9/1973); 859 (1/1974); 807, 713, 831 (2/1974); 883 (4/1974); 847 (9/1974); 865 (12/1974); 717 (4/1975); 846 (6/1975); 867 (7/1976); 868 (9/1976); 819, 836, 840 (10/1976); 715, 878 (12/1976).

See also FRAM.

Displacement: 2425 tons (standard), 3479 tons (full load) *Length:* 119 m (390 ft 6 in) oa *Beam:* 15 m (49 ft) *Draught:* 5.79 m (19 ft) maximum *Machinery:* 2-shaft geared steam turbines, 60 000 shp=34 knots *Armament:* 6 5-in (127-mm)/38-cal (3×2); 4-6 3-in (76-mm)/50-cal (2-3×2); 4-16 40-mm (1.57-in) quad and twin mounts; 8-15 20-mm (0.79-in); 5-10 21-in (53-cm) torpedo tubes (1-2×5) *Crew:* 336-367

Gebauer

Hungarian-developed machine-gun. This weapon deserves a mention because it was (when it worked) the fastest-firing single-barrel machine-gun ever made. It was developed in the early 1930s by the Danuvia company of Budapest and was designed by Jan Gebauer and Paul Kiraly. Gebauer was a ballistics expert employed at various times by the Czech war department, while Kiraly was an ordnance engineer who designed a variety of automatic weapons for various makers.

The Gebauer gun was a belt-fed weapon working by a combination of gas piston action and short recoil of the barrel, and it was designed for fixed, synchronized, installation in fighter aircraft. The mechanism was extremely complicated, the rate of fire was 2000 rds/min, and it promised much; but whenever it was tested it displayed an alarming lack of reliability. It was tried by the RAF in 1934 when they were looking for a machine-gun for the new monoplane fighters but was discarded in favour of the Browning. Development appears to have been abandoned in about 1937 and Gebauer and Kiraly went their separate ways.

Gecko

Soviet surface-to-air missile. The SA-8 Gecko is a vehicle-mounted low-level surface-to-air missile in approximately the same class as the Thomson-CSF Crotale. It was revealed to the West in November 1975 and was probably deployed operationally by 1977. The SA-8 is fired from a four-round launcher carried on a new type of six-wheeled vehicle, which is thought to be amphibious and may be fitted with a waterjet propulsion unit. Gecko provides all-weather air defence for forward units of the Soviet army and operates alongside the SA-9 Gaskin missile and ZSU-23-4SP Shilka radar-directed cannon.

The Gecko vehicle carries its own surveillance radar with a detection range of about 30 km (18.6 miles) against a fighter-sized target. The rotating antenna can be folded down for transport, but the vehicle is too large to be

USS *Gurke*, a *Gearing* Class destroyer, at San Diego on August 18, 1967, after FRAM conversion

George F Dale

The mechanism of the Gebauer machine-gun

I V Hogg

carried by any aircraft except the An-22 Cock and the Mi-12 Homer helicopter. Targets are tracked by a central flat antenna with a maximum range exceeding 20 km (12 miles).

Four missiles are carried on rails to the rear of the radar assembly. The round is probably virtually identical to that used in the naval SA-N-4 system, with the addition of a tail-mounted flare for use in the optical guidance mode. This clear-weather mode, used when the radar is being jammed or the target is near the ground or flying in close formation with other aircraft, employs a television tracker mounted on top of the main radar assembly. In the all-weather mode the radar tracker is thought to track missiles in flight in addition to the target, commands being transmitted via dishes on each side of the main antenna. Gathering is generally understood to be performed by a small monopulse aerial and command horn mounted under each command dish.

Length: 3.2 m (10 ft 6 in) *Span:* 64 cm (25 in) *Diameter:* 21 cm (8.3 in) *Weight:* 180-200 kg (396-440 lb) *Range:* 12-15 km (7.5-9.3 miles) *Maximum altitude:* approx 3000 m (9840 ft) *Warhead:* 40-50 kg (88-110 lb)

IWM

***Gefion*, a German cruiser launched in 1893 but soon outclassed in the naval race with Britain**

Gefion

German cruiser, launched 1893. The third class cruiser *Gefion* was ordered under the 1891 Programme as a unit of the 'J' Class. It was the intention of the Imperial naval office under Admiral Hollmann to evaluate several types of cruiser and assess their imperfections and advantages. As a result no immediate orders for more vessels of the 'J' Class were placed. The naval division of the German high command under Admirals Senden and Tirpitz were pressing for the mass construction of units designed to build up the fleet.

Among their ideas were plans for a large class of cruisers whose design would be based on *Gefion*. The disagreement between the two parties over the priorities for naval construction arose from the role of the naval office, which had responsibility for preparing the budget and in dealing with the parliamentarians of the Reichstag (who at that time were opposed to any heavy expenditure on armaments), on the one hand and the high command responsibility for strategy on the other. At that time the high command was bent on building up the strength of the German navy with new battleships and cruisers as a counter to foreign naval aspirations. Their opponents were expected to be Russia or France. Shortly afterwards, the advent of the Boer war and tacit German support for the Boers against the British, made the Royal Navy a more likely opponent. During the 1890s the naval office ordered ships without consultation with the high command. This gave rise to certain types of ship being built which were not suited to the tasks required of them by the high command. In an attempt to arrive at a satisfactory design, the naval office concentrated on building ships to a one-off design. This was an attempt to seek the most suitable design rather than concentrating on a good design and building it in numbers to increase the strength of the navy. One of the good designs available at that time was *Gefion*, but following naval office policy only the one ship was ordered. The Kaiser himself pressed for an increased naval construction plan in 1895, plans which included a large number of protected cruisers (nine First Class, 15 Second Class and 12 Third or Fourth Class). Again the design of *Gefion* was omitted from further consideration.

The arguments over the type of ships to be built and the political and military arguments over the size of the fleet led to a long drawn out battle which was not resolved until Admiral Tirpitz became state secretary of the naval office in June 1897, and shortly afterward succeeded in pushing his plans for the expansion of the German navy through the Reichstag.

The long delay in building up navy strength caused by these arguments meant that, when the decision was finally reached to embark on a large programme of construction, the design of *Gefion* had become outdated as a result of the rapid technological advances in armament and naval construction techniques.

At the time of her construction, *Gefion* was a well-protected and armed ship and more than a match for comparable vessels in the French or Russian fleets. She was constructed on a transverse and longitudinal framed system. The lower part of the stem was of bronze and the upper part of steel.

Gefion was laid down at the Schichau yard at Danzig in 1892 and launched on May 31, 1893, and completed in 1894. She spent the period between 1897 and 1901 on foreign service, after which she underwent a three-year refit at the dockyard in Wilhelmshaven. She was downgraded to an accommodation ship at Danzig in 1916 and was removed from the fleet on November 5, 1919, and sold. She was converted for merchant use, renamed *Adolf Sommerfeld*, and finally scrapped at Danzig in 1923.

Displacement: 3687 tons (normal) *Length:* 110.4 m (362 ft 2½ in) *Beam:* 13.2 m (43 ft 3½ in) *Draught:* 6.5 m (21 ft 4 in) full load *Machinery:* 2-shaft reciprocating vertical triple expansion, 9000 ihp=19 knots *Protection:* Deck 31.7 mm (1.25 in) *Armament:* 10 4.1-in (105-mm)/35-cal (10×1); 6 4-pdr (50-mm)/40-cal (6×1); 4 mg; 2 deck-mounted 18-in (46-cm) torpedo tubes *Crew:* 302

Geier

German homing torpedo. A successor to the cancelled Boje was introduced, with an active acquisition range of 256 m (280 yards), and it was christened Geier (vulture). The transducer was suspended to stabilize the variation of reverberation with the time of transmission, and two receiver-amplifiers were used. The first was a time-varied gain type to follow the decay of the reverberation and the second was an AGC type to compensate for variations from day-to-day changes in the sea state.

The prototype was succeeded by Geier 2, whose listening hydrophone operated over two different band-widths. The self-noise was different in each channel but the echo was at the same level, and thus by appropriate amplification and subtraction the self-noise was reduced to give a much improved ratio of signal-to-noise. Another important improvement was a facility for 'preferring a side', with the homer responding only to echoes from one predetermined sector.

The first Geiers appeared in March 1944 and Geier 2 began tests the following autumn, becoming operational in the closing months of the war. No details of the Geier have been released since 1945, presumably because the knowledge was incorporated into British programmes, but it is known that Geier 3 was on the drawing board in May 1945.

See also Boje.

Gekko Japanese name for Nakajima J1N fighter/attack aircraft See **J1N**

General Dynamics US aircraft See **F-16, F-111**

General Electric

US aircraft guns. The Armaments Division (now Aircraft Equipment Division) of the General Electric company became involved in the development of aircraft guns at the end of the Second World War when they were awarded a contract by the USAAF under the code-name 'Project Vulcan' for the design of a new high-speed aircraft weapon. They revived an idea developed by Richard Jordan Gatling, who had fitted one of his famous mechanical machine-guns with an electric motor to produce the extraordinarily high rate of fire of 3000 rds/min. The principle was tested and proved sound, and by 1949 a prototype 0.6-in (15.24-mm) six-barrelled gun had been tested, producing 6000 rds/min. The calibre was increased to 20-mm (0.79-in) to allow explosive shells to be fired, and by 1956 the M61, or Vulcan, entered service, initially on F-104 Starfighters. The Vulcan is described separately, but from the original weapon a series of multi-barrelled guns in various calibres have been developed.

The first was a smaller-calibre weapon for helicopters, and this emerged in the early 1960s as the M134, or GAU-2, Minigun, a six-barrelled externally-powered 7.62-mm (0.30-in) gun working on the same principle as the Vulcan and firing at up to 6000 rds/min. More recently the five-barrelled XM214 5.56-mm (0.219-in) version has been developed, and prototypes of this lightweight weapon can fire bursts of between three and 1500 rounds at up to 10 000 rds/min. A number of three-barrelled weapons have also been produced, including the 20-mm M197 and the lightweight 30-mm (1.18-in) XM188 used on the Bell YAH-63 AAH prototype. The most powerful of the company's guns is the massive 30-mm GAU-8 Avenger (also described separately) used on the Fairchild A-10 ground-attack aircraft. The XM188 is used as the basis for General Electric's design for a CHAG (Compact High-Performance Aerial Gun), the first prototypes of which were due to be handed over in mid-1979.

(M134 Minigun) *Calibre:* 7.62-mm (0.30-in) *Weight:* 20.64 kg (45 lb 8 oz) *Muzzle velocity:* 853 m/sec (2800 ft/sec) *Rate of fire:* up to 6000 rds/min

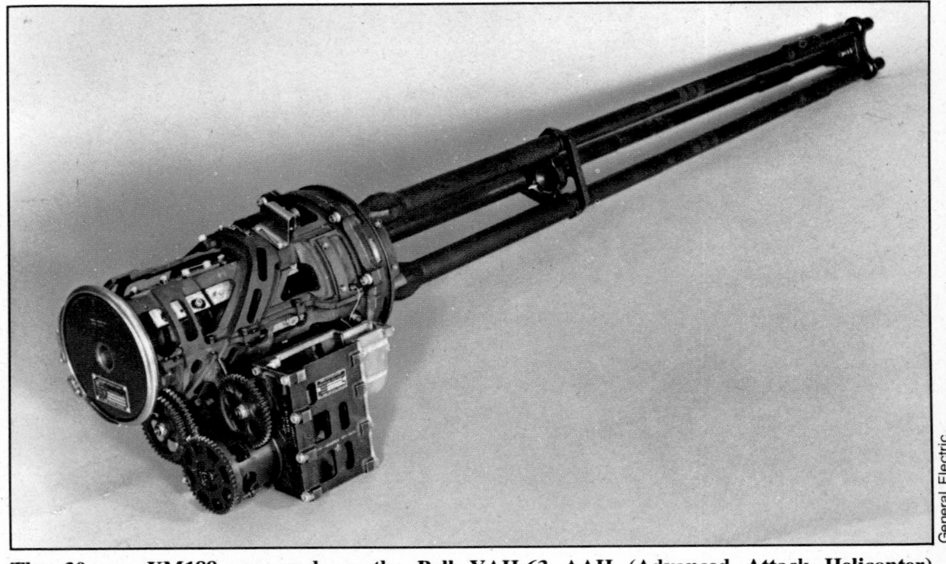

General Electric

The 30-mm XM188, as used on the Bell YAH-63 AAH (Advanced Attack Helicopter)

(XM214) *Calibre:* 5.56-mm (0.219-in) *Length:* 68.6 cm (27 in) *Weight:* 15 kg (33 lb) with drive *Muzzle velocity:* 990 m/sec (3250 ft/sec) *Rate of fire:* up to 10 000 rds/min

(M197) *Calibre:* 20-mm (0.79-in) *Length:* 189.2 cm (74.5 in) *Weight:* 66 kg (145 lb 8 oz) *Muzzle velocity:* 1036 m/sec (3400 ft/sec) *Rate of fire:* 400-1500 rds/min

(XM188) *Calibre:* 30-mm (1.18-in) *Length:* 147.3 cm (58 in) *Weight:* 54.4 kg (120 lb) *Muzzle velocity:* 670 m/sec (2200 ft/sec) *Rate of fire:* up to 2000 rds/min

The General Electric 20-mm M197 is fitted to a number of helicopter gunships

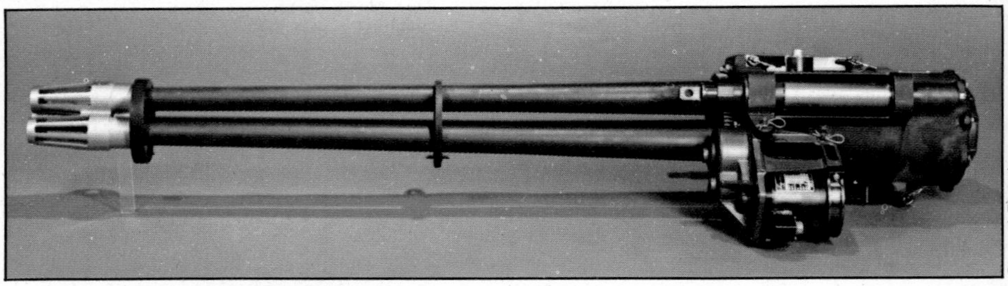

General Electric

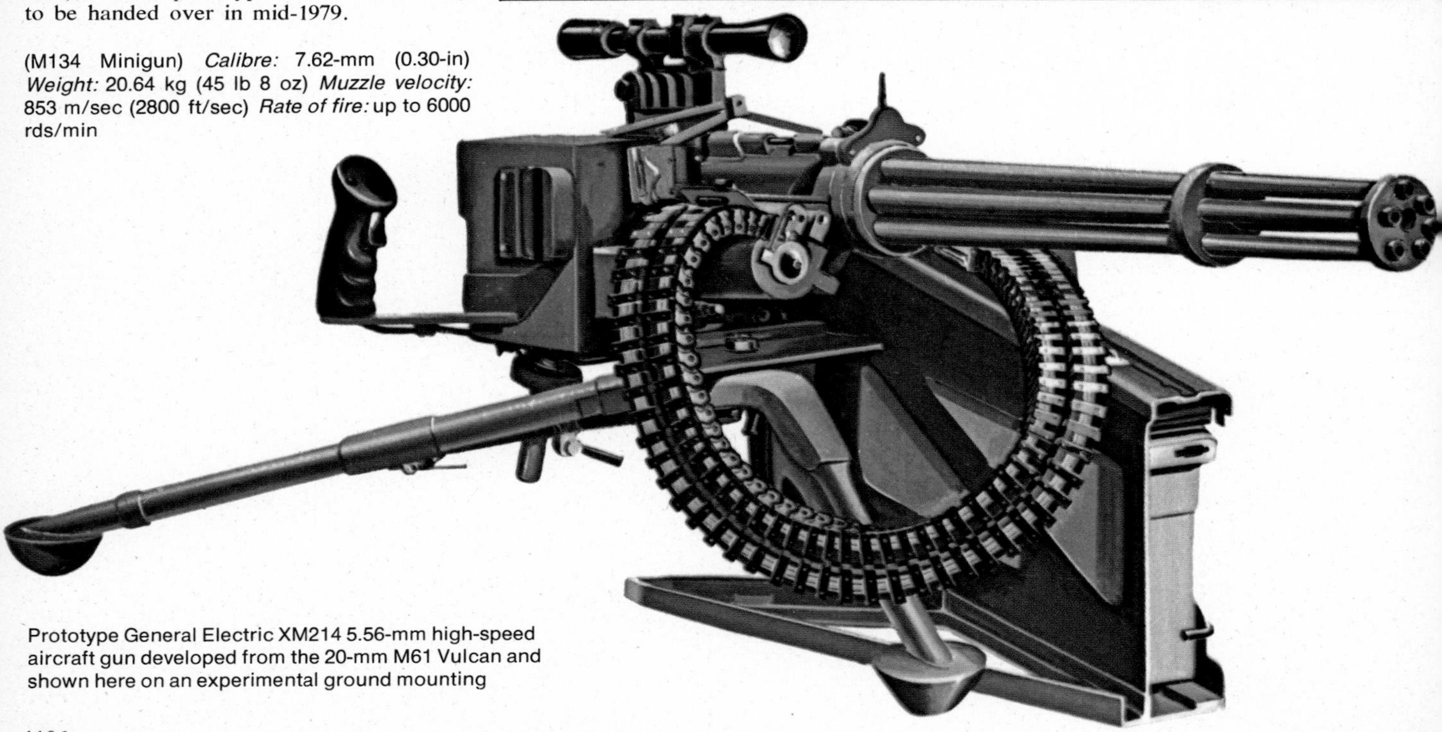

Prototype General Electric XM214 5.56-mm high-speed aircraft gun developed from the 20-mm M61 Vulcan and shown here on an experimental ground mounting

The South African war revealed a major deficiency in British artillery equipments, in that they had no heavy siege howitzer, and in 1900 eight 24-cm (9.45-in) howitzers were bought from Skoda of Pilsen and shipped secretly to South Africa to be used in the siege of Pretoria. According to barrack-room legend they were sent in crates marked 'pianos'. However they went, they arrived too late and were not used. One or two appear to have been sent to China in 1902, but evidence on this is scanty. Eventually all appeared in England and were used for training, since they bore a superficial resemblance to a new British design, the 9.2-in (234-mm) howitzer, which was then under development. The 24-cm calibre was translated into 9.45-in for the benefit of the British nomenclature, and ever afterwards these howitzers were known to the army as the 'Quarter-to-Ten Guns'. Although not officially obsolete until 1920, they were never used in the First World War.

9.2-in Howitzer Mk 1

As a result of seeing the 9.45-in (240-mm), the War Office approached the Coventry Ordnance Works in 1910 with a request for a heavy howitzer, and since 9.2-in (234-mm) was a service calibre, and ammunition and barrel-making machinery existed for it, this was selected. The new howitzer was a well thought-out design, based on a segment-shaped ground platform built up from sections. On top of this sat the gun carriage, pivoting on a roller race, and bearing the gun in a cradle with hydro-pneumatic recoil system. Since the mounting had to be compact for transport, it tended to rear up when fired. To counter this a large 'earth box' of steel was assembled at the front of the ground platform and had to be filled with nine tons of earth when the gun was emplaced. When the time came to move, nine tons of earth had, of course, to be shovelled out again. The weapon was dismantled by a portable hoist into three units for transportation. Each load weighed about 5 tons.

I V Hogg

A 12-in (304-mm) howitzer in France in 1940

9.2-in Howitzer Mk 2

Production of the 9.2-in (234-mm) Mark 1 began in 1913, and in November 1914 the prototype model went to France where it was christened 'Mother'. It was first used at Neuve Chapelle. Up to the end of 1916, 233 had been made, but by then the army were asking for more range, and a Mark 2 version was produced. This used a longer barrel but the mounting was much the same as before, and only slight improvements were necessary. Over 800 were made and supplied to the Russian and American armies.

12-in Howitzer Mk 2

The Mark 2 had been built by Vickers, and when they were asked in late 1916 to produce an even heavier weapon, they simply scaled-up the 9.2-in (234-mm) to 12-in (304-mm) calibre to make the 12-in howitzer Mark 2 (the Mark 1 was a railway equipment). The principal difference, as the gunners now saw it, was that the earth box had to have 20 tons of soil shovelled into it. As soon as the Mark 2 was in production, Vickers, looking ahead, began work on a better design.

I V Hogg

Right: The howitzer shop at Woolwich arsenal in 1916. The First World War saw a massive increase in the demand for artillery of all calibres and Woolwich expanded to meet this, bringing women in to swell the labour force

The 9.2-in (234-mm) Mk 1 Howitzer had a platform built up in sections, held stable by an 'earth box' which was filled with nine tons of earth. It fired a 132-kg (290-lb) shell to a maximum range of 9200 m (10060 yards) and weighed 13577 kg (29930 lb) in action

A British 8-in (203-mm) Howitzer in action near Aveluy in September 1916 during the First World War. The 8-in was a stop-gap weapon which used a 6-in (152-mm) cut short, with an enlarged bore and chamber. One hundred were ordered and the carriages were constructed by railway workshops throughout England. By 1919 they were obsolete having been replaced by the 8-in BL Mk 6 Howitzer which was five tons lighter

IWM

12-in Howitzer Mk 4

When approached in 1917, Vickers had the Mark 4 howitzer ready. This had a longer barrel and a more modern breech, a stronger mounting, ammunition hoists, and a power-operated rammer, probably the first time such a device was ever seen on a field equipment. It was driven by air compressed in a special cylinder during the recoil movement of the gun. Both the 12-in (304-mm) models were dismantled into six loads for travelling, drawn by traction engines or Holt tractors. Their road speed was about 8 km/h (5 mph) and they were familiarly known throughout the army as the 'Twelve Inch Road Hogs'. Several were retained in service after the First World War, four went to France in 1939 and were left there in 1940. The few remaining in Britain were used as anti-invasion defences and training weapons.

15-in Howitzer Mk 1

When the Coventry Ordnance Works had produced their successful 9.2-in (234-mm) howitzer, they decided to produce something bigger in the hope of interesting the army, and by scaling-up the 9.2-in they produced a massive 15-in (381-mm) model. Once built and tested, the Ordnance Works had the problem of persuading the army to buy it, and here things took an unexpected and amusing turn. One of the company directors was Admiral Reginald Bacon, retired from the Royal Navy, and he, expecting the news to be passed on to the War Office, informed the Admiralty of the new howitzer. To Bacon's surprise, Winston Churchill, First Lord of the Admiralty, decided that here was an opportunity to get the navy into the limelight on the Western Front. The navy took the 15-in howitzer, manned it with Royal Marines, and sent it to France, and then ordered the building of another eleven. To add a final flourish to this, Bacon was recommissioned as a colonel of the Royal Marines and sent to France to command the howitzer battery.

8-in Howitzer Mk 1

By the middle of 1916, however, the navy decided they had better things to do than man howitzers in Flanders, and handed the weapons over to the army. The army were not entirely pleased, feeling that the weapons did not have enough performance to make them worth emplacing. Attempts to develop a lighter shell and thus get a longer range came to nothing. Although the army soldiered on with the 15-in (381-mm) until the end of the war, using them where ranges were short, they rapidly scrapped them in 1920. With the coming of the Second World War, the British heavy artillery consisted of a collection of 8-in (203-mm), 9.2-in (234-mm) and 12-in (305-

I V Hogg

Above: A 12-in (304-mm) Mk 4 howitzer showing the loading hoists, breech and power rammer
Below: Loading a shell into a 15-in (381-mm) howitzer in France in the spring of 1916

Below: The 8-in (203-mm) howitzer Mk 6 with a shell in position on the loading trolley

COMPARATIVE DATA

Gun	Calibre	Shell weight (kg/lb)	Muzzle velocity (m/sec/ft/sec)	Maximum range (m/yards)	Weight in action (kg/lbs)	Elevation (degrees)	Traverse (degrees left and right)
7.2-in Howitzer Mk 1	183-mm	91/200	518/1700	15 450/16 900	10 282/22 670	0+45	4
7.2-in Howitzer Mk 6	183-mm	91/200	586/1925	17 925/19 600	14 764/32 550	−2+63	30
8-in Howitzer Mk 1	203-mm	91/200	396/1300	9600/10 500	13 920/30 688	−5+45	nil
8-in Howitzer Mk 8	203-mm	91/200	457/1500	11 245/12 300	9017/19 880	0+45	4
9.2-in Howitzer Mk 1	234-mm	132/290	361/1185	9200/10 060	13 577/29 932[1]	−3+55[3]	30
9.2-in Howitzer Mk 2	234-mm	132/290	488/1600	12 745/13 935	16 460/36 288[2]	0+50[3]	30
9.45-in Howitzer Mk 1	240-mm	127/280	283/928	6995/7650	8687/19 152	0+63[4]	9½
12-in Howitzer Mk 2	305-mm	340/750	364/1195	10 370/11 340	37 186/81 981[5]	0+65[6]	30
12-in Howitzer Mk 4	305-mm	340/750	448/1470	13 120/14 350	41 504/91 502[5]	−3+65[6]	30
15-in Howitzer Mk 1	381-mm	635/1400	340/1117	10 035/10 975	N/A	−5+45[7]	12½

Notes: 1) Plus 9 tons of earth 2) Plus 11 tons of earth 3) Minimum firing angle 15° 4) Minimum firing angle 42° 5) Plus 20 tons of earth 6) Minimum firing angle 20° 7) Minimum firing angle 25°

I V Hogg

A 7.2-in (183-mm) Howitzer Mk 6 on its 155-mm (6.1-in) carriage. It served into the 1960s

mm) howitzers left over from the last war. None of them were felt to be suited to a modern war of movement. They were slow to move, slow to bring into and out of action, and their ranges were short.

7.2-in Howitzer Mk 1

In 1940 it was decided to develop a new weapon which could be mounted on the carriages of the 8-in (203-mm) howitzers, and after some tests a 7.2-in (183-mm) barrel firing a 91-kg (200-lb) shell was chosen. All the remaining 8-in (203-mm) howitzers were taken away, their barrel liners removed, and they were relined with 7.2-in (183-mm) barrels, with the breech mechanism altered to suit. The resulting weapons were introduced as the 7.2-in Mark 1 in 1941. Shortly after this a number of 8-in howitzers were obtained from the US. They were the same as the British design, having either been supplied to the US Army in 1917-18 or built to British designs in the US. These were also converted, and given different mark numbers according to the pattern of 8-in from which they had originated.

7.2-in Howitzer Mk 6

All these designs used the two-wheeled box trail of the old 8-in (203-mm), and the force of recoil from the new 7.2-in (183-mm) was more than the recoil system could absorb. As a result, the whole carriage jumped backwards when the gun fired. On wet ground they were extremely dangerous, and to try to effect some control large wedges, called variously 'scotches' or 'quoins', were placed behind the wheels. When the gun fired, the wheels ran up these wedges, stopped, and then ran back down to the firing position again. Even so, firing the 7.2 was a hair-raising experience.

In 1943 first supplies of the American 155-mm (6.1-in) Gun M1 arrived in Britain, and the carriage of this gun could be adjusted to mount an 8-in howitzer. In April 1943 a trial was made of fitting a 7.2-in barrel to the American mounting, which proved to be a success, and as a result the combination was approved as the 7.2 in-Howitzer Mark 5 in November 1943.

But then it was realized that taking a modern carriage and putting the extempore 7.2 on top was wasting the carriage. As a result, a completely new barrel, longer and capable of more power, was designed and produced expressly for fitting to the 155-mm carriage. This was adopted in December 1943 as the Mark 6, and no Mark 5 pattern was ever made. The Mark 6 was an excellent weapon which increased the maximum range by two miles or so and was rock steady when fired. It replaced the earlier models and remained in service until replaced by the American 8-in howitzer, under NATO standardization, in the 1960s.

The advent of the heavier-than-air craft and its ability to cross water probably had a greater effect on Britain than on any other country in the early 1900s, with its implied threat of aerial reconnaissance of naval bases and surveillance of the fleet, if nothing worse. As a result, antiaircraft guns were being examined as early as 1905. By 1913 a number of Maxim 1-pdr pom-pom cannon had been fitted to high angle mountings, both mobile and static, and design work was in progress on a 3-in (76-mm) antiaircraft gun.

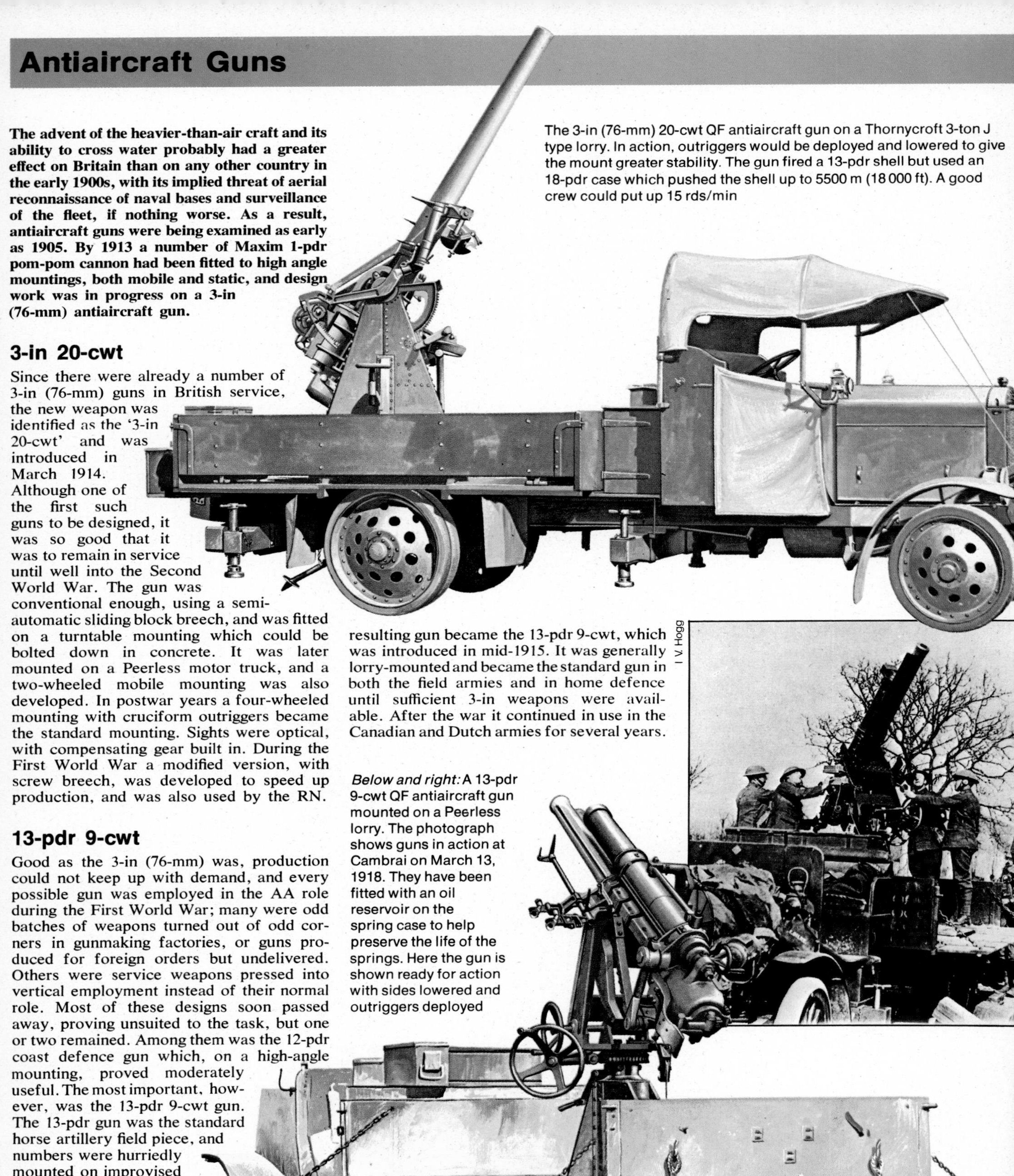

The 3-in (76-mm) 20-cwt QF antiaircraft gun on a Thornycroft 3-ton J type lorry. In action, outriggers would be deployed and lowered to give the mount greater stability. The gun fired a 13-pdr shell but used an 18-pdr case which pushed the shell up to 5500 m (18 000 ft). A good crew could put up 15 rds/min

I V. Hogg

Below and right: A 13-pdr 9-cwt QF antiaircraft gun mounted on a Peerless lorry. The photograph shows guns in action at Cambrai on March 13, 1918. They have been fitted with an oil reservoir on the spring case to help preserve the life of the springs. Here the gun is shown ready for action with sides lowered and outriggers deployed

3-in 20-cwt

Since there were already a number of 3-in (76-mm) guns in British service, the new weapon was identified as the '3-in 20-cwt' and was introduced in March 1914. Although one of the first such guns to be designed, it was so good that it was to remain in service until well into the Second World War. The gun was conventional enough, using a semi-automatic sliding block breech, and was fitted on a turntable mounting which could be bolted down in concrete. It was later mounted on a Peerless motor truck, and a two-wheeled mobile mounting was also developed. In postwar years a four-wheeled mounting with cruciform outriggers became the standard mounting. Sights were optical, with compensating gear built in. During the First World War a modified version, with screw breech, was developed to speed up production, and was also used by the RN.

13-pdr 9-cwt

Good as the 3-in (76-mm) was, production could not keep up with demand, and every possible gun was employed in the AA role during the First World War; many were odd batches of weapons turned out of odd corners in gunmaking factories, or guns produced for foreign orders but undelivered. Others were service weapons pressed into vertical employment instead of their normal role. Most of these designs soon passed away, proving unsuited to the task, but one or two remained. Among them was the 12-pdr coast defence gun which, on a high-angle mounting, proved moderately useful. The most important, however, was the 13-pdr 9-cwt gun. The 13-pdr gun was the standard horse artillery field piece, and numbers were hurriedly mounted on improvised carriages in 1914 to act as AA guns. At the same time the 18-pdr field gun was also tried out.

Neither was very good, but some unknown genius suggested relining the 18-pdr gun to 3-in calibre so that the 13-pdr shell could be propelled by the 18-pdr cartridge. This plan worked extremely well, and the resulting gun became the 13-pdr 9-cwt, which was introduced in mid-1915. It was generally lorry-mounted and became the standard gun in both the field armies and in home defence until sufficient 3-in weapons were available. After the war it continued in use in the Canadian and Dutch armies for several years.

A 4.5-in (114-mm) AA gun, one of the many installed around London during the Second World War. With electric ramming equipment they could put up eight rds/min—impressive when each shell weighed 24.5 kg (54 lb)

3.7-in Mk 1

After the war a good deal of work went into the study of AA guns; an excellent 3.6-in (91-mm) gun was developed from 1919 onward, but no money was available to put it into production and as better ideas came along the project was abandoned. In 1928 a specification called for a 3.7-in (94-mm) gun firing an 11.3-kg (25-lb) shell, and designs were worked on for some years. Finally, in 1933, a firm specification appeared and in 1935 designs appeared from Woolwich arsenal and from Vickers. The Vickers design was chosen, and in April 1936 the pilot gun passed acceptance tests. Production was authorized in April 1937, and the first production guns were delivered in January 1938. Production continued until 1945.

The 3.7-in gun was an extremely advanced weapon for its time, having facilities for electric data transmission and a very complicated mounting. It was, however, rather heavy, and at first was not particularly liked by gunners accustomed to the lighter and handier 3-in (76-mm). But its vastly better performance soon made people forget the weight, and by the middle of the war it was acclaimed as one of the best weapons of its type in existence. It was constantly being improved, and one of the most important modifications was the addition of the Molins fuze setter and rammer. With this device it was no longer necessary to set the shell's time fuze by hand before manually loading the round into the breech. The round was dropped on to a tray and the operating flap —affectionately known as the 'pig's ear' from its shape—was pressed. From then on, operation was entirely automatic. The fuze setting machine slid back over the nose of the shell to set the fuze, and then retracted; the tray swung across into line with the open breech and the round was rammed; the breech closed automatically, the tray swung clear, and the gun fired. Not only did this lighten the work and speed up the rate of fire, but it also imposed a fixed 'dead time' between setting the fuze and firing it, which helped in predicting the gun data.

4.5-in Mk 1

Considering that it was the outcome of a 1928 specification, the 3.7-in (94-mm) coped well. Nevertheless, as early as January 1941 the War Office had begun looking ahead for its replacement.

During the 1920s some desultory work on a design for for a 4.7-in (120-mm) gun had been done, but by 1937 it was obvious that with all available energy and money going into the 3.7-in gun there would be no chance of producing the larger calibre gun as well. It was then suggested that the army adopt the naval 4.5-in (114-mm) gun. The performance was close to that of the proposed 4.7-in. It was a tried and tested weapon already in production, and since most of the places the army had intended to install these heavy weapons were naval base areas, there would be a simplification of ammunition supply. The 4.5-in (114-mm) was formally taken into army use in 1938.

The 4.5-in was a fairly simple weapon on a static mounting, and was usually protected by an all-enveloping shield. Hand ramming was originally used, but in 1940 an electric rammer was fitted which brought the rate of fire up to 8 rds/min. Guns sited near the coast were also issued with AP (armour piercing) shells for use against invasion craft if the necessity arose. It never did.

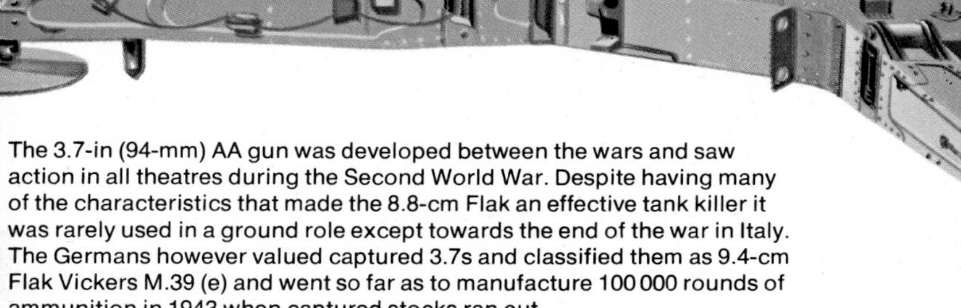

The 3.7-in (94-mm) AA gun was developed between the wars and saw action in all theatres during the Second World War. Despite having many of the characteristics that made the 8.8-cm Flak an effective tank killer it was rarely used in a ground role except towards the end of the war in Italy. The Germans however valued captured 3.7s and classified them as 9.4-cm Flak Vickers M.39 (e) and went so far as to manufacture 100 000 rounds of ammunition in 1943 when captured stocks ran out

3.7-in Mk 6

But even with the 4.5-in (114-mm) gun, the army was apprehensive about the future. After several possible ideas had been explored, it was decided to develop a new, longer 3.7-in (94-mm) barrel with an enlarged chamber, and fit it into the body of the 4.5-in gun. This became the 3.7-in Mk 6, and was issued in 1943. Among other features, the gun had a new form of rifling in which the bottom of the rifling grooves gradually came up to meet the lands (the raised parts of the rifling), so that the last few inches of the barrel were smooth. To go with this, a special shell was developed with copper centring bands in the body as well as the usual driving band. The effect of the shallowing rifling and smoothbore section was to smooth out the bands and eject the shell with no protuberances to disturb the airflow. This, together with the enlarged chamber and the new, more powerful, cartridge, gave the gun an extremely high velocity and it could reach up to destroy anything in the air at that time.

5.25-in Mk 1

The 3.7-in (94-mm) Mk 6 was chosen as an interim solution because it offered good performance for relatively little work and cost. The long-term solution was to go to another naval equipment, the 5.25-in (133-mm) high angle gun. Three twin mountings were obtained by the army in 1942 and redesigned into single-gun equipments. The first, Mark 1A, was solely an AA gun and was turntable mounted with an open-backed mild steel shield. The second, Mark 1B, was a dual-role AA/coast defence gun mounted in an armoured turret. The equipment was complex, with powered ammunition feed from a magazine under the mounting, chain rammer, powered elevation and traverse, remote control capability, air blast to clear the bore and keep fumes out of the turret, electrical firing and many other features. They were the most complex antiaircraft equipments ever seen in British or any other service, and according to uncomfirmed reports each gun, complete with turret, engine house and magazine, cost a quarter of a million pounds when installed.

Numbers of 5.25-in guns were emplaced around the major dockyard target areas—London, Portsmouth, Tyne, and the Humber—in 1944-45 and installation continued after

I V Hogg

Above: **A 5.25-in (133-mm) AA Mk 1B DP gun. *Left:* The 3.7-in (94-mm) AA Mk 6 at maximum elevation. It was first issued in 1943**

BRITISH ANTI-AIRCRAFT DATA

Gun	Calibre	Shell weight (kg/lb)	Muzzle velocity (m/sec/ft/sec)	Ground range (m/yards)	Effective ceiling (m/ft)	Weight in action (kg/tons)	Rate of fire (rds/min)
12-pdr 12-cwt	76-mm	5.7/12.5	670/2200	9235/10 100	6700/22 000	N/A	8
13-pdr Mk 3	76-mm	5.9/13	510/1675	5395/5900	5180/17 000	7110/7[1]	10
13-pdr 9-cwt	76-mm	5.9/13	655/2150	7315/8000	5790/19 000	7620/7.5[1]	10
3-in 20-cwt	76-mm	5.7/12.5	762/2500	9965/10 900	7160/23 500	2720/2.7	20
40-mm Bofors	40-mm	0.9/2.0	823/2700	9875/10 800	1525/5000	1980/1.9	120
2-pdr Mk 8	40-mm	0.9/2.0	693/2275	6860/7500	1830/6000	7570/7.4	60
6-pdr 6-cwt	57-mm	2.7/6.0	945/3100	13 720/15 000	6400/21 000	11 180/11	35
3.7-in Mk 1	94-mm	12.7/28	792/2600	18 835/20 600	9750/32 000	9317/9.2[2]	25
3.7-in Mk 6	94-mm	12.7/28	1044/3425	23 410/25 600	13 700/45 000	17 400/17.1	19
4.5-in Mk 1	114-mm	24.5/54	732/2400	20 850/22 800	10 500/34 500	14 987/14.7	8
5.25-in Mk 1	133-mm	36.3/80	853/2800	24 690/27 000	13 100/43 000	50 294/49.5[3]	10
40-mm L/70	40-mm	1.0/2.2	1000/3280	12 500/13 670	3000/9850	4800/4.7	240

Notes: 1) On motor truck mounting. 2) Figures for mobile; the static model weighed 1047 kg (10.3 tons). 3) AA/CD (antiaircraft/coast defence) version in armoured turret.

I V Hogg

A Bofors 40-mm L/70 in 1975. It can be used in the ground role where its high rate of fire with AP rounds is effective against light armour

the war. The development of guided missiles, however, curtailed the programme and the guns were declared obsolete in 1959 and scrapped.

2-pdr Mk 8

So far the guns reviewed have been those concerned with high-flying targets, but in the early 1930s the threat of tactical air attacks by low-flying strafing planes became apparent. Due to the usual shortage of money, the main problem was to find some existing weapon which could be put to use. Once again, a naval gun was the answer. The 2-pdr Mk 8 twin gun, the navy's pom-pom, was adopted in April 1937. In the first instance the standard naval mounting would be adopted, and work would then go ahead on a fresh design which would be more easily portable, for the naval gun had been built for bolting down to ship's decks.

40-mm Bofors

At the same meeting which approved the 2-pdr, another gun was suggested for use by the field armies—the 40-mm (1.57-in) Bofors gun, a lightweight weapon on a four-wheeled carriage capable of being towed at high speed and, if need be, fired from its wheels. Approval was given to buy 100 guns and half a million rounds of ammunition from Sweden. This was followed by purchase of more guns from Poland, who were building them under licence from Bofors, and eventually the negotiation of a building licence for Britain. As experience was gained, it was seen that the Bofors was vastly preferable to the 2-pdr, and plans for the latter gun were modified. No more than 60 were made and as soon as sufficient Bofors guns were available to replace them they were returned to the navy.

The 40-mm Bofors was the most widely-used AA gun of the Second World War. Both Axis and Allied forces used licence-built and captured weapons, and even the Japanese used Dutch-built guns captured in Java

6-pdr 6-cwt

While the Bofors gun could deal with targets up to about 1500 m (5000 ft), the 3.7-in could not deal with targets in the 1500-2500 m (5000-8000 ft) band at that time, since it could not swing fast enough to keep up with them. It was decided that a third type of gun, an 'intermediate' gun, was needed, and a 57-mm (2.24-in) 6-pdr was planned. This was to be a twin gun with automatic feed and a high rate of fire. Although much effort went into the 6-pdr 6-cwt twin design, it was never successful and never entered service.

40-mm L/70

After the Second World War the 3.7-in (94-mm), 5.25-in (133-mm) and 40-mm (1.57-in) continued in service. Several new designs were under development, including a 102-mm (4-in) water-cooled gun firing at 70 rds/min and a 5-in (127-mm) smoothbore firing a discarding sabot fin-stabilized shell. Before these could be perfected, the guided missile arrived and made AA guns redundant except in small calibres. The Bofors company produced a new gun, the L/70, with power operation and double the rate of fire, and this was adopted in the early 1960s. It was still in service in 1978, but was rapidly being phased out in favour of the latest generation of missiles such as 'Rapier' and 'Blowpipe'. It is likely that during the 1980s AA guns will be phased out of British service altogether.

Antitank Guns

Britain in the late 1920s and early 1930s, like many other countries, considered that antitank shooting was to be an infantry task, best performed by some small-calibre portable weapons, and spent much time trying out various 20-mm (0.79-in) guns with little result. Eventually the 0.55-in (14-mm) Boys antitank rifle was issued for front-line infantry use, while a heavier weapon, a 2-pdr gun, was developed for more serious work. However, it was belatedly realized that the infantry had more than enough to do, and in 1938 the Royal Artillery were given the responsibility for antitank defence, including the 2-pdr gun.

2-pdr

Like most of its contemporaries the 2-pdr was of 40-mm (1.57-in) calibre and fired a small piercing shot capable of dealing with the tanks of the mid-1930s. It was, however, rather more elegantly engineered than other designs, with an ingenious three-legged carriage which allowed the travelling wheels to be lifted clear of the ground so that the gun could traverse through 360°. The traversing gear was a two-speed device giving fast movement for picking up targets and slow movement for precise aiming. A shield protected the gunners and carried a ready-use locker of ammunition.

All this complication meant slow production, and late in 1938, worried by the lack of antitank guns, the army purchased a number of 25-mm (1-in) Mle 34 Hotchkiss antitank guns from the French. Though efficient-looking weapons, their performance was poor, but they served as training weapons until sufficient 2-pdrs were available, and were later issued to infantry battalions, who used them in France in 1939-40.

Bofors 37-mm Gun

Woolwich arsenal appreciated that the 2-pdr gun would soon be out of date, and in 1938 began designing a 57-mm (2.24-in) 6-pdr with a low priority. A pilot model was built and fired in 1939, after which the design was shelved until such time as it might be needed.

Shortly before the war the Sudan government purchased a number of 37-mm (1.46-in) guns from AB Bofors of Sweden, and on the outbreak of war these were made available to British Army units in the Western Desert to make up for their lack of 2-pdrs. This was an excellent gun with a performance slightly below that of the 2-pdr and proved extremely valuable in the early part of the desert campaign until the increased weight of armour carried by German tanks made it obsolete, along with the 2-pdr.

Ordnance, QF, 2-pdr, or 'Two Pounders', on portee mountings in North Africa. Outclassed in the desert they proved effective in the Far East against lightly-armoured Japanese tanks

IWM

I V Hogg

6-pdr

After the fall of France, with several hundred 2-pdr guns left behind, the British Army was short of antitank guns. The 6-pdr was now proposed to replace the 2-pdr, but to place the 6-pdr in production would have absorbed all the facilities then in use for making 2-pdr guns. In the summer of 1940 a gun in the hand was worth any number of better guns in the production pipeline. The 2-pdr was a gun with which the troops were familiar, whereas the 6-pdr would mean retraining before it could become a useful weapon. So the 2-pdr stayed in production at the expense of the 6-pdr. Although a contract for 400 6-pdrs was actually placed in June 1940 it was not until 2-pdr demand had been satisfied that work could begin. It was November 1941 before the first 6-pdr guns appeared.

By that time the 2-pdr was well outclassed by German armour in the desert which, armed with a heavier 50-mm (1.96-in) or 75-mm (2.95-in) gun, could stand off, out of danger from the 2-pdr, and shell the antitank gun into submission. It took skilful and daring handling to bring the 2-pdr gun into a position to do damage to German tanks.

The issue of the 6-pdr changed this and evened up the battle; it also had the beneficial effect of allowing many 25-pdr field guns to get back to their primary task of infantry support instead of being sequestered as antitank weapons.

***Left:* The 6-pdr antitank gun was delivered late in 1941 but by 1942 it was obsolescent since it could not penetrate the armour of the newer German tanks. However, for a year in North Africa it had given the British a much needed replacement for the 2-pdr**

BRITISH ANTITANK GUN DATA

Gun	Calibre	Shot type (see notes)	Shot weight (kg/lb)	Muzzle velocity (m/sec/ft/sec)	Maximum range (m/yards)	Weight in action (kg/lb)	Penetration (see notes)
25-mm Mle 1934	25-mm	AP	0.32/0.7	950/3110	1800/1975	496/1095	12 mm/1000 m
2-pdr QF	40-mm	AP	0.91/2	807/2650	7315/8000	796/1757	42 mm/1000 m
6-pdr QF	57-mm	HE	2.7/6	823/2700	5030/5500	1597/3521	—
		AP	2.7/6	821/2693			74 mm/1000 m
		APCBC	3.2/7	846/2775			88 mm/1000 m
		APCR	1.8/4	1075/3528			90 mm/1000 m
		APDS	1.5/3.2	1234/4050			146 mm/1000 m
17-pdr QF	76-mm	HE	7.0/15.4	846/2775	9150/10000	2097/4624	—
		AP	7.7/16.9	883/2900			109 mm/1000 m
		APC	7.7/16.9	883/2900			118 mm/1000 m
		APDS	3.5/7.8	1204/3950			231 mm/1000 m
37-mm Bofors	37-mm	AP/HE	0.7/1.5	800/2625	4500/4925	335/738	40 mm/1000 m

Notes: AP= Armour piercing shot; AP/HE= armour-piercing shell; APC= capped shot; APBC= capped, ballistic capped, shot; APDS= discarding sabot shot; APCR= composite rigid (tungsten corded) shot.
Penetration figures given at 30° angle of impact against homogeneous plate.

Antitank Guns

A British 2-pdr antitank gun on a portee mounting in North Africa. The gun is camouflaged with desert scrub and the truck carries ammunition and the personal effects of the crew. Officially the 2-pdr was not meant to be fired from this mount, but in action it gave the crew mobility which meant the difference between life and death when in contact with enemy tanks. The 2-pdr was withdrawn from service in mid-1942 and handed over to the infantry. Though it was outclassed in Europe and Africa it served until 1945 in the Far East

IWM

A 'Pheasant' 17-pdr AT gun on a 25-pdr carriage, known officially as a 17-pdr Mk 2. A hundred of these were flown out to North Africa in 1943

The 32-pdr was the last of the conventional antitank guns and like the Pak 43/41 its size made it difficult to handle in the field

17-pdr

In November 1940 the question of eventual replacement of the 6-pdr was raised—before the 6-pdr was even in production—and a 3-in (76-mm) gun firing a 17 lb (7.7 kg) shot was proposed. By early 1942 pilots had been tested and approved, and the 17-pdr gun was formally introduced in May 1942. This was a considerable leap forward and the 17-pdr was to become one of the most formidable antitank guns of the war. At the time the first guns were being produced, news was received of the imminent arrival in North Africa of the new German Tiger tank, and a number of 17-pdr guns were hastily fitted to 25-pdr carriages, since the proper 17-pdr split-trail carriage had not yet been built. These, code-named 'Pheasant', proved to be surprisingly stable and robust and served until the correct mountings were available. It should perhaps be pointed out that the first Tiger tank fell victim to an Allied 6-pdr gun.

32-pdr

Once the 17-pdr had been approved, thoughts turned to the day when it would need replacement, and in October 1942 the General Staff demanded a weapon with a 25% performance increase over the 17-pdr. After much debate, the solution adopted was a 3.7-in (94-mm) 32-pdr gun, little more than a made-over 3.7-in (94-mm) AA gun barrel on a massive two-wheeled split-trail carriage. A handful of pilot models were made, but they were not completed until 1945. It was then obvious that these weapons had gone beyond the limit of feasibility, being far too heavy and cumbersome to act as antitank weapons, even though they promised a staggering performance. After some trials had been carried out the 32-pdr guns were scrapped, with the exception of one which remains in the Rotunda Museum at Woolwich.

The 32-pdr gun was the last conventional antitank gun to be developed in Britain, since it showed that guns relying upon kinetic energy—smashing power—to pierce armour had now become impractical. The place of the specialist antitank gun was taken by the recoilless gun firing chemical-energy (explosive) projectiles, though the 6-pdr and 17-pdr were retained in service until the late 1950s, before being replaced by the 120-mm BAT (battalion antitank) recoilless gun.

Antitank Ammunition

In speaking of British antitank guns, consideration must be given to their ammunition, since without an understanding of this, knowledge of their development is incomplete. The basic projectile was the armour-piercing (AP) shot, solid steel and with a hard point, which would simply smash through armour and do damage inside the tank resulting from the splinters and fragments of armour knocked off. The British Army never had much faith in AP shells, ie pointed projectiles with a small charge of explosive and a base fuze. In the British view, the small amount of explosive did little more damage beyond what was already being done by splinters inside the tank, and it added far too much complication in the way of base fuzes and base adapters which hold the fuze in place during the piercing action.

AP shot was satisfactory against homogeneous armour; against face-hardened armour it tended to shatter. To counter this, a penetrating cap of steel was placed over the point; this became the APC (armour-piercing capped) shot. Since the penetrating cap was blunt, a light steel cap of more pointed form was placed on it as a wind-shield, leading to the APCBC (armour-piercing capped, ballistic cap) shot, the ultimate in solid shot design.

To deal with harder and thicker armour, tungsten carbide was adopted as the penetrating material. Since this was much heavier than steel, it was not possible to make a simple shot, so a core of tungsten was surrounded by a steel and light alloy body to make APCR shot (armour-piercing composite rigid). While this had a high velocity and good piercing power at short and medium ranges, its velocity fell off rapidly in flight until at longer ranges it was soon dropped in favour of APDS (armour-piercing discarding sabot) in which the alloy sheath was stripped away as the shot left the muzzle, and the tungsten core flew to the target at high velocity. This was introduced for the 6-pdr and 17-pdr in 1944 and with APDS shot the 17-pdr became the most powerful tank-killer in Europe in 1944-5.